Glencoe Science Life's Structure and Function
Contents in Brief

Teacher Wraparound Edition

Student Edition

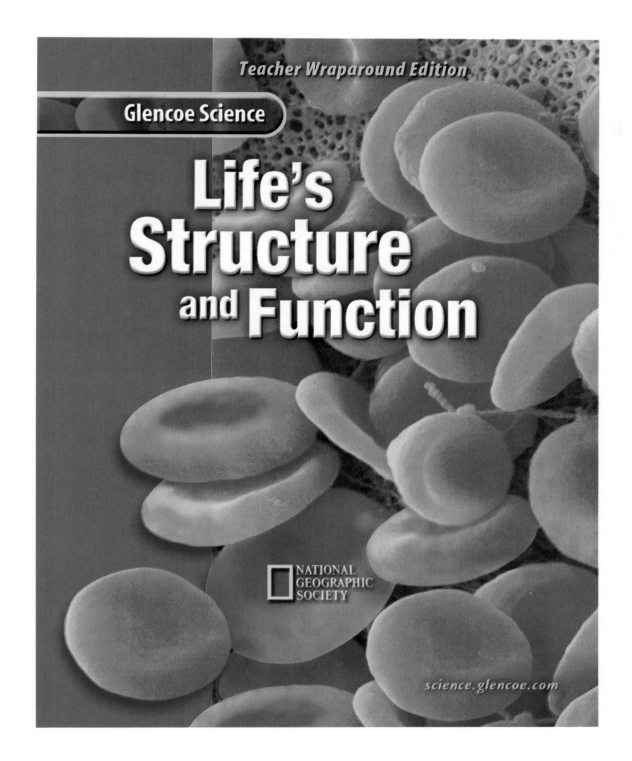

Teacher Wraparound Edition

Glencoe Science

Life's Structure and Function

NATIONAL GEOGRAPHIC SOCIETY

science.glencoe.com

Glencoe McGraw-Hill

New York, New York   Columbus, Ohio   Woodland Hills, California   Peoria, Illinois

GLENCOE SCIENCE
Life's Structure and Function

Student Edition
Teacher Wraparound Edition
Interactive Teacher Edition CD-ROM
Interactive Lesson Planner CD-ROM
Lesson Plans
Content Outline for Teaching
   Directed Reading for Content Mastery
   Foldables: Reading and Study Skills
Assessment
   Chapter Review
   Chapter Tests
   ExamView Pro Test Bank Software
   Assessment Transparencies
   Performance Assessment in the Science Classroom
   The Princeton Review Test Practice Booklet
Spanish Directed Reading for Content Mastery
Spanish Resources
Reinforcement
Enrichment

Activity Worksheets
Section Focus Transparencies
Teaching Transparencies
Laboratory Activities
Science Inquiry Labs
Critical Thinking/Problem Solving
Reading and Writing Skill Activities
Mathematics Skill Activities
Cultural Diversity
Laboratory Management and Safety
Mindjogger Videoquizzes and Teacher Guide
Interactive Explorations and Quizzes CD-ROM
   with Presentation Builder
Vocabulary Puzzlemaker Software
Cooperative Learning
Environmental Issues in the Science Classroom
Home and Community Involvement
Using the Internet in the Science Classroom
Dinah Zike's Teaching Science with Foldables

THE PRINCETON REVIEW

"Test-Taking Tip," "Study Tip," and Test practice features in this book were written by The Princeton Review, the nation's leader in test preparation. Through its association with McGraw-Hill, The Princeton Review offers the best way to help students excel on standardized assessments.

The Princeton Review is not affiliated with Princeton University or Educational Testing Service.

Glencoe/McGraw-Hill
A Division of The McGraw-Hill Companies

Send all inquiries to:

Glencoe/McGraw-Hill
8787 Orion Place
Columbus, OH 43420

ISBN 0-07-825554-6

Printed in the United States of America

1 2 3 4 5 6 7 8 9 10 027/043 10 09 08 07 06 05 04 03 02 01

Authors, Reviewers, and Consultants

for the *Custom Curriculum Series*

Authors

Alton Biggs
Biology Teacher
Allen High School
Allen, Texas

Lucy Daniel, PhD
Teacher/Consultant
Rutherfordton-Spindale
 High School
Rutherfordton, North Carolina

Cathy Ezrailson
Science Department Head
Academy for Science and Health
 Professions
Conroe, Texas

Ralph M. Feather Jr., PhD
Science Department Chair
Derry Area School District
Derry, Pennsylvania

Nicholas Hainen
Chemistry/Physics Teacher
Worthington City Schools
Worthington, Ohio

Patricia Horton
Mathematics/Science Teacher
Summit Intermediate School
Etiwanda, California

Norman G. Lederman, PhD
Professor of Science and Math
 Education
Oregon State University
Corvallis, Oregon

Deborah Lillie
Math and Science Writer
Sudbury, Massachusetts

Thomas McCarthy, PhD
Science Department Chair
St. Edwards School
Vero Beach, Florida

Edward Ortleb
Science Consultant
St. Louis Public Schools
St. Louis, Missouri

Susan Leach Snyder
Earth Science Teacher,
 Consultant
Jones Middle School
Upper Arlington, Ohio

Peter Rillero, PhD
Professor of Science Education
Arizona State University West
Phoenix, Arizona

Eric Werwa, PhD
Department of Physics and
 Astronomy
Otterbein College
Westerville, Ohio

Dinah Zike
Educational Consultant
Dinah-Might Activities, Inc.
San Antonio, Texas

Margaret K. Zorn
Science Writer
Yorktown, Virginia

Reviewers

Sandra K. Enger, PhD
Coordinator
UAL Institute for Science Education
Huntsville, Alabama

Lee Meadows, PhD
Associate Professor of Science Education
University of Alabama
Birmingham, Alabama

Gilbert Naizer, PhD
Assistant Professor of Elementary Education
Texas A&M University
Commerce, Texas

Kimberly S. Roempler, PhD
Associate Director
Eisenhower National Clearinghouse
 for Math and Science
The Ohio State University
Columbus, Ohio

Cultural Diversity Consultants

Nedaro Bellamy
Associate Director,
 Rice Model Science Laboratory
Lanier Middle School, Houston ISD
Houston, Texas

Joyce Hilliard-Clark, PhD
Director, Imhotep Academy
North Carolina State University
Raleigh, North Carolina

Inclusion Strategies Consultant

Barry Barto
Special Education Teacher
John F. Kennedy Elementary School
Manistee, Michigan

Introducing the
Glencoe Science Custom Curriculum Series

Teach science your way!

With the 15 Life, Earth, and Physical Science titles in our modular series, you can select the science topics you want to cover and customize your science curriculum in any way you choose.

The Glencoe Custom Curriculum Series provides:

- Flexibility—you can easily meet your curriculum requirements.
- Convenience—the books are easy for students to carry and ideal for whenever locker space isn't available.
- A sense of accomplishment—as students complete each book, they can see the progress they're making.

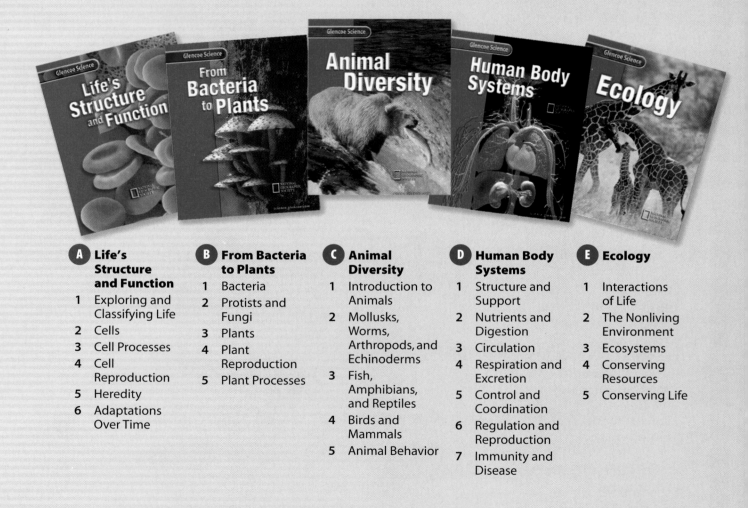

A Life's Structure and Function
1 Exploring and Classifying Life
2 Cells
3 Cell Processes
4 Cell Reproduction
5 Heredity
6 Adaptations Over Time

B From Bacteria to Plants
1 Bacteria
2 Protists and Fungi
3 Plants
4 Plant Reproduction
5 Plant Processes

C Animal Diversity
1 Introduction to Animals
2 Mollusks, Worms, Arthropods, and Echinoderms
3 Fish, Amphibians, and Reptiles
4 Birds and Mammals
5 Animal Behavior

D Human Body Systems
1 Structure and Support
2 Nutrients and Digestion
3 Circulation
4 Respiration and Excretion
5 Control and Coordination
6 Regulation and Reproduction
7 Immunity and Disease

E Ecology
1 Interactions of Life
2 The Nonliving Environment
3 Ecosystems
4 Conserving Resources
5 Conserving Life

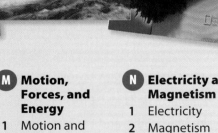

Correlation to **Benchmarks**

The five **Life Science** books in the *Custom Curriculum Series* address many of the Benchmarks for Science Literacy.

A	Life's Structure and Function
B	From Bacteria to Plants
C	Animal Diversity
D	Human Body Systems
E	Ecology

Benchmark	Book and Chapter
4	**The Physical Setting**
4B. The Earth	A6, C1, E2, E3
4C. Processes That Shape the Earth	A6, E2, E4
4D. Structure of Matter	A3, E2
4E. Energy Transformation	A3, B5, E1, E3
5	**The Living Environment**
5A. Diversity of Life	A1, A2, A5, B1, B2, B3, B4, B5, C1, C2, C3, C4, E5
5B. Heredity	A4, A5, B4
5C. Cells	A2, A3, A4, B1, B2, C1, D7
5D. Interdependence of Life	B1, B2, B4, C1, C2, C4, C5
5E. Flow of Matter and Energy	A3, B1, B2, B5, E1, E2, E3, E4, E5
5F. Evolution of Life	A1, A4, A5, A6, B1, B2, B3, C1, C2, C3, C4, D7
6	**The Human Organism**
6A. Human Identity	D1, D2, D3, D4, D5, D6, D7
6B. Human Development	D6
6C. Basic Functions	C5, D1, D2, D3, D4, D5, D6, D7
6D. Learning	C5, D5
6E. Physical Health	B1, B2, C1, D1, D2, D3, D4, D5, D6, D7
8	**The Designed World**
8F. Health Technology	A2, A5, B1, B2, C1, D1, D2, D3, D4, D5, D6, D7
9	**The Mathematical World**
9A. Numbers	All Math Skills and Problem-Solving Activities
9B. Symbolic Relationships	All Math Skills and Problem-Solving Activities
9C. Reasoning	All Math Skills and Problem-Solving Activities
10	**Historical Perspectives**
10G. Explaining the Diversity of Life	A1, A4, A5, C1, C2, C3, C4
10I. Discovering Germs	A2, B1
12	**Habits of Mind**
12A. Values and Attitudes	A1, All "Oops, Accidents in Science!," "Science and History," and "Science and Language Arts" features
12B. Computation and Estimation	Math Skills and Problem-Solving Activities
12D. Communication Skills	All Activities and Skill Builders

Correlation to National Science Education Standards

The following chart illustrates how the five **Life Science** books in the *Custom Curriculum Series* address the National Science Education Standards.

Content Standard	Book, Chapter, and Section
(UCP) Unifying Concepts and Processes	
1. Systems, order, and organization	A1-4, A2-1, A2-2, A3-3, B2-1, B2-2, B3-1, B5-1, B5-2, D1-1, D1-2, D1-3, D2-2, D3-1, D4-1, D4-2, D5-1, D5-2, D6-1, D6-2, D7-1, E1-1, E1-2, E1-3, E2-1, E2-2, E2-3, E3-1, E3-2, E3-3, E5-1, E5-2
2. Evidence, models, and explanation	A1-1, A1-2, A1-3, A3-1, A5-1, A5-2, A5-3, B1-2, D7-2, E4-1, E4-2, E4-3
3. Change, constancy, and measurement	A4-1, A4-2, A4-3, B4-1, C2-1, C2-2, C2-3, C2-4, C3-1, C3-2, C3-3, C3-4, C4-1, C4-2, C5-1, C5-2, D2-1, D6-2, E3-1
4. Evolution and equilibrium	A3-2, A4-2, A4-3, A6-1, A6-2, A6-3, D7-3, E5-1, E5-2
5. Form and function	A2-1, A2-3, B1-1, B2-1, B2-2, B3-2, B3-3, B4-2, B4-3, C1-1, C1-2, C1-3, D3-2, D3-3, D6-1, D6-3
(A) Science as Inquiry	
1. Abilities necessary to do scientific inquiry	A1-1, A1-4, A2-1, A2-2, A2-3, A3-1, A3-2, A3-3, A4-1, A4-3, A5-1, A5-2, A5-3, A6-1, A6-3, B1-1, B1-2, B2-1, B2-2, B3-2, B3-3, B4-1, B4-2, B4-3, B5-1, B5-2, C1-1, C1-2, C1-3, C2-3, C2-4, C3-1, C3-2, C3-3, C3-4, C4-1, C4-2, C5-1, C5-2, D1-1, D1-2, D1-3, D2-1, D2-2, D3-1, D3-2, D3-3, D4-1, D4-2, , D5-1, D5-2, D6-2, D6-3, D7-1, D7-2, D7-3, E1-1, E1-2, E1-3, E2-1, E2-2, E2-3, E3-2, E3-3, E4-1, E4-2, E4-3, E5-1, E5-2
2. Understandings about scientific inquiry	A1-1, A1-3, A1-4, A6-1, C5-2
(B) Physical Science	
1. Properties and changes of properties in matter	A1-1, A3-1, E2-2, E2-3
2. Motions and forces	D1-1, D1-2, E2-3
3. Transfer of energy	A3-3, E2-3
(C) Life Science	
1. Structure and function in living systems	A1-2, A1-3, A1-4, A2-1, A2-2, A2-3, A3-1, A3-2, A3-3, A4-1, A4-3, A6-1, A6-2, A6-3, B1-1, B2-1, B2-2, B3-1, B3-2, B3-3, B4-1, B4-2, B4-3, B5-1, B5-2, C1-1, C1-2, C1-3, C2-1, C2-2, C2-3, C2-4, C3-1, C3-2, C3-3, C3-4, C4-1, C4-2, D1-1, D1-2, D1-3, D2-1, D2-2, D3-1, D3-2, D3-3, D4-1, D4-2, D5-1, D5-2, D6-1, D6-2, D6-3, D7-1, D7-2, D7-3, E1-1, E1-2, E1-3, E2-1, E2-2, E2-3, E5-1, E5-2
2. Reproduction and heredity	A2-3, A4-2, A4-3, A5-1, A5-2, A5-3, A6-1, A6-2, A6-3, B1-1, B2-2, B4-1, B4-2, B4-3, C2-3, C3-2, C3-3, C3-4, C4-1, C4-2, C5-2, D6-2, D6-3
3. Regulation and behavior	A3-2, B1-1, B5-1, B5-2, C1-1, C1-2, C1-3, C2-4, C3-1, C3-2, C3-3, C3-4, C4-1, C4-2, C5-1, C5-2, D1-3, D2-2, D5-1, D5-2, D6-1, D6-2, D6-3, D7-1, D7-2, D7-3
4. Populations and ecosystems	A1-2, A3-3, B1-2, C1-2, C3-2, C3-3, C3-4, C4-2, E1-1, E1-2, E1-3, E2-1, E2-2, E2-3, E3-1, E3-2, E3-3, E5-1, E5-2
5. Diversity and adaptations of organisms	A6-1, A6-2, A6-3, B1-1, B2-1, B2-2, B3-1, B3-2, B3-3, B4-2, B4-3, C1-1, C1-2, C1-3, C2-1, C2-2, C2-3, C2-4, C3-1, C3-2, C3-3, C3-4, C4-1, C4-2, C5-1, C5-2, D7-1, D7-2, D7-3, E3-2, E3-3, E5-1, E5-2
(D) Earth and Space Science	
1. Structure of the Earth system	E2-1, E2-2, E2-3
2. Earth's history	A1-3, A6-1, A6-2
3. Earth in the solar system	E2-3
(E) Science and Technology	
1. Abilities of technological design	A5-3, D7-3
2. Understandings about science and technology	A2-3, A4-3, A5-3, B3-3, B4-3, D2-2, D7-3, E4-2, E4-3
(F) Science in Personal and Social Perspectives	
1. Personal Health	A2-3, A5-2, B1-2, C1-3, D1-2, D1-3, D2-1, D2-2, D3-2, D3-3, D4-1, D4-2, D6-2, D6-3, D7-1, D7-2, D7-3, E4-2
2. Populations, resources, and environments	C1-2, C2-1, C2-2, C2-4, C4-2, E2-1, E2-2, E2-3, E3-1, E3-2, E3-3, E4-1, E4-2, E4-3, E5-1, E5-2
3. Natural hazards	E3-1
4. Risks and benefits	B3-2, D7-3, E4-1, E4-2, E4-3
5. Science and technology in society	A1-4, A4-3, A5-3, B1-2, B2-2, B3-3, B4-3, C3-4, E1-3, E4-1, E4-2, E4-3, E5-1, E5-2
(G) History and Nature of Science	
1. Science as a human endeavor	A1-1, A3-3, A4-3, A5-3, A6-1, A6-3, B2-2, B5-2, C2-4, C4-2, C5-2, D5-2, D7-3, E1-3, E3-3, E4-3
2. Nature of science	A1-4, A6-2, A6-3, B1-2, B3-3, D1-3
3. History of science	A1-3, A1-4, A2-3, A5-1, A6-1, A6-2, A6-3, C1-3, C4-2, C5-1, D1-3, D3-3, D4-2, D7-2, E1-3

Technology Resources

Online Science

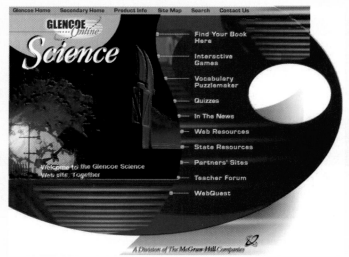

The Glencoe Science Web site **science.glencoe.com** is an invaluable resource for all teachers and students. You will find current information, Web links, chapter content, and Internet activities that allow students to connect to other students worldwide.

Interactive CD-ROM Program

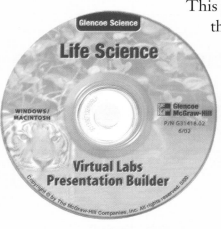

This program provides students the opportunity to develop hypotheses, manipulate variables, build presentations, review content, and think critically.

ExamView Pro Computer TestMaker Software

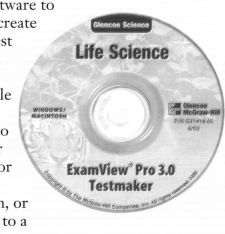

Use this software to design and create your own test instruments in minutes. This versatile program allows you to create paper tests, tests for your school LAN system, or tests posted to a class Web site.

Interactive Lesson Planner

Here's the perfect solution for help in planning your lessons and organizing your resources. Every page of your Teacher Classroom Resources is available in this product at the click of a mouse.

MindJogger Videoquizzes

The interactive quiz-show format of this program, with three levels of difficulty, provides excitement for your students in reviewing key concepts for every chapter. It's a fun way to help you assess students' understanding of science content.

Vocabulary PuzzleMaker Software

This software program allows you to create crossword puzzles, jumble puzzles, or word searches in minutes to review chapter vocabulary. The puzzles can be printed or played on the computer screen.

Guided Reading Audio Program
English/Spanish

Students can listen to complete chapter texts read in English and Spanish. They're perfect for students who are auditory learners or for English Language Learners.

Interactive Teacher Edition

You can view your entire *Teacher Wraparound Edition* and Teacher Classroom Resources on your computer screen. Export all worksheet masters to your own word processor for editing, if you choose.

Teacher Classroom Resources

Chapter Resources Booklets

We've organized all of the materials you need for each chapter into convenient chapter-based booklets! The Fast File system provides an easy way to stay organized.

Each **Chapter Resources** booklet contains:

Reproducible Student Pages

Assessment
- Chapter Review
- Chapter Test

Hands-On Activities
- Activity Worksheets for each activity in the *Student Edition*
- Two additional laboratory activities
- Foldables: Reading and Study Skills

Meeting Individual Needs
- Extension and Intervention
- Directed Reading for Content Mastery

- Directed Reading for Content Mastery *in Spanish*
- Reinforcement
- Enrichment
- Note-taking Worksheets

Transparency Activities
- Section Focus Activity
- Teaching Transparency Activity
- Assessment Transparency Activity

Teacher Support and Planning
- Content Outline for Teaching
- Spanish Resources
- Teacher Guide and Answers

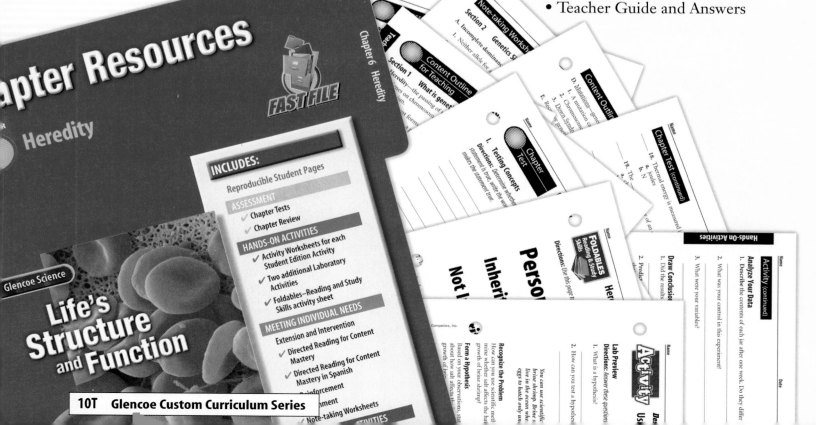

Additional Resources

Glencoe Professional Series

Foldables: Improving Reading and Study Skills

Students love Foldables because they're fun. Teachers love them because they're effective.

What is a Foldable?

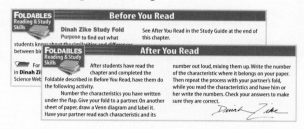

Foldables are three-dimensional, interactive graphic organizers. As students fold paper, cut tabs, write, and manipulate what they have made, they are kinesthetically involved in learning. These unique, hands-on tools for studying and reviewing were created exclusively for Glencoe Science by teaching specialist Dinah Zike.

Foldables are Useful!

Reading in the Content Area

Foldables help students develop ways of organizing information that are fun and creative. These useful activities help students practice basic writing skills, find and report main ideas, organize information, review key vocabulary terms, and much more!

Every chapter begins with a Foldable activity. Students make the physical structure of a Foldable that incorporates one of many prereading strategies. Then, as students read through the chapter and do the activities, students record information as they learn it in the appropriate part of the foldable. In the Chapter Study Guide, the After You Read feature gives students a strategy for using the fold they made to help them review the chapter concepts.

FOLDABLES Reading & Study Skills — **Before You Read**

Dinah Zike Study Fold
Purpose to find out what students know about the similarities and differences between bir...

See After You Read in the Study Guide at the end of this chapter.

For... in **Dinah Zi...** Science Web...

FOLDABLES Reading & Study Skills — **After You Read**

After students have read the chapter and completed the Foldable described in Before You Read, have them do the following activity.

Number the characteristics you have written under the flap. Give your fold to a partner. On another sheet of paper, draw a Venn diagram and label it. Have your partner read each characteristic and its number out loud, mixing them up. Write the number of the characteristic where it belongs on your paper. Then repeat the process with your partner's fold, while you read the characteristics and have him or her write the numbers. Check your answers to make sure they are correct.

Dinah Zike

Review One advantage of Foldables is that they result in an organized study guide. The Foldables then can be used not only while preparing for the chapter test, but they can also be used for reviewing for unit tests, end of course exams, and even standardized tests.

Assessment Foldables present an ideal opportunity for you to probe the depth of your students' knowledge. You'll get detailed feedback on exactly what they know and what misconceptions they may have.

Foldables are Easy!

Anyone who has paper, scissors, and maybe a stapler or some glue can implement Foldables in the classroom. Glencoe's Foldables have been tested with teachers and middle school students to make sure the directions are easy for both students and teachers. After doing a couple of them, your class will quickly become seasoned experts. Don't be surprised if you find them inventing their own for use in projects and reports in all of their classes!

A message from **the creator of Foldables,** Dinah Zike

You might not know my name or me, but I bet you have seen at least one of my graphic organizers or folds used in supplemental programs or teacher workshops. Today, my graphic organizers and manipulatives are used internationally. I present workshops and keynote presentations to over 50,000 teachers a year, sharing the manipulatives I began inventing, designing, and adapting over thirty years ago. Around the world, students of all ages are using them as daily work, note-taking activities, student-directed projects, forms of alternative assessment, science lab journals, quantitative and qualitative observation books, graphs, tables, and more. But through all my years of teaching, designing, and publishing, my materials had never been featured in a middle school textbook. When Glencoe/McGraw-Hill approached me to share some of my three-dimensional, manipulative graphic organizers with you in this new and innovative science series, I was thrilled.

Working with Glencoe, we all had the vision that Foldables should be an integral part of the curriculum, not simply tacked on. What we ended up with was a strategy that will help students read and learn science concepts. One of the advantages of using the same manipulative repeatedly is that students are immersed in what they are learning. It is not out of sight and out of mind. How long is your average student actively involved with a duplicated activity sheet? Ten minutes? Fifteen? Students will use the Foldable at the beginning of each chapter, before reading the chapter, during reading, and after reading. That's a lot of immersion!

Dinah Zike

Reading and Writing in the Content Area

Glencoe Custom Curriculum Series is designed to increase science literacy through improving reading comprehension and deepening students' understanding of ideas and concepts. The reading strategies are active, constructive, and engaging.

In the Student Edition

Reading Checks throughout each chapter stimulate quick recall to keep students focused on main ideas and important details.

> ✔ **Reading Check**
>
> *How does fertilization occur in plants?*

Caption Questions throughout each chapter help students to comprehend what they have read through interpreting the visual. This is especially useful for less proficient readers.

> **Figure 17**
> **This energy pyramid shows that each feeding level contains less energy than the level below it.** *What would happen if the hawks and snakes outnumbered the rabbits and mice in this ecosystem?*

Skill Builder Activities in each Section Assessment often include questions that directly address reading and writing skills. Students are referred to the *Science Skill Handbook* for help.

> **Communicating** In your Science Journal write your own analogy about the diploid and haploid stages of a plant life cycle. **For more help, refer to the** Science Skill Handbook.

The Before You Read and After You Read Activities in every chapter set a purpose for reading and help students to construct a graphic organizer to use for learning content and as a study aide.

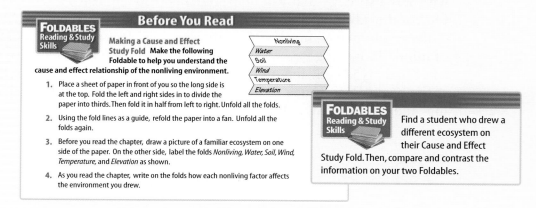

FOLDABLES Reading & Study Skills

Before You Read

Making a Cause and Effect Study Fold Make the following Foldable to help you understand the cause and effect relationship of the nonliving environment.

Nonliving / Water / Soil / Wind / Temperature / Elevation

1. Place a sheet of paper in front of you so the long side is at the top. Fold the left and right sides in to divide the paper into thirds. Then fold it in half from left to right. Unfold all the folds.
2. Using the fold lines as a guide, refold the paper into a fan. Unfold all the folds again.
3. Before you read the chapter, draw a picture of a familiar ecosystem on one side of the paper. On the other side, label the folds *Nonliving, Water, Soil, Wind, Temperature,* and *Elevation* as shown.
4. As you read the chapter, write on the folds how each nonliving factor affects the environment you drew.

FOLDABLES Reading & Study Skills

Find a student who drew a different ecosystem on their Cause and Effect Study Fold. Then, compare and contrast the information on your two Foldables.

Print and Technology Resources to Promote Reading and Writing in the Content Area

Ancillaries

Chapter Resources

- Directed Reading for Content Mastery pages *(in English and Spanish)*
- Foldables: Reading and Study Skills Worksheets
- Note-taking Worksheets

Dinah Zike's Teaching Science with Foldables

Reading and Writing Skill Activities

Technology

- **Guided Reading Audio Program *(English and Spanish)***
- **MindJogger VideoQuizzes**
- **Interactive CD-ROM**
- **Vocabulary PuzzleMaker**
- **Glencoe Science Online**

Students often make personal, educational, and career choices on their own that can influence the rest of their lives. Throughout their school years, they acquire skills that help them make these decisions. The development of keen mathematical skills can ensure that students have a wide variety of life options.

Principles and Standards for School Mathematics of the National Council of Teachers of Mathematics describes the foundation of mathematical concepts and applications that can provide students with the necessary mathematical skills to help achieve their life goals.

The ten categories of mathematical concepts and applications, as shown in the table below, allow students to increase their abilities to visualize, describe, and analyze situations in mathematical terms.

In *Glencoe Custom Curriculum Series*, each Math Skill Activity and Problem-Solving Activity provides students with the opportunity to practice and apply some of the mathematical concepts and applications described in the Standards. These activities serve to reinforce mathematical skills in real-life situations, thus, preparing students to meet their needs in an ever-changing world.

A	Life's Structure and Function	C	Animal Diversity	E	Ecology
B	From Bacteria to Plants	D	Human Body Systems		

Correlation of Math Skills Activities and Problem Solving Activities in the Life Science books, *Glencoe Custom Curriculum Series,* to NCTM Standards Grades 6–8

Standard	Book and Page
1. Number and Operations	D-11, A-13, E-15, C-25, D-40, A-46, C-52, A-74, D-78, E-80, C-82, D-104, A-109, B-112, E-114, E-129, A-133, D-133, C-147, D-147, D-185
2. Algebra	D-11, E-15, C-25, E-40, C-52, A-74, E-80, C-82, B-112, E-114, D-133, B-135, D-147
3. Geometry	D-11, A-46
4. Measurement	D-11, E-15, D-40, E-40, A-46, E-80, C-82, D-133
5. Data Analysis and Probability	A-13, D-78, E-114, C-117, E-129, A-133, B-135, C-147, D-185
6. Problem Solving	D-11, A-13, E-15, B-20, C-25, D-40, B-41, C-52, B-70, A-74, D-78, E-80, C-82, D-104, A-109, B-112, E-114, C-117, A-133, B-135, C-147, D-147, A-159, D-185
7. Reasoning and Proof	D-40, B-41
8. Communication	A-13, E-15, B-20, D-40, B-41, A-46, C-52, B-70, D-78, C-82, D-104, A-109, E-114, C-117, E-129, C-147, A-159, D-185
9. Connections	D-11, A-13, E-15, B-20, C-25, D-40, E-40, B-41, A-46, C-52, B-70, A-74, D-78, E-80, C-82, D-104, A-109, B-112, E-114, C-117, E-129, A-133, D-133, B-135, C-147, D-147, A-159, D-185
10. Representation	E-40, B-70, D-78, E-114, E-129, A-133

Materials List

It is assumed that goggles, laboratory aprons, tap water, textbooks, paper, calculators, pencils, and pens are available for all activities.

All laboratory activities have been thoroughly reviewed by a safety expert.

All full-length labs were bench tested by Science Kit to ensure quality and safety.

Materials support is provided by Science Kit® & Boreal® Laboratories. Call Science Kit at 1-800-828-7777 to get your activity materials folder. This folder makes it easy for you to order materials and equipment for the program.

Consumables

Item	EXPLORE ACTIVITY Page	Mini LAB Page	Activity Chapter/Section
Beads			6-1
Beans, red (100)			5-1
Beans, white (100)			5-1
Cardboard			6-1
Crayons			6-1
Elodea, sprig			3-2
Food coloring		77	
Food-carrot	67		
Food-corn syrup			3-1
Food-egg, unshelled			3-1
Food-fruit from one plant species			6-2
Food-gelatin, prepared		73	
Food-gelatin, unflavored		42	
Food-pineapple pieces, fresh		73	
Food-salt	67		
Glue		103	6-1
Graph paper			6-2
Labels	67	77	1-2
Magazine pictures of furniture		27	
Marker(s)		77, 103	5-2, 6-1
Modeling clay			6-1
Newspaper		52	
Paper bag(s)			5-1
Paper towel(s)	97		
Paper, black	155		
Paper, colored		103	
Pencils, colored			6-1
Plastic bag, self-sealing	97		
Poster board		103	5-2
Salt solution, strong			1-2
Salt solution, weak			1-2
Seeds, bean	97		

Materials List

Consumables *continued*

Item	EXPLORE ACTIVITY Page	Mini LAB Page	Activity Chapter/Section
Seeds, packet of 10 kinds			1-1
Seeds, from one plant species			6-2
Sequins			6-1
Sponge		11	
Spoon, plastic			1-2
Tape		173	
Thread		103	
Toothpick(s)		103	
Water	67, 97	11, 52, 77, 103	1-2, 2-1, 2-2, 3-1, 3-2
Wax pencil		77	
Yarn		103	

Non-Consumables

Item	EXPLORE ACTIVITY Page	Mini LAB Page	Activity Chapter/Section
Balance	67	11	3-1
Beaker(s)	67		
Bowl(s)	67	52	
Clock	67	77	
Clock with second hand	155		
Compound light microscope			2-2
Container(s)		42	1-2, 3-1
Coverslip			2-1, 2-2
Cups, small		73	
Dropper		77	2-1, 2-2
Dropper bottle(s)			3-2
Flashlight		42	
Forceps			2-1
Glass, clear		52	
Glasses, clean (12)		77	
Hand lens	39, 97	52	1-1, 1-2, 6-2
Hole punch	155		
Insect collection	7		
Microscope			2-1, 4-1
Microscope slide			2-1, 2-2
Petri dishes, plastic			2-2
Prepared slide of human cheek cells			2-1
Prepared slide of onion root tip			4-1
Reference-newspaper classified ads	155		

Non-Consumables *continued*

Item	EXPLORE ACTIVITY Page	Mini LAB Page	Activity Chapter/Section
Spoon			3-1
Stereomicroscope			2-2
Stirring rod			3-2
Stirrer	67		
Test tubes			3-2
Test-tube rack			3-2
Test-tube stopper(s)			3-2
Watch	67		

Chemical Supplies

Item	EXPLORE ACTIVITY Page	Mini LAB Page	Activity Chapter/Section
Bromothymol blue solution			3-2

Live Organisms

Item	EXPLORE ACTIVITY Page	Mini LAB Page	Activity Chapter/Section
Brine shrimp eggs			1-2
Elodea plant			2-1

Lab Safety

The activities in *Glencoe Custom Curriculum Series* have been tested in the laboratory and have been reviewed by safety consultants. Even so, there are no guarantees against accidents. For additional help, refer to the *Laboratory Management and Safety* booklet, which contains safety guidelines and masters to test students' lab and safety skills.

General Guidelines

- Post safety guidelines, fire escape routes, and a list of emergency procedures in the classroom. Make sure students understand these procedures. Remind them at the beginning of *every* lab session.

  - Understand and make note of the Safety Symbols used in each activity.

  - Have students fill out a safety contract. Students should pledge to follow the rules, to wear safety attire, and to conduct themselves in a responsible manner.

- Know where emergency equipment is stored and how to use it.

- Supervise students at all times. Check assembly of all setups.

- Perform all activities before you allow students to do so.

- Instruct students to follow directions carefully.

- Make sure that all students are wearing proper safety attire. They should secure long hair and loose clothing.

Handling Chemicals

- Always wear safety goggles, gloves, and an apron when handling chemicals. Treat all chemicals as potentially dangerous.

- Never ingest chemicals. Use proper techniques to smell solutions.

- Use a fume hood when handling chemicals that are poisonous or corrosive or that give off a vapor.

- *Always add acids to water, never the reverse.*

- Prepare solutions by adding the solid to a small amount of distilled water, then diluting with water to the volume listed. If you use a hydrate that is different from the one specified, adjust the amount of hydrate to obtain the correct concentration.

- Consider purchasing premixed solutions from a scientific supply house.

- Maintain appropriate MSDS (Materials Safety Data Sheets).

- Do not permit wearing contact lenses, even with safety glasses; splashing chemicals could infuse under a lens and cause eye damage.

Laboratory **Management** and **Safety** IN THE SCIENCE CLASSROOM

Disclaimer
Glencoe/McGraw-Hill makes no claims to the completeness of this discussion of laboratory safety and chemical handling. The material presented is not all-inclusive, nor does it address all of the hazards associated with handling, storage, and disposal of chemicals, or with laboratory management.

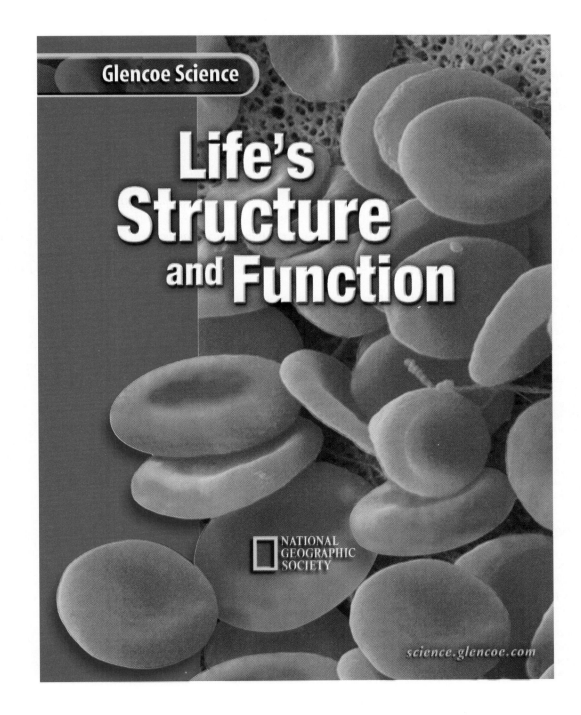

Glencoe Science

Life's Structure and Function

NATIONAL GEOGRAPHIC SOCIETY

science.glencoe.com

Glencoe McGraw-Hill

New York, New York   Columbus, Ohio   Woodland Hills, California   Peoria, Illinois

Glencoe Science

Life's Structure and Function

Student Edition
Teacher Wraparound Edition
Interactive Teacher Edition CD-ROM
Interactive Lesson Planner CD-ROM
Lesson Plans
Content Outline for Teaching
Dinah Zike's Teaching Science with Foldables
Directed Reading for Content Mastery
Foldables: Reading and Study Skills
Assessment
   Chapter Review
   Chapter Tests
   ExamView Pro Test Bank Software
   Assessment Transparencies
   Performance Assessment in the Science Classroom
   The Princeton Review Standardized Test Practice Booklet
Directed Reading for Content Mastery in Spanish
Spanish Resources
English/Spanish Guided Reading Audio Program
Reinforcement

Enrichment
Activity Worksheets
Section Focus Transparencies
Teaching Transparencies
Laboratory Activities
Science Inquiry Labs
Critical Thinking/Problem Solving
Reading and Writing Skill Activities
Mathematics Skill Activities
Cultural Diversity
Laboratory Management and Safety in the Science Classroom
Mindjogger Videoquizzes and Teacher Guide
Interactive Explorations and Quizzes CD-ROM with
   Presentation Builder
Vocabulary Puzzlemaker Software
Cooperative Learning in the Science Classroom
Environmental Issues in the Science Classroom
Home and Community Involvement
Using the Internet in the Science Classroom

Glencoe/McGraw-Hill
A Division of The **McGraw·Hill** Companies

Cover Images: These human red blood cells are part of a liquid tissue—blood.

Send all inquires to:
Glencoe/McGraw-Hill
8787 Orion Place
Columbus, OH 43240

ISBN 0-07-825553-8
Printed in the United States of America.
1 2 3 4 5 6 7 8 9 10 027/043 06 05 04 03 02 01

Authors

Alton Biggs
Biology Teacher
Allen High School
Allen, Texas

Lucy Daniel, PhD
Teacher/Consultant
Rutherfordton-Spindale High School
Rutherfordton, North Carolina

Dinah Zike
Educational Consultant
Dinah-Might Activities, Inc.
San Antonio, Texas

Content Consultants

Leanne Field, PhD
Lecturer Molecular Genetics and
Microbiology
University of Texas
Austin, Texas

Connie Rizzo, MD
Professor of Biology
Pace University
New York, New York

Homer Montgomery, PhD
Department of GeoSciences
University of Texas at Dallas
Richardson, Texas

Dominic Salinas, PhD
Middle School Science Supervisor
Caddo Parish Schools
Shreveport, Louisiana

Safety Consultant

Sandra West, PhD
Associate Professor of Biology
Southwest Texas State University
San Marcos, Texas

Math Consultant

Teri Willard, EdD
Department of Mathematics
Montana State University
Belgrade, Montana

Reading Consultants

Elizabeth Babich
Special Education Teacher
Mashpee Public Schools
Mashpee, Massachusetts

Carol A. Senf, PhD
Associate Professor of English
Georgia Institute of Technology
Atlanta, Georgia

Reviewers

Maureen Barrett
Thomas E. Harrington Middle School
Mt. Laurel, New Jersey

Diane Lutz
Denmark Middle School
Denmark, Wisconsin

Janice Bowman
Coke R. Stevenson Middle School
San Antonio, Texas

Amy Morgan
Berry Middle School
Hoover, Alabama

Cory Fish
Burkholder Middle School
Henderson, Nevada

Michelle Punch
Northwood Middle School
Houston, Texas

Linda V. Forsyth
Merrill Middle School
Denver, Colorado

Billye Robbins
Lomax Junior High School
LaPorte, Texas

Tammy Ingraham
Westover Park Intermediate School
Canyon, Texas

Delores Stout
Bellefonte Middle School
Bellefonte, Pennsylvania

Series Activity Testers

José Luis Alvarez, PhD
Math/Science Mentor Teacher
Yseleta ISD
El Paso, Texas

Mary Helen Mariscal-Cholka
Science Teacher
William D. Slider Middle School
El Paso, Texas

Nerma Coats Henderson
Teacher
Pickerington Jr. High School
Pickerington, Ohio

José Alberto Marquez
TEKS for Leaders Trainer
Yseleta ISD
El Paso, Texas

Science Kit and Boreal Laboratories
Tonawanda, New York

CONTENTS

CONTENTS

CHAPTER 6

Interdisciplinary Connections/Activities

Feature Contents

Glencoe Science Life's Structure and Function
Contents in Brief

Teacher Wraparound Edition

Student Edition

Genome Sequencing

Introduction

This feature introduces students to scientific inquiry by discussing the sequencing of genomes. It is important to note that scientists who have sequenced the genomes of various organisms could complete their work only because of the background work done by generations of chemists and biologists. Sequencing of genomes is an excellent example of the interdependent nature of the different fields of science. Scientists who have developed and refined computers and software are vital to rapid, high-volume sequencing. Genome sequencing will benefit scientists in many fields, as well as the general public. Advances in medicine and agriculture due to genome research have the potential to enhance life for the human race.

1 Motivate

Have students discuss potential advantages and disadvantages of genome sequencing. Encourage students to think creatively. Record student's responses in two side-by-side lists on the board or overhead. Discuss the relative number of positive and negative responses.

Genome Sequencing

Figure 1
The DNA in your cells makes up your genetic material.

Figure 2
99.99% of all human genes are the same from individual to individual. It takes only 0.01% of your genes for your unique combination of traits.

Your genome determines your traits—everything from your eye color and blood type to the likelihood that you might get certain diseases. A genome is the set of genes in a one-celled or many-celled organism. Each gene plays a part in the expression of a specific trait. Organisms like protists, fungi, plants, and animals have their genes on chromosomes in the nucleus of each cell. In the human genome, there are 30,000 to 40,000 genes on 23 pairs of chromosomes.

Sequencing the genome of any organism—bacteria, protist, fungus, plant, or animal—is complex. Each gene's message involves four chemicals called bases—adenine (A), cytosine (C), guanine (G), and thymine (T). The bases are linked in pairs, adenine with thymine and cytosine with guanine. Each gene is a unique chain of paired bases. The average size of a human gene is about 3,000 paired bases. The sequence carries instructions for making a specific protein. Depending on the string of bases in a gene, the protein might control the formation of a certain type of tissue or it might be an enzyme that drives a biochemical reaction. Many human disorders and diseases including Huntington's Disease and sickle cell anemia are the result of a person's genetic make up.

Curriculum Connection

Mathematics The great variety of genes that make up the genome of organisms are formed using only four different chemical bases in varying sequences. Have students determine the number of possible sequences of an eight-base length of DNA. Because there are four possible bases at each position of the sequence, the students can find the answer by using the formula $4 \times 4 \times 4 \times 4 \times 4 \times 4 \times 4 \times 4$; or 4^8. Students should find that there are 65,536 combinations possible in an eight-base length of DNA.

Decoding the Genome

To decode a genome, scientists first have to identify the bases and their correct sequence. Then they must determine which parts of the sequence are genes. Only 3 percent of the human genome are useful genes.

Powerful supercomputers and inventive software make it possible to collect, sequence, and analyze genetic data faster than ever before. In one method, scientists mark chromosomes and then cut them into manageable fragments. Through chemical processes, each of the bases is dyed a different color then displayed in a pattern read by super-fast machines. The machines convert the base sequences into digital data. A super-computer then puts the fragments in the proper sequence, using markers from the first stage of the process.

By March 2001, the complete genome of some organisms in every kingdom—eubacteria, archaebacteria, protists, fungi, plants, and animals—was known including the human genome. These accomplishments would not have been possible without modern computer technology and the research of many scientists worldwide.

Figure 3
The genetic material passed from parents to offspring determines individual characteristics.

2 Teach

Content Background

Decoding the genomes of organisms has been possible only because of advances in sequencing technology. The first practical sequencing methods, called the Sanger method and the Maxam-Gilbert method, provide accurate results, but are time and labor intensive. These methods are still being used to sequence small areas of high interest, but would have been impractical for sequencing an entire genome. The estimated cost per base sequenced using these methods is between \$1.00 and \$2.00. Newer methods of sequencing include resonance ionization spectroscopy, florescence detection of bases in flow cytometry, and scanning tunnel microscopy. These methods all increase the possible rate of sequencing. The cost per base is decreased with these newer, more efficient methods.

Discussion

Why are scientists interested in sequencing the genomes of organisms other than humans? Answers will vary. Students should note that comparisons of different genomes will help scientists discover the function of different genes and the relationships between various organisms.

Science Journal

Genomes of Different Organisms Have students consider ways that the human genome might be similar to and different from the genome of other organisms. In a paragraph in their Science Journals, have the students discuss some of the expected similarities and differences. L3 **Linguistic**

Activity

Have students consider how scientists in different fields have contributed to the technology of genome sequencing. Remind students that the work being performed today would not be possible without the previous work of other scientists. Have small groups of students select a specific scientist (anyone from Gregor Mendel to Craig Venter) or group of scientists (biologists, engineers, computer scientists, and so on) to research. Have each student group write a newspaper article describing the contributions their subject has made to the sequencing process. L2 COOP LEARN IS **Interpersonal**

Extension

Have interested students monitor information about progress in sequencing the Human Genome and the genomes of other organisms on a weekly basis. Have students report major breakthroughs and milestones to the class. Encourage students to continue this project throughout the school year. L2

THE NATURE OF SCIENCE

Science

Scientists often collect and analyze data to find answers to questions or solve problems. When you collect data and analyze it to answer questions or solve problems, you are doing science.

Genetics is a part of life science, the study of all Earth's living organisms. It includes zoology and botany. In this book, you'll learn about the structures that make up organisms, including genes, and their functions.

Science Today

Through science, scientists now have a better understanding than ever before of the world and its inhabitants. New scientific discoveries build on many that came before them. Future scientists might work to understand the long lines of genetic code that today's scientists have uncovered. Each step in decoding genomes will add to the understanding of what each of the genes does. Understanding the human genome is an important key to solving many medical problems. Some day, it might be possible to genetically identify health problems in advance and treat them before they develop.

Improved technology is another important part of science. Many advances in science would not be possible without new equipment to perform experiments and collect data. Sequencing the human genome would be impossible without the technology that allows scientists to see, manipulate, and record the genetic material. Sequencing machines and supercomputers have allowed scientists to map the human genome more quickly and accurately than was previously possible. The transfer of computerized data over the Internet also has made it possible for the Human Genome Project's scientists to share the details of their results instantly.

Figure 4
These machines, called 3700s, ran nonstop to sequence the human genome. They filter the DNA and digitally record it.

Benefits for Society

New scientific discoveries often benefit society. Science has made work easier, has helped to keep people safer, and led to medical advances that allow people to live longer and healthier lives. Scientists working on the Human Genome Project hope that their work will help provide a better explanation of how living organisms are constructed and how they function. A complete understanding of the genome will tell us more about the physical makeup of humans than we have ever known before.

Inclusion Strategies

Learning Disabled Reinforce that all living things—plants, animals, protists, bacteria, and fungi—have DNA in their cells. Scientists are interested in sequencing the genomes of many living things. Remind students that every characteristic of their bodies is affected by their DNA, even those things we can't see, such as digestive enzymes, structure of bones, and make up of blood.

Where Do Scientists Work?

Scientists work in a variety of places for a variety of reasons. Most of the American scientists who sequenced the human genome worked for either the United States government as part of the federally funded Human Genome Project, or for private companies. Both groups have the same goal even though their methods vary. These scientists worked with sensitive equipment in university laboratories and research centers. Scientists, who apply genetic research to medicine, work with the data provided by the new genetic maps. They might test hypotheses about genetic therapy through clinical experimentation.

Figure 5
Some results from the Human Genome Project are available on the Internet.

A Geneticist

Dr. John Carpten is a molecular geneticist working on the Human Genome Project. His focus is on the gene that makes some men at higher risk for developing prostate cancer. Geneticists like Dr. Carpten may do research in laboratories, analyze data in lab settings, or do diagnostic work with patients.

Dr. John Carpten

The human genome is sequenced and the locations of genes for human traits and illnesses are known. If you had the power to choose a project that uses the genome map to create something new or solve a problem, what would you choose to do and why? How would the sequenced genome help you?

Figure 6
Some day, a physician might consult a patient's genome before prescribing medicine or other treatment for a disease.

Discussion

Imagine that a doctor knew that a patient's genetic make-up caused that person to be more likely to develop a disease. How could the doctor use this information to help the patient? The doctor may be able to advise the patient on preventative medicine or lifestyle changes, such as diet or exercise, that might help the patient avoid the disease. The patient may also have time to prepare for the onset of symptoms of the disease. Students may also point out the negative aspects of knowing in advance the possibility of being afflicted with a disease or illness.

Use Science Words

Word Origin Genome is a word constructed from two root words. Have students determine the language origin of the word genome, and the meanings of the two root words that were combined in the 1930's to develop this term. Students should find that the term *genome* was developed by combining the German words for *gene* and *chromosome*.

③ Assess

Use the questions in the You Do It to assess understanding. Answers should relate to the use of the completed genome map to solve a problem or to make something new and should be a specific as possible.

You Do It

Lead students through this exercise as a class. Remind students that while the sequencing of the Human Genome is an achievement unto itself, there are many ways that this application will lead to advances in many areas of science. List student's responses on the board or overhead. Emphasize that there are no right or wrong answers. Encourage students to think creatively.

Section/Objectives	Standards		Activities/Features
	National	**State/Local**	
Chapter Opener	See p. 6T for a Key to Standards.		**Explore Activity:** Use features to classify organisms, p. 7 **Before You Read,** p. 7
Section 1 What is science? 🕐 2 sessions 📦 1 block 1. **Apply** scientific methods to problem solving. 2. **Demonstrate** how to measure using scientific units.	National Content Standards: UCP2, A1, A2, B1, G1		**Science Online,** p. 10 **MiniLAB:** Analyzing Data, p. 11 **Problem-Solving Activity:** Does temperature affect the rate of bacterial reproduction?, p. 13
Section 2 Living Things 🕐 2 sessions 📦 1 block 1. **Distinguish** between living and nonliving things. 2. **Identify** what living things need to survive.	National Content Standards: UCP2, C1, C4		**Science Online,** p. 17 **Health Integration,** p. 19
Section 3 Where does life come from? 🕐 1 session 📦 0.5 block 1. **Describe** experiments about spontaneous generation. 2. **Explain** how scientific methods led to the idea of biogenesis. 3. **Examine** how chemical compounds found in living things might have formed.	National Content Standards: UCP2, A2, C1, D2, G3		**Visualizing the Origins of Life,** p. 22 **Earth Science Integration,** p. 23
Section 4 How are living things classified? 🕐 3 sessions 📦 1.5 blocks 1. **Describe** how early scientists classified living things. 2. **Explain** the system of binomial nomenclature. 3. **Demonstrate** how to use a dichotomous key.	National Content Standards: UCP1, A1, A2, C1, F5, G2, G3		**Science Online,** p. 25 **MiniLAB:** Communicating Ideas, p. 27 **Activity:** Classifying Seeds, p. 29 **Activity:** Using Scientific Methods, pp. 30–31 **Science and Society:** Monkey Business, pp. 32–33

NATIONAL GEOGRAPHIC   **Teacher's Corner**

PRODUCTS AVAILABLE FROM GLENCOE
To order call 1-800-334-7344:
Books
National Geographic Book of Mammals
Field Guide to the Birds of North America
CD-ROMs
Mammals: A Multimedia Encyclopedia

NGS PictureShow: Classifying Plants and Animals
Curriculum Kits
GeoKit: Cells and Organisms
GeoKit: Fish, Reptiles, and Amphibians
GeoKit: Plants
Transparency Set

NGS PicturePack: Classifying Plants and Animals
PRODUCTS AVAILABLE FROM NATIONAL GEOGRAPHIC SOCIETY
To order call 1-800-368-2728:
Video
Plant Classification

Activity Materials	Reproducible Resources	Section Assessment	Technology
Explore Activity: insect collection	**Chapter Resources Booklet** Foldables Worksheet, p. 15 Directed Reading Overview, p. 17 Note-taking Worksheets, pp. 33–35	GLENCOE'S ASSESSMENT ADVANTAGE	
MiniLAB: pan balance, sponge, water	**Chapter Resources Booklet** Transparency Activity, p. 44 MiniLAB, p. 3 Enrichment, p. 29 Reinforcement, p. 25 Lab Activity, pp. 9–10 Directed Reading, p. 18	**Portfolio** Science Journal, p. 9 **Performance** MiniLAB, p. 11 Problem-Solving Activity, p. 13 Skill Builder Activities, p. 15 **Content** Section Assessment, p. 15	Section Focus Transparency Interactive CD-ROM/DVD Guided Reading Audio Program
Need materials? Contact Science Kit at 1-800-828-7777 or www.sciencekit.com on the Internet.	**Chapter Resources Booklet** Transparency Activity, p. 45 Enrichment, p. 30 Reinforcement, p. 26 Directed Reading, p. 18	**Portfolio** Curriculum Connection, p. 18 **Performance** Skill Builder Activities, p. 20 **Content** Section Assessment, p. 20	Section Focus Transparency Interactive CD-ROM/DVD Guided Reading Audio Program
	Chapter Resources Booklet Transparency Activity, p. 46 Enrichment, p. 31 Reinforcement, p. 27 Directed Reading, p. 19	**Portfolio** Reteach, p. 23 **Performance** Skill Builder Activities, p. 23 **Content** Section Assessment, p. 23	Section Focus Transparency Interactive CD-ROM/DVD Guided Reading Audio Program
MiniLAB: magazine picture of a piece of furniture **Activity:** packets of seeds (10 different kinds), metric ruler, hand lens **Activity:** 3 500-mL, wide-mouthed containers; brine shrimp eggs; small plastic spoon; distilled water; weak salt solution; strong salt solution; 3 labels; hand lens	**Chapter Resources Booklet** Transparency Activity, p. 47 MiniLAB, p. 4 Enrichment, p. 32 Reinforcement, p. 28 Directed Reading, pp. 19, 20 Transparency Activity, pp. 49–50 Lab Activity, pp. 11–13 Activity Worksheets, pp. 5–6, 7–8 **Lab Management and Safety,** p. 65	**Portfolio** Assessment, p. 28 **Performance** MiniLAB, p. 27 Skill Builder Activities, p. 28 **Content** Section Assessment, p. 28	Section Focus Transparency Teaching Transparency Interactive CD-ROM/DVD Guided Reading Audio Program

End of Chapter Assessment

Blackline Masters	Technology	Professional Series
Chapter Resources Booklet Chapter Review, pp. 37–38 Chapter Tests, pp. 39–42 **Standardized Test Practice by The Princeton Review,** pp. 7–10	MindJogger Videoquiz CD-ROM Explorations and Quizzes Vocabulary Puzzle Makers ExamView Pro Test Bank Interactive Lesson Planner Interactive Teacher's Edition	Performance Assessment in the Science Classroom (PASC)

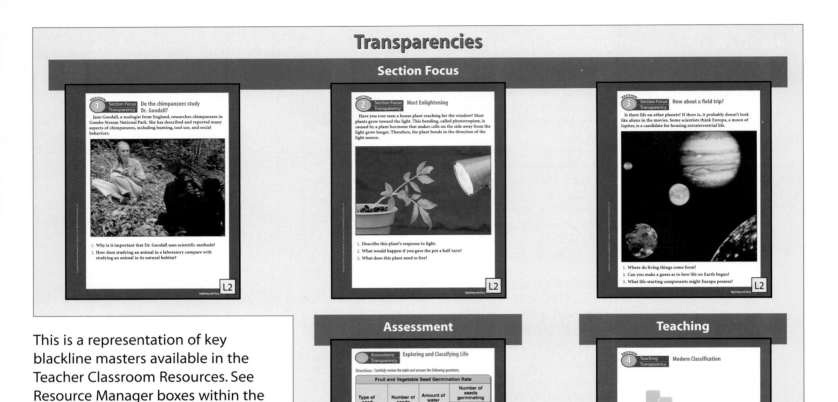

Transparencies

Section Focus

Section Focus Transparency 1 — Do the chimpanzees study Dr. Goodall?

Jane Goodall, a zoologist from England, researches chimpanzees in Gombe Stream National Park. She has described and reported many aspects of chimpanzees, including hunting, tool use, and social behaviors.

1. Why is it important that Dr. Goodall uses scientific methods?
2. How does studying an animal in a laboratory compare with studying an animal in its natural habitat?

L2

Section Focus Transparency 2 — Most Enlightening

Have you ever seen a house plant reaching for the window? Most plants grow toward the light. This bending, called phototropism, is caused by a plant hormone that makes cells on the side away from the light grow longer. Therefore, the plant bends in the direction of the light source.

1. Describe this plant's response to light.
2. What would happen if you gave the pot a half turn?
3. What does this plant need to live?

L2

Section Focus Transparency 3 — How about a field trip?

Is there life on other planets? If there is, it probably doesn't look like aliens in the movies. Some scientists think Europa, a moon of Jupiter, is a candidate for housing extraterrestrial life.

1. Where do living things come from?
2. Can you make a guess as to how life on Earth began?
3. What life-starting components might Europa possess?

L2

This is a representation of key blackline masters available in the Teacher Classroom Resources. See Resource Manager boxes within the chapter for additional information.

Key to Teaching Strategies

The following designations will help you decide which activities are appropriate for your students.

| L1 | Level 1 activities should be appropriate for students with learning difficulties. |

| L2 | Level 2 activities should be within the ability range of all students. |

| L3 | Level 3 activities are designed for above-average students. |

| ELL | ELL activities should be within the ability range of English Language Learners. |

| COOP LEARN | Cooperative Learning activities are designed for small group work. |

| LS | Multiple Learning Styles logos are used throughout to indicate strategies that address different learning styles. |

| P | These strategies represent student products that can be placed into a best-work portfolio. |

Assessment

Assessment Transparency — Exploring and Classifying Life

Directions: Carefully review the table and answer the following questions.

Fruit and Vegetable Seed Germination Rate

Type of seed	Number of seeds	Amount of water added (mL)	Number of seeds germinating Day 3	Day 5	Day 7
Orange	10	50	0	0	1
Lemon	10	50	0	1	1
Cucumber	10	50	6	7	7
Onion	10	50	7	9	10

1. Which hypothesis was probably being tested?
   A Less than 25 percent of vegetable seeds will germinate.
   B Seeds prefer to grow in soil versus sand.
   C Vegetable seeds germinate faster than fruit seeds.
   D A period of one week is required before seeds will germinate.
2. Which of the following would improve an experiment to compare the rate of seed germination?
   F using more types of seeds
   G measuring the length of the plants
   H adding 100mL of water to each seed
   J conducting the experiment for a shorter time
3. Which factor would have the LEAST effect on the results?
   A the amount of light to which the seeds were exposed
   B the amount of soil used for the seeds
   C the color of the pots used
   D the depth the seeds were planted in the soil

L2

Teaching

Teaching Transparency 4 — Modern Classification

Kingdom — Animalia
Phylum — Chordata
Class — Mammalia
Order — Cetacea
Family — Delphinidae
Genus — Tursiops
Species — Tursiops truncatus

L2

Hands-on Activities

Activity Worksheets

Activity — Classifying Seeds

Lab Preview
Directions: Answer these questions before you begin the Activity.

1. Why should seeds that are meant for planting not be tasted or eaten?

2. What is one feature of a seed that might be used for classifying seeds?

Scientists use classification systems to show how organisms are related. How do they determine what features to use to classify organisms? In this activity, you will observe seeds and use their features to classify them.

What You'll Investigate
How can the features of seeds be used to develop a key to identify the seed?

Materials
packets of seeds (10 different kinds)
hand lens
metric ruler

Goals
Observe the seeds and notice their features.
Classify seeds using those features.

Safety Precautions
Do not eat any seeds or put them in your mouth. Some may have been treated with chemicals.

Procedure
1. Record the features of each seed in the table below.
2. Use the features to develop a key.
3. Exchange keys with another group. Can you use their key to identify seeds?

Features	Type of Seed
Color	
Length (mm)	
Shape	
Texture	

L2

Laboratory Activities

Laboratory Activity 1 — The Scientific Method

When scientists are asked questions, they may not know the answers. They think of the possible answers, called hypotheses, and experiment to find the correct answers. Using the results of the experiment, they may need to form another hypothesis and test it. This way of solving a problem is called the scientific method.

Strategy
You will predict whether or not red cabbage juice will remain red when chemicals are added to it.
You will test your prediction with an experiment.
You will observe what happens and record your observations.
You will draw conclusions based on your observations.

Materials
apron   labels   chemical X (vinegar): Keep containers
goggles   3 droppers   closed when not in use.
4 test tubes (18 – 150 mm) graduated cylinder (25 mL)   chemical Y (ammonia)
test tube rack   40 mL red cabbage juice   chemical Z (baking soda solution)

Procedure
1. In the space below, predict what will happen to the red cabbage juice when chemicals X, Y and Z are added to it.

2. Label four test tubes, 1, 2, 3, and 4.
3. Add 10 mL of red cabbage juice to each test tube. CAUTION: Do not spill chemicals X, Y, or Z on clothes or skin. Rinse with water if spilled.

4. Add 10 drops of chemical X to test tube 1.
5. Add 10 drops of chemical Y to test tube 2.
6. Add 10 drops of chemical Z to test tube 3.
7. Do not add anything to test tube 4. This is the control. The control is a part of the experiment that is not tested.
8. Record your observations in Table 1.

Data and Observations
Table 1

Test tube	Substance added	Color
1		
2		
3		
4		

L2

Meeting Different Ability Levels

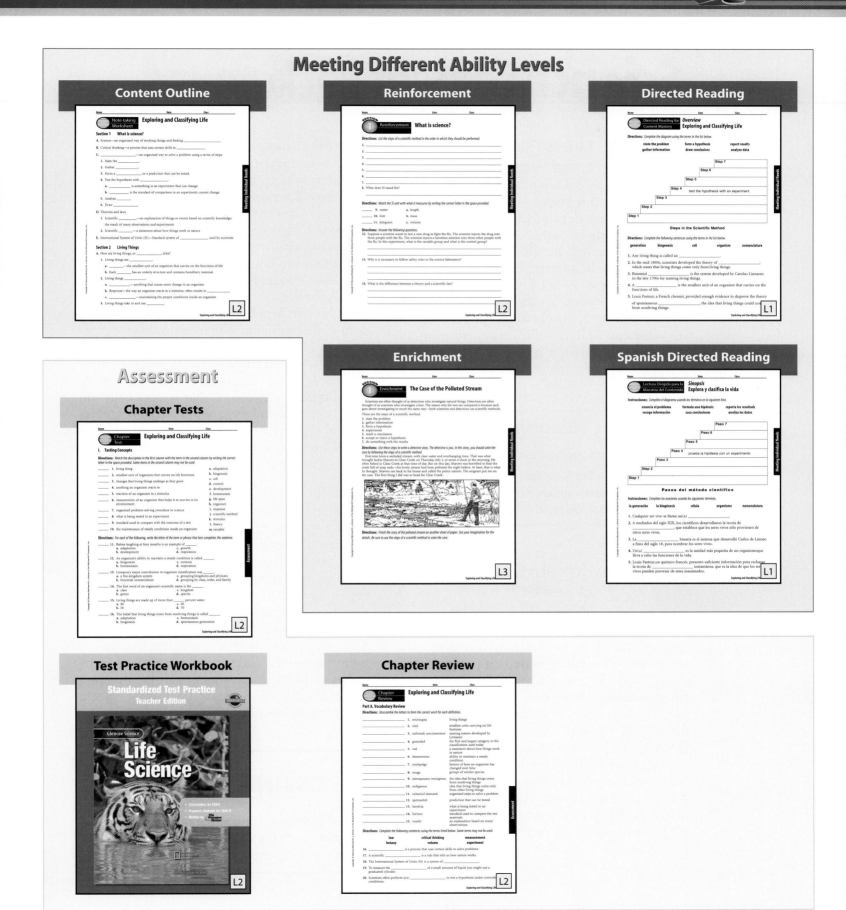

Content Outline

Reinforcement

Directed Reading

Assessment

Chapter Tests

Enrichment

Spanish Directed Reading

Test Practice Workbook

Chapter Review

Science Content Background

SECTION 2

Living Things
Living Versus Nonliving

Living organisms consist of highly organized systems that interact and are dependent upon one another. Living systems are open systems requiring a constant source of energy. All living organisms have a metabolic process by which the energy in carbohydrates is released for use. All living organisms respond to their environment in adaptive ways, including physiological responses as well as behaviors. Living organisms must also have a means of reproduction, growth, and development if their species is to continue.

Student Misconception

All things that move are alive.

Refer to the facing page for teaching strategies to address this misconception. Refer to pages 16–19 for content related to this topic.

SECTION 4

How are living things classified?
Modern Classification

This textbook uses a combination of phenetics and cladistics to classify organisms. Phenetics is based on particular features. Cladistics uses shared, derived characteristics to classify organisms. By comparing DNA nucleotide sequences between species and by measuring the amount of bonding between DNA from different species, taxonomists infer the degree of similarity between organisms. Scientists hypothesize that organisms with similar proteins are closely related. A comparison of the amino acid sequences between species' proteins provides objective, quantitative data for taxonomists because the structure of proteins is genetically determined.

Scientific Names

Most taxonomists currently divide the six-kingdom system into groups called domains. The three domains are Eubacteria, Archaea, and Eukarya. The domains Eubacteria and Archaea contain Kingdom Eubacteria and Kingdom Archaebacteria, respectively. Domain Eukarya contains four kingdoms—Kingdom Protista, Kingdom Fungi, Kingdom Plantae, and Kingdom Animalia.

The two kingdoms of prokaryotes, Kingdom Eubacteria and Kingdom Archaebacteria, differ. All eubacteria have muramic acid in their cell walls, but archaebacteria do not. The RNA sequences of eubacteria and archaebacteria are also different. Organisms that possess cells with membrane-bound organelles are eukaryotes. Several organelles—mitochondria, chloroplasts, and Golgi apparatus—are approximately the size of a prokaryotic cell.

Tools for Identifying Organisms

A system of classification avoids ambiguity among species, reflects the phylogeny (evolutionary history) of organisms, and provides clues about the organism's habits and possible features shared with similar organisms. The second word of a scientific name is called the specific epithet, usually an adjective that describes the organism, indicates the organism's place of origin, or is a Latinized surname to honor someone. Subspecies have two specific epithets. Today, species names are a mixture of Latin and Greek. At least 1.5 million species of organisms have been named.

SCIENCE *Online*

For additional content background on this topic, go to the Glencoe Science Web site at science.glencoe.com.

IDENTIFYING ▷ **Misconceptions**

Find Out What Students Think

Students may think that . . .

• **All things that move are alive.**

Students generally define "living" according to the characteristics of large animals. Hence they associate "living" with movement. Students often do not consider plants and fungi to be alive because they do not appear to move, but may classify rivers or clouds as living because they do move. Students may add other mammalian characteristics to their definitions of life such as eating, breathing, or the presence of a heartbeat.

Clouding the concept further is the confusion between "nonliving" and "dead." Students may classify both a dead animal and a rock as "nonliving" objects, even though they classify animals in general as alive.

Discussion
Place a rock, a houseplant, and a living animal (such as a caged hamster or a volunteer student) in view of the class. Ask students if they think any of the three items are alive. As students respond, ask them why the think the item is or is not alive. From this, generate a list of characteristics that students believe belong to all living organisms. Students will probably recognize that the animal is alive. Some will understand that the plant is alive, but have difficulty explaining why. Most will know that the rock is not alive.

Promote Understanding

Activity
Have the students read **Section 2** in this chapter, then review the list they generated in the discussion suggestion above. Ask the students if they want to change anything on the list.

Next, place a candle in full view of the class and light it. Ask students if they think the flame is alive. Then do the following:

• Blow gently on the flame to show that it responds.

• Light another candle or a match from the flame to show that the flame can reproduce.

• Point out that the wax of the candle is being consumed, showing that the flame uses energy.

Remind students that many nonliving things have some characteristics of living things.

• Ask the class what characteristics the candle flame lacks. Students should recognize that the flame is not highly organized, it is not made up of organic molecules, and it contains no cells.

Assess
After completing the chapter, see *Identifying Misconceptions* in the Study Guide.

Exploring and Classifying Life

Chapter Vocabulary

scientific methods
hypothesis
control
variable
theory
law
organism
cell
homeostasis
spontaneous generation
biogenesis
phylogeny
kingdom
binomial nomenclature
genus

What do you think?

Science Journal The animals in the picture are tube sponges. Tube sponges remain attached to one place. They remove oxygen and food from water that flows through a series of canals in their bodies.

Exploring and Classifying Life

How many different living things do you see in this picture? Did your answer include the living coral? What do all living things have in common? How are they different? In this chapter, you will read the answers to these questions. You also will read how living things are classified. In the first part of the chapter, you will read how scientific methods may be used to solve many everyday and scientific problems.

What do you think?

Science Journal Look at the picture below with a classmate. Discuss what you think these might be. Here's a hint: *You could really clean up with these things.* Write your answer or best guess in your Science Journal.

6 ◆ A

Theme Connection

Systems and Interactions Scientists have devised systems for classifying organisms. These systems use an organism's traits, which have changed over time as a result of organisms' interactions with the environment.

EXPLORE ACTIVITY

Life scientists discover, describe, and name hundreds of organisms every year. How do they decide if a certain plant belongs to the iris or orchid family of flowering plants, or if an insect is more like a grasshopper or a beetle?

Use features to classify organisms

1. Observe the organisms on the opposite page or in an insect collection in your class.
2. Decide which feature could be used to separate the organisms into two groups, then sort the organisms into the two groups.
3. Continue to make new groups using different features until each organism is in a category by itself.

Observe

What features would you use to classify the living thing in the photo above? How do you think scientists classify living things? List your ideas in your Science Journal.

FOLDABLES
Reading & Study Skills

Before You Read

Making a Vocabulary Study Fold To help you study the interactions of life, make the following vocabulary Foldable. Knowing the definition of vocabulary words in a chapter is a good way to ensure you have understood the content.

1. Place a sheet of notebook paper in front of you so that the short side is at the top. Fold the paper in half from the left to the right side.
2. Through one thickness of paper, cut along every third line from the outside edge to the center fold, forming ten tabs as shown.
3. On the front of each tab, write a vocabulary word listed on the first page of each section in this chapter. On the back of each tab, write what you think the word means. Add to or change the definitions as you read.

A ◆ 7

Purpose Use the Explore Activity to introduce students to classification. In this chapter students will learn how characteristics of organisms are used in classification. L2 COOP LEARN
IS Interpersonal
Preparation Use the opening photo to promote a discussion of how organisms are classified. If insect collections are available, use them to supplement the discussion.
Materials chapter-opening photo or an insect collection
Alternate Materials collection of leaves
Teaching Strategies
• Make sure students can identify the differences between the organisms in the coral reef or in the insect collection.
• Accept any logical classification groupings devised by students.

Observe

Scientists identify the traits of an organism. They compare these traits with those of other living things. The organism is then placed into a group of living things with similar traits.

✓ Assessment

Oral Have students explain the reasons behind the choices they made. Use **Performance Assessment in the Science Classroom**, p. 121.

FOLDABLES
Reading & Study Skills

Before You Read

Dinah Zike Study Fold
Purpose Use the Activity to expose students to the chapter's content and vocabulary before they read, and to encourage a search for terms and definitions as they read. The resulting Foldable can be used as an assessment tool and study guide before, during and after reading.

📁 For additional help, see Foldables Worksheet, p. 15 in **Chapter Resources Booklet,** or go to the Glencoe Science Web site at **science.glencoe.com.** See After You Read in the Study Guide at the end of this chapter.

What is science?

What is science?

1 Motivate

Bellringer Transparency

Display the Section Focus Transparency for Section 1. Use the accompanying Transparency Activity Master. L2

ELL

Section Focus Transparency — Do the chimpanzees study Dr. Goodall?

Jane Goodall, a zoologist from England, researches chimpanzees in Gombe Stream National Park. She has described and reported many aspects of chimpanzees, including hunting, tool use, and social behaviors.

1. Why is it important that Dr. Goodall uses scientific methods?
2. How does studying an animal in a laboratory compare with studying an animal in its natural habitat?

Exploring and Classifying Life

Tie to Prior Knowledge

Students use problem-solving skills daily. Discuss how they solve everyday problems, such as deciding what outfit to wear or how to manage homework with sports schedules. Relate solving everyday problems to scientific methods.

Text Question Answer

bacteria

As You Read

What You'll Learn

- **Apply** scientific methods to problem solving.
- **Demonstrate** how to measure using scientific units.

Vocabulary

scientific methods   variable
hypothesis   theory
control   law

Why It's Important

Learning to use scientific methods will help you solve ordinary problems in your life.

The Work of Science

Movies and popcorn seem to go together. So before you and your friends watch a movie, sometimes you pop some corn in a microwave oven. When the popping stops, you take out the bag and open it carefully. You smell the mouthwatering, freshly popped corn and avoid hot steam that escapes from the bag. What makes the popcorn pop? How do microwaves work and make things hot? By the way, what are microwaves anyway?

Asking questions like these is one way scientists find out about anything in the world and the universe. Science is often described as an organized way of studying things and finding answers to questions.

Types of Science Many types of science exist. Each is given a name to describe what is being studied. For example, energy and matter have a relationship. That's a topic for physics. A physicist could answer most questions about microwaves.

On the other hand, a life scientist might study any of the millions of different animals, plants, and other living things on Earth. Look at the objects in **Figure 1.** What do they look like to you? A life scientist could tell you the objects are living plants and not just pretty rocks. Life scientists who study plants are botanists, and those who study animals are zoologists. What do you suppose a bacteriologist studies?

Figure 1

Are these all rocks? **Examine the picture carefully. Some of these objects are actually *Lithops* plants. They commonly are called stone plants and are native to deserts in South Africa.**

8   A

Section ✓*Assessment* Planner

PORTFOLIO
Science Journal, p. 9
PERFORMANCE ASSESSMENT
MiniLAB, p. 11
Problem-Solving Activity, p. 13
Skill Builder Activities, p. 15
See page 36 for more options.

CONTENT ASSESSMENT
Section, p. 15
Challenge, p. 15
Chapter, pp. 36–37

Critical Thinking

Whether or not you become a trained scientist, you are going to solve problems all your life. You probably solve many problems every day when you sort out ideas about what will or won't work. Suppose your CD player stops playing music. To figure out what happened, you have to think about it. That's called critical thinking, and it's the way you use skills to solve problems.

If you know that the CD player does not run on batteries and must be plugged in to work, that's the first thing you check to solve the problem. You check and the player is plugged in so you eliminate that possible solution. You separate important information from unimportant information—that's a skill. Could there be something wrong with the first outlet? You plug the player into a different outlet, and your CD starts playing. You now know that it's the first outlet that doesn't work. Identifying the problem is another skill you have.

Solving Problems

Scientists use the same types of skills that you do to solve problems and answer questions. Although scientists don't always find the answers to their questions, they always use critical thinking in their search. Besides critical thinking, solving a problem requires organization. In science, this organization often takes the form of a series of procedures called **scientific methods. Figure 2** shows one way that scientific methods might be used to solve a problem.

State the Problem Suppose a veterinary technician wanted to find out whether different types of cat litter cause irritation to cats' skin. What would she do first? The technician begins by observing something she cannot explain. A pet owner brings his four cats to the clinic to be boarded while he travels. He leaves his cell phone number so he can be contacted if any problems arise. When they first arrive, the four cats seem healthy. The next day however, the technician notices that two of the cats are scratching and chewing at their skin. By the third day, these same two cats have bare patches of skin with red sores. The technician decides that something in the cats' surroundings or their food might be irritating their skin.

Figure 2
The series of procedures shown below is one way to use scientific methods to solve a problem.

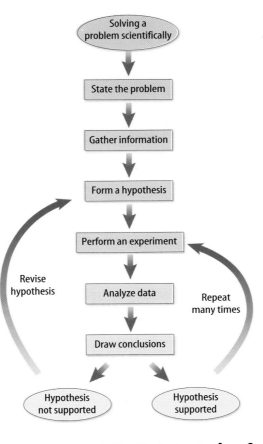

SECTION 1 What is science? **A ◆ 9**

Science Journal

Critical-Thinking Log Ask students to keep in their journals a log of instances in which they used critical thinking to solve problems. Logs should note the date, problem, and solution. At the end of one week, have students share their logs with classmates. Guide students in recognizing that critical thinking is a life skill.
L2 IS **Interpersonal** P

The Work of Science

Activity

Divide the class into small groups. Ask: **What do you think life scientists do? Where might they work?** Allow time for groups to discuss the questions and record their responses. Have each group use their results to write a Help Wanted advertisement seeking a life scientist. Ask groups to present their advertisements to the class. COOP LEARN
IS **Interpersonal**

Critical Thinking

IDENTIFYING Misconceptions

Science is often thought of as a discipline out of reach of most people. Many believe that only well-educated or specially trained people can practice science. Explain that science is a process of understanding and that anyone can use the methods of science in daily life.

Solving Problems

Visual Learning

Figure 2 Are all the steps shown here always followed in the exact same sequence? No; if a hypothesis is not supported, the scientist starts over by forming a new hypothesis. Sometimes, only a few of the steps are used.

Quick Demo

Fill a 4-L glass with pond water and place it in a well-lighted area. Have students hypothesize how the water will appear in ten days. Collect the written hypotheses. At the end of ten days, have students check their hypotheses against the conditions in the jar. L1

LS Linguistic

Teacher FYI

The first scientist credited with using the scientific method was Galileo. In his investigation of falling objects, the steps he used were (1) observation, (2) hypothesis, (3) mathematical analysis or deduction from hypothesis, (4) experimental test, and (5) revision of hypothesis.

SCIENCE Online
Internet Addresses

_____
_____
_____
_____

Explore the Glencoe Science Web site at **science.glencoe.com** to find out more about topics in this section.

Figure 3
Observations can be made in many different settings.

A Laboratory investigations   **B** Computer models

C Fieldwork

SCIENCE Online

Research Visit the Glencoe Science Web site at **science.glencoe.com** for more information about how scientists use controlled experiments. Communicate to your class what you learn.

Gather Information Laboratory observations and experiments are ways to collect information. Some data also are gathered from fieldwork. Fieldwork includes observations or experiments that are done outside of the laboratory. For example, the best way to find out how a bird builds a nest is to go outside and watch it. **Figure 3** shows some ways data can be gathered.

The technician gathers information about the problem by watching the cats closely for the next two days. She knows that cats sometimes change their behavior when they are in a new place. She wants to see if the behavior of the cats with the skin sores seems different from that of the other two cats. Other than the scratching and chewing, all four cats' behavior seems to be the same.

The technician calls the owner and tells him about the problem. She asks him what brand of cat food he feeds his cats. Because his brand is the same one used at the clinic, she decides that food is not the cause of the skin irritation. She decides that the cats probably are reacting to something in their surroundings. There are many things in the clinic that the cats might react to. How does she decide what it is?

During her observations she notices that the cats seem to scratch and chew themselves most after using their litter boxes. The cat litter used by the clinic contains a deodorant. The technician calls the owner and finds out that the cat litter he buys does not contain a deodorant.

Form a Hypothesis Based on this information, the next thing the veterinary technician does is form a hypothesis. A **hypothesis** is a prediction that can be tested. After discussing her observations with the clinic veterinarian, she hypothesizes that something in the cat litter is irritating the cats' skin.

Test the Hypothesis with an Experiment The technician gets the owner's permission to test her hypothesis by performing an experiment. In an experiment, the hypothesis is tested using controlled conditions. The technician reads the labels on two brands of cat litter and finds that the ingredients of each are the same except that one contains a deodorant.

LAB DEMONSTRATION

Purpose to compare observations and inferences

Materials one red apple

Alternate Materials one purple grape for each student pair

Preparation Wash apples.

Procedure Have students record visual observations of the fruit and then classify the following statements as observations or inferences. 1. The apple's covering is red. 2. The apple is edible. 3. There are seeds inside the apple.

Expected Outcome 1 is an observation; 2 and 3 are inferences.

✓ Assessment

How are observations and inferences different? Observations are information gathered through the senses. Inferences result from past observations and knowledge.

Controls The technician separates the cats with sores from the other two cats. She puts each of the cats with sores in a cage by itself. One cat is called the experimental cat. This cat is given a litter box containing the cat litter without deodorant. The other cat is given a litter box that contains cat litter with deodorant. The cat with deodorant cat litter is the control.

A **control** is the standard to which the outcome of a test is compared. At the end of the experiment, the control cat will be compared with the experimental cat. Whether or not the cat litter contains deodorant is the variable. A **variable** is something in an experiment that can change. An experiment should have only one variable. Other than the difference in the cat litter, the technician treats both cats the same.

Reading Check *How many variables should an experiment have?*

Analyze Data The veterinary technician observes both cats for one week. During this time, she collects data on how often and when the cats scratch or chew, as shown in **Figure 4.** These data are recorded in a journal. The data show that the control cat scratches and chews more often than the experimental cat does. The sores on the skin of the experimental cat begin to heal, but those on the control cat do not.

Draw Conclusions The technician then draws the conclusion—a logical answer to a question based on data and observation—that the deodorant in the cat litter probably irritated the skin of the two cats. To accept or reject the hypothesis is the next step. In this case, the technician accepts the hypothesis. If she had rejected it, new experiments would have been necessary.

Although the technician decides to accept her hypothesis, she realizes that to be surer of her results she should continue her experiment. She should switch the experimental cat with the control cat to see what the results are a second time. If she did this, the healed cat might develop new sores. She makes an ethical decision and chooses not to continue the experiment. Ethical decisions, like this one, are important in deciding what science should be done.

Figure 4
Collecting and analyzing data is part of scientific methods.

Mini LAB

Analyzing Data

Procedure
1. Obtain a **pan balance.** Follow your teacher's instructions for using it.
2. Record all data in your **Science Journal.**
3. Measure and record the mass of a dry **sponge.**
4. Soak this sponge in **water.** Measure and record its mass.
5. Calculate how much water your sponge absorbed.
6. Combine the class data and calculate the average amount of water absorbed.

Analysis
What other information about the sponges might be important when analyzing the data from the entire class?

Discussion

Is it possible to form a hypothesis without first making observations? Explain. No; a hypothesis is formed from observations.

Reading Check

Answer one

Mini LAB

Purpose to obtain data using a pan balance L1
IS Logical-Mathematical
Materials pan balance, sponge, water, Science Journal
Teaching Strategies
• Demonstrate the use of a balance.
• Review techniques for transporting a balance: be sure all riders are back to the zero point; place one hand under the balance and the other hand on the beam's support to carry the balance.

Analysis
Accept all reasonable answers. Students may suggest that the size of the sponges or how long each was soaked in water would affect results.

Assessment

Performance Have students use a meterstick to measure the length and width of their lab tables. Ask them to explain how they decided which units of measure to use. Use **PASC,** p. 97.

Resource Manager

Chapter Resources Booklet
    MiniLAB, p. 3
    Reinforcement, p. 25
Life Science Critical Thinking/Problem Solving, p. 4

Curriculum Connection

Language Arts Have students research a major discovery in life science and the person who made the discovery. Possible research subjects include Francesco Redi, William Harvey, Alexander Fleming, Barbara McClintock, and George Washington Carver. Have students use their findings to write newspaper articles describing their discoveries. L1 **IS** Linguistic

Developing Theories

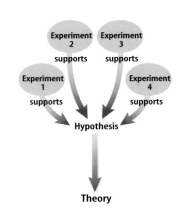

Figure 5
If data collected from several experiments over a period of time all support the hypothesis, it can finally be called a theory.

Report Results When using scientific methods, it is important to share information. The veterinary technician calls the cats' owner and tells him the results of her experiment. She tells him she has stopped using the deodorant cat litter.

The technician also writes a story for the clinic's newsletter that describes her experiment and shares her conclusions. She reports the limits of her experiment and explains that her results are not final. In science it is important to explain how an experiment can be made better if it is done again.

Developing Theories

After scientists report the results of experiments supporting their hypotheses, the results can be used to propose a scientific theory. When you watch a magician do a trick you might decide you have an idea or "theory" about how the trick works. Is your idea just a hunch or a scientific theory? A scientific **theory** is an explanation of things or events based on scientific knowledge that is the result of many observations and experiments. It is not a guess or someone's opinion. Many scientists repeat the experiment. If the results always support the hypothesis, the hypothesis can be called a theory, as shown in **Figure 5.**

✓ Reading Check *What is a theory based on?*

A theory usually explains many hypotheses. For example, an important theory in life sciences is the cell theory. Scientists made observations of cells and experimented for more than 100 years before enough information was collected to propose a theory. Hypotheses about cells in plants and animals are combined in the cell theory.

A valid theory raises many new questions. Data or information from new experiments might change conclusions and theories can change. Later in this chapter you will read about the theory of spontaneous generation and how this theory changed as scientists used experiments to study new hypotheses.

Laws A scientific **law** is a statement about how things work in nature that seems to be true all the time. Although laws can be modified as more information becomes known, they are less likely to change than theories. Laws tell you what will happen under certain conditions but do not necessarily explain why it happened. For example, in life science you might learn about laws of heredity. These laws explain how genes are inherited but do not explain how genes work. Due to the great variety of living things, laws that describe them are few. It is unlikely that a law about how all cells work will ever be developed.

Scientific Methods Help Answer Questions You can use scientific methods to answer all sorts of questions. Your questions may be as simple as "Where did I leave my house key?" or as complex as "Will global warming cause the polar ice caps to melt?" You probably have had to find the answer to the first question. Someday you might try to find the answer to the second question. Using these scientific methods does not guarantee that you will get an answer. Often scientific methods just lead to more questions and more experiments. That's what science is about—continuing to look for the best answers to your questions.

Activity

Have students obtain articles from science magazines, journals, or newspapers that describe scientific studies. As they read their articles, have students circle passages that describe the use of scientific methods. Ask them each to prepare an oral report that summarizes the content of the article and describes how scientific methods were used. L2
IS **Logical-Mathematical**

Problem-Solving Activity

Does temperature affect the rate of bacterial reproduction?

Some bacteria make you sick. Other bacteria, however, are used to produce foods like cheese and yogurt. Understanding how quickly bacteria reproduce can help you avoid harmful bacteria and use helpful bacteria. It's important to know things that affect how quickly bacteria reproduce. How do you think temperature will affect the rate of bacterial reproduction? A student makes the hypothesis that bacteria will reproduce more quickly as the temperature increases.

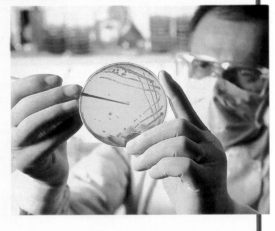

Identifying the Problem
The table below lists the reproduction-doubling rates at specific temperatures for one type of bacteria. A rate of 2.0 means that the number of bacteria doubled two times that hour (e.g., 100 to 200 to 400).

Bacterial Reproductive Rates	
Temperature (°C)	**Doubling Rate per Hour**
20.5	2.0
30.5	3.0
36.0	2.5
39.2	1.2

Look at the table. What conclusions can you draw from the data?

Solving the Problem
1. Do the data in the table support the student's hypothesis?
2. How would you write a hypothesis about the relationship between bacterial reproduction and temperature?
3. Make a list of other factors that might have influenced the results in the table.
4. Are you satisfied with these data? List other things that you wish you knew.
5. Describe an experiment that would help you test these other ideas.

SECTION 1 What is science? **A ◆ 13**

Problem-Solving Activity

National Math Standards
Correlation to Mathematics Objectives
1, 5, 6, 8, 9

Answers
1. Not completely; doubling increases to a certain temperature, and then decreases.
2. Possible answer: Bacteria reproduce more quickly as temperature rises until a certain temperature is reached; then rate falls.
3. Other possible influences: Was the light always the same? Did the bacteria have the same amount of space to grow? Were the bacteria always in the same medium? Check that student's experiments test only one variable at a time.
4. Answer will vary. Accept reasonable responses.
5. Answers will vary depending on responses to question 4. Look for variables and controls in student descriptions.

Inclusion Strategies

Learning Disabled Invite students to design a bulletin board showing the steps in scientific methods using pictures from magazines. L1
IS **Visual-Spatial**

Resource Manager

Chapter Resources Booklet
  Enrichment, p. 29
Mathematics Skill Activities, p. 33

Measuring with Scientific Units

Quick Demo

Show students a nickel and a dime. Tell them the nickel has a mass of about 5 g and the dime is 1 mm thick. Have students determine the mass, thickness, and volume of other coins they may have.

IDENTIFYING Misconceptions

Students may not understand that the weight of an object can vary, depending on the force of gravity. Explain that an object on the moon weighs less than an object on Earth because the pull of gravity is weaker on the moon than on Earth. However, the amount of matter (mass) that makes up the object does not change with location.

Teacher FYI

The U.S. is the only industrialized country that has not officially adopted SI. This has caused difficulties in the area of trade and commerce. To successfully compete in world markets, many products made in the U.S. are labeled in both SI and customary units. Invite students to conduct an SI measurement hunt in their homes to find five items that are marked with both types of measures.

Figure 6
Your food often is measured in metric units.

A The label of this juice bottle shows you that it contains 473 mL of juice.

B Nutritional information on the label is listed in grams or milligrams.

Nutrition Facts
Serv. Size 8 fl oz (240 mL)
Servings 2

Amount Per Serving
Calories 110

	% Daily Value*
Total Fat 0g	0%
Sodium 25mg	1%
Potassium 480mg	14%
Total Carb 27g	9%
Sugars 24g	
Protein 0g	

Vitamin C 100% • Thiamin 8%

Not a significant source of fat cal., sat. fat, cholest, fiber, vitamin A, calcium and iron.

*Percent Daily Values are based on a 2,000 calorie diet.

Measuring with Scientific Units

An important part of most scientific investigations is making accurate measurements. Think about things you use every day that are measured. Ingredients in your hamburger, hot dog, potato chips, or soft drink are measured in units such as grams and milliliters, as shown in **Figure 6.** The water you drink, the gas you use, and the electricity needed for a CD player are measured, too.

In your classroom or laboratory this year, you will use the same standard system of measurement scientists use to communicate and understand each other's research and results. This system is called the International System of Units, or SI. For example, you may need to calculate the distance a bird flies in kilometers. Perhaps you will be asked to measure the amount of air your lungs can hold in liters or the mass of an automobile in kilograms. Some of the SI units are shown in **Table 1.**

Table 1 Common SI Measurements

Measurement	Unit	Symbol	Equal to
Length	1 millimeter	mm	0.001 (1/1,000) m
	1 centimeter	cm	0.01 (1/100) m
	1 meter	m	1 m
	1 kilometer	km	1,000 m
Volume	1 milliliter	mL	0.001 (1/1,000) L
	1 liter	L	1,000 mL
Mass	1 gram	g	1,000 mg
	1 kilogram	kg	1,000 g
	1 tonne	t	1,000 kg = 1 metric ton

Resource Manager

Chapter Resources Booklet
Lab Activity, pp. 9–10

Reading and Writing Skill Activities,
pp. 17, 33

Cultural Diversity

Ancient Measurements The ancient Chinese system of weights and measures included an acoustical dimension. The quantity of content in a vessel was defined by both weight and by the pitch produced when the vessel was struck. Have students research and report on other measurement instruments and systems. Students might investigate the cubit and thermoscope or the history of the metric system.

Safety First

Doing science is usually much more interesting than just reading about it. Some of the scientific equipment that you will use in your classroom or laboratory is the same as what scientists use. Laboratory safety is important. In many states, a student can participate in a laboratory class only when wearing proper eye protection. Don't forget to wash your hands after handling materials. Following safety rules, as shown in **Figure 7,** will protect you and others from injury during your lab experiences. Symbols used throughout your text will alert you to situations that require special attention. Some of these symbols are shown below. A description of each symbol is in the Safety Symbols chart at the front of this book.

Figure 7
Proper eye protection should be worn whenever you see this safety symbol.

Safety First

Discussion

What is the purpose of safety symbols? Each safety symbol alerts experimenters to a potential danger associated with a particular situation.

③ Assess

Reteach

Divide the class into groups. Give each student in a group a slip of paper labeled with a step of a scientific method. After all the papers have been distributed, have students arrange themselves in a line that shows the order in which the steps are often carried out. Have groups compare their results and discuss why each group may not necessarily have the steps in the same order.

Challenge

A scientist shares the results of her experiment with others. Three scientists repeat the experiment and get different results. **What might you conclude about the first scientist's experiment?** Possible answers: The experiment was not well designed, the procedure was not clearly stated, or variables exist that the first scientist did not identify.

✓ Assessment

Portfolio Safety is just as important at home as it is in the laboratory. For each safety symbol in the chart at the front of the book, have students write one safety rule to follow at home in the kitchen, bathroom, or outdoors. Use **Performance Assessment in the Science Classroom,** p. 157.

Section ① Assessment

1. Identify steps that might be followed when using scientific methods.
2. Why is it important to test only one variable at a time during an experiment?
3. What SI unit would you use to measure the width of your classroom?
4. How is a theory different than a hypothesis?
5. **Think Critically** Can the veterinary technician in this section be sure that the deodorant caused the cats' skin problems? What could she change in her experiment to make it better?

Skill Builder Activities

6. **Communicating** Write a newsletter article that explains what the veterinary technician discovered from her experiment. **For more help, refer to the** Science Skill Handbook.
7. **Converting Units** Sometimes temperature is measured in Fahrenheit degrees. Normal human body temperature is 98.6°F. What is this temperature in degrees Celsius? Use the English to metric conversion chart at the back of this book. **For more help, refer to the** Math Skill Handbook.

Answers to Section Assessment

1. State the problem, gather information, form a hypothesis, test the hypothesis with an experiment, analyze data, and draw conclusions.
2. so the scientist can understand which condition caused the results
3. meters
4. theory—an explanation based on many observations; hypothesis—a testable prediction
5. Possible answer: Both cats may not be allergic to the same thing. She could repeat the experiment, this time giving the other cat non-deodorized litter. If the skin problem clears up, she has likely identified the problem.
6. The newspaper article should include the observations that led to stating the problem, how she gathered the information to form the hypothesis, how she tested the hypothesis with an experiment, analyzed the data, drew conclusions, and reported the results.
7. 37°C

SECTION

Living Things

1 Motivate

Bellringer Transparency

Display the Section Focus Transparency for Section 2. Use the accompanying Transparency Activity Master. L2

ELL

SECTION 2 Section Focus Transparency | Most Enlightening

Have you ever seen a house plant reaching for the window? Most plants grow toward the light. This bending, called phototropism, is caused by a plant hormone that makes cells on the side away from the light grow longer. Therefore, the plant bends in the direction of the light source.

1. Describe this plant's response to light.
2. What would happen if you gave the pot a half turn?
3. What does this plant need to live?

Exploring and Classifying Life

Tie to Prior Knowledge

Students will have ideas about characteristics and needs of all living things. Ask them to name traits and needs that all organisms share. Record responses on the board.

As You Read

***What* You'll Learn**
- **Distinguish** between living and nonliving things.
- **Identify** what living things need to survive.

Vocabulary
organism
cell
homeostasis

***Why* It's Important**
All living things, including you, have many of the same traits.

What are living things like?

What does it mean to be alive? If you walked down your street after a thunderstorm, you'd probably see earthworms on the sidewalk, birds flying, clouds moving across the sky, and puddles of water. You'd see living and nonliving things that are alike in some ways. For example, birds and clouds move. Earthworms and water feel wet when touched. Yet, clouds and water are nonliving things, and birds and earthworms are living things. Any living thing is called an **organism.**

Organisms vary in size from the microscopic bacteria in mud puddles to gigantic oak trees and are found just about everywhere. They have different behaviors and food needs. In spite of these differences, all organisms have similar traits. These traits determine what it means to be alive.

Living Things Are Organized If you were to look at almost any part of an organism, like a plant leaf or your skin, under a microscope, you would see that it is made up of small units called cells. A **cell** is the smallest unit of an organism that carries on the functions of life. Some organisms are composed of just one cell while others are composed of many cells. Cells take in materials from their surroundings and use them in complex ways. Each cell has an orderly structure and contains hereditary material. The hereditary material contains instructions for cellular organization and function. **Figure 8** shows some organisms that are made of many cells. All the things that these organisms can do are possible because of what their cells can do.

Magnification: 106×

Muscle cells

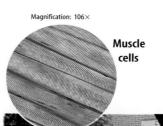

Nerve cells

Figure 8
Your body is organized into many different types of cells. Two types are shown.

Magnification: 2,000×

Section ✓ Assessment Planner

PORTFOLIO
Curriculum Connection, p. 18
PERFORMANCE ASSESSMENT
Skill Builder Activities, p. 20
See page 36 for more options.

CONTENT ASSESSMENT
Section, p. 20
Challenge, p. 20
Chapter, pp. 36–37

Living Things Respond Living things interact with their surroundings. Watch your cat when you use your electric can opener. Does your cat come running to find out what's happening even when you're not opening a can of cat food? The cat in **Figure 9** ran in response to a stimulus—the sound of the can opener. Anything that causes some change in an organism is a stimulus (plural, *stimuli*). The reaction to a stimulus is a response. Often that response results in movement, such as when the cat runs toward the sound of the can opener. To carry on its daily activity and to survive, an organism must respond to stimuli.

Living things also respond to stimuli that occur inside them. For example, water or food levels in organisms' cells can increase or decrease. The organisms then make internal changes to keep the right amounts of water and food in their cells. Their temperature also must be within a certain range. An organism's ability to keep the proper conditions inside no matter what is going on outside the organism is called **homeostasis.** Homeostasis is a trait of all living things.

> ✔ **Reading Check** *What are some internal stimuli living things respond to?*

Figure 9
Some cats respond to a food stimulus even when they are not hungry. *Why does a cat come running when it hears a can opener?*

Living Things Use Energy Staying organized and carrying on activities like homeostasis requires energy. The energy used by most organisms comes either directly or indirectly from the Sun. Plants and some other organisms use the Sun's energy and the raw materials carbon dioxide and water to make food. You and most other organisms can't use the energy of sunlight directly. Instead, you take in and use food as a source of energy. You get food by eating plants or other organisms that ate plants. Most organisms, including plants, also must take in oxygen in order to release the energy of foods.

Some bacteria live at the bottom of the oceans and in other areas where sunlight cannot reach. They can't use the Sun's energy to produce food. Instead, the bacteria use energy stored in some simple chemical compounds and the raw material carbon dioxide to make food. Unlike most other organisms, many of these bacteria do not need oxygen to release the energy that is found in their food.

Research Visit the Glencoe Science Web site at **science.glencoe.com** for more information about homeostasis. Communicate to your class what you learn.

SECTION 2 Living Things   **A ◆ 17**

2 Teach

What are living things like?

Quick Demo

Responses in plants are usually less obvious than in animals. However, if you touch a mimosa plant, all the small leaflets on the branch fold upward. Obtain a mimosa plant to demonstrate this rapid response.

Caption Answer

Figure 9 The cat is responding to the stimulus of the can opener.

✔ Reading Check

Answer water and food levels, temperature

Use an Analogy

Compare the homeostasis that must be maintained by the body to the conditions necessary for a car to function. For example, a car must have fuel, oil, and other fluids in proper balance in order to run. In the same way, organisms must have fuel and other materials in order to remain alive.

SCIENCE *Online*
Internet Addresses
_____
_____
_____
_____

Explore the Glencoe Science Web site at **science.glencoe.com** to find out more about topics in this section.

Inclusion Strategies

Learning Disabled Have students choose and draw a scene on poster board or mural paper. Have them label the objects in the drawing as living or nonliving. L1 IS **Visual-Spatial**

Resource Manager

Chapter Resources Booklet
Transparency Activity, p. 45
Directed Reading for Content Mastery, p. 18
Science Inquiry Labs, p. 3

What are living things like?, continued

Discussion

How does an acorn grow and develop? An acorn sprouts and produces roots, stems, a trunk, and leaves that continue to grow for years. As it grows, it takes in substances from the air and soil and changes those substances into living cells. It continues to add new material to replace parts that wear out.

IDENTIFYING
Misconceptions

Students may think that all things that move are alive. Refer to page 6F for teaching strategies that address this misconception.

Teacher FYI

Nonliving things obtain and use energy just as living things do. Windmills, solar calculators, solar panels, and thunderclouds all absorb energy from their environments and change it into different forms. Living things take in energy from their environments and use it for specialized purposes such as growth, development, and reproduction.

Living Things Grow and Develop When a puppy is born, it might be small enough to hold in one hand. After the same dog is fully grown, you might not be able to hold it at all. How does this happen? The puppy grows by taking in raw materials, like milk from its mother, and making more cells. Growth of many-celled organisms, such as the puppy, is mostly due to an increase in the number of cells. In one-celled organisms, growth is due to an increase in the size of the cell.

Organisms change as they grow. Puppies can't see or walk when they are first born. In eight or nine days, their eyes open, and their legs become strong enough to hold them up. All of the changes that take place during the life of an organism are called development. **Figure 10** shows how four different organisms changed as they grew.

The length of time an organism is expected to live is its life span. Adult dogs can live for 20 years and a cat for 25 years. Some organisms have a short life span. Mayflies live only one day, but a land tortoise may live for more than 180 years. Some bristlecone pine trees have been alive for more than 4,600 years. Your life span is about 80 years.

Figure 10
Complete development of an organism can take a few days or several years. The pictures below show the development of **A** a dog, **B** a human, **C** a pea plant, and **D** a butterfly.

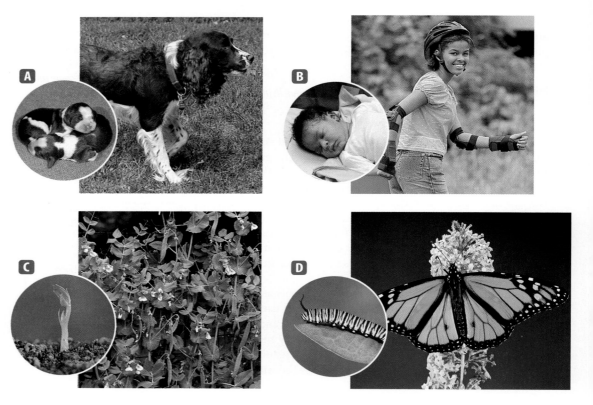

Science Journal

Characteristics of Living Things Have students choose an animal that they have observed. In their Science Journals, have them write an essay explaining how their observations show that the animal is a living organism. L2
Linguistic

Curriculum Connection

Math Have students obtain data that illustrates how they have changed as they have grown older. Ask them to research their heights at three different ages. (If this information is not available at home, have students obtain the data from their school records.) Then have students work in pairs to measure their current heights. Ask students to present their results as bar graphs. L2 **Logical-Mathematical** P

Figure 11
Living things reproduce themselves in many different ways. **A** A *Paramecium* reproduces by dividing into two. **B** Beetles, like most insects, reproduce by laying eggs. **C** Every spore released by these puffballs can grow into a new fungus.

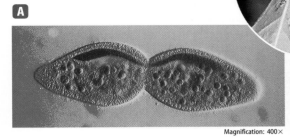

Magnification: 400×

Living Things Reproduce

Cats, dogs, alligators, fish, birds, bees, and trees eventually reproduce. They make more of their own kind. Some bacteria reproduce every 20 minutes while it might take a pine tree two years to produce seeds. **Figure 11** shows some ways organisms reproduce.

Without reproduction, living things would not exist to replace those individuals that die. An individual cat can live its entire life without reproducing. However, if cats never reproduced, all cats soon would disappear.

✔ Reading Check *Why is reproduction important?*

What do living things need?

What do you need to live? Do you have any needs that are different from those of other living things? To survive, all living things need a place to live and raw materials. The raw materials that they require and the exact place where they live can vary.

A Place to Live

An organism's surroundings limit where it can live. Not many kinds of organisms can live in extremely hot or extremely cold environments. Most cannot live at the bottom of the ocean or on the tops of mountains. All organisms also need living space in their surroundings. For example, thousands of penguins build their nests on an island. When the island becomes too crowded, the penguins fight for space and some may not find space to build nests. An organism's surroundings must provide for all of its needs.

Health
INTEGRATION

Human infants can't take care of themselves at birth. Research to find out what human infants can do at different stages of development. Make a chart that shows changes from birth to one year old.

What do living things need?, continued

Caption Answer

Figure 12 Plants take in water through their roots.

Reteach

Write the characteristics of living things on 3" x 5" cards. Have students draw a card and give an example of the characteristic. L1

Challenge

Which characteristic of life is important to survival of a species rather than to the organism itself? Explain. Reproduction; a living thing can survive without reproducing, but the species would not survive if none of its members reproduced.

Assessment

Process Have students heat water in a beaker and dissolve as much sugar in the beaker as they can. Tie a string around a stirring rod. Place the rod across the top of the beaker so the string is immersed in the cooled water. Leave the string in the beaker until sugar crystals begin to grow. Ask students why these crystals are not alive. They have none of the other characteristics of living things. Use **Performance Assessment in the Science Classroom,** p. 97.

Figure 12
You and a corn plant each take in and give off about 2 L of water in a day. Most of the water you take in is from water you drink or from foods you eat. *Where do plants get water to transport materials?*

Raw Materials Water is important for all living things. Plants and animals take in and give off large amounts of water each day, as shown in **Figure 12**. Organisms use homeostasis to balance the amounts of water lost with the amounts taken in. Most organisms are composed of more than 50 percent water. You are made of 60 to 70 percent water. Organisms use water for many things. For example, blood, which is about 90 percent water, transports digested food and wastes in animals. Plants have a watery sap that transports materials between roots and leaves.

Living things are made up of substances such as proteins, fats, and sugars. Animals take in most of these substances from the foods they eat. Plants and some bacteria make them using raw materials from their surroundings. These important substances are used over and over again. When organisms die, substances in their bodies are broken down and released into the soil or air. The substances can then be used again by other living organisms. Some of the substances in your body might once have been part of a butterfly or an apple tree.

At the beginning of this section, you learned that things such as clouds, sidewalks, and puddles of water are not living things. Now do you understand why? Clouds, sidewalks, and water do not reproduce, use energy, or have other traits of living things.

Section 2 Assessment

1. What is the main source of energy used by most organisms?
2. List five traits most organisms have.
3. Why would you expect to see cells if you looked at a section of a mushroom cap under a microscope?
4. In order to survive, what things do most organisms need?
5. **Think Critically** Why is homeostasis important to organisms?

Skill Builder Activities

6. **Comparing and Contrasting** What are the similarities and differences between a goldfish and the flame of a burning candle? **For more help, refer to the** Science Skill Handbook.
7. **Using a Database** Use references to find the life span of ten animals. Use your computer to make a database. Then graph the life spans from shortest to longest. **For more help, refer to the** Technology Skill Handbook.

Answers to Section Assessment

1. the Sun
2. Living things are organized, respond, take in and use energy, grow and develop, and reproduce.
3. All living things are made of cells.
4. Organisms need raw materials and a place to live.
5. Without homeostasis—the maintaining of proper conditions inside an organism regardless of external conditions—the organism would die.
6. The goldfish is made of cells, takes in and uses energy, responds, grows and develops, reproduces, and needs a place to live and raw materials. The candle flame moves, responds to wind, uses energy from the candle, gives off heat energy, produces waste products, and uses oxygen to burn.
7. Life spans will vary in different references. Sample data (in years): humans: 76; horses: 30; cows: 24; dogs: 15; cats: 12; turtles: 125; elephants: 60; penguins: 23; shrews: 1; snakes: 11; spiders: 3

SECTION 3 Where does life come from?

Life Comes from Life

You've probably seen a fish tank, like the one in **Figure 13,** that is full of algae. How did the algae get there? Before the seventeenth century, some people thought that insects and fish came from mud, that earthworms fell from the sky when it rained, and that mice came from grain. These were logical conclusions at that time, based on repeated personal experiences. The idea that living things come from nonliving things is known as **spontaneous generation.** This idea became a theory that was accepted for several hundred years. When scientists began to use controlled experiments to test this theory, the theory changed.

✔ **Reading Check** *According to the theory of spontaneous generation, where do fish come from?*

Spontaneous Generation and Biogenesis From the late seventeenth century through the middle of the eighteenth century, experiments were done to test the theory of spontaneous generation. Although these experiments showed that spontaneous generation did not occur in most cases, they did not disprove it entirely.

It was not until the mid-1800s that the work of Louis Pasteur, a French chemist, provided enough evidence to disprove the theory of spontaneous generation. It was replaced with **biogenesis** (bi oh JEN uh suhs), which is the theory that living things come only from other living things.

As You Read

***What* You'll Learn**

- **Describe** experiments about spontaneous generation.
- **Explain** how scientific methods led to the idea of biogenesis.
- **Examine** how chemical compounds found in living things might have formed.

Vocabulary
spontaneous generation
biogenesis

***Why* It's Important**
You can use scientific methods to try to find out about events that happened long ago or just last week. You can even use them to predict how something will behave in the future.

Figure 13
The sides of this tank were clean and the water was clear when the aquarium was set up. Algal cells, which were not visible on plants and fish, reproduced in the tank. So many algal cells are present now that the water is cloudy.

SECTION 3 Where does life come from? **A** **21**

SECTION 3

Where does life come from?

1 Motivate

Bellringer Transparency
Display the Section Focus Transparency for Section 3. Use the accompanying Transparency Activity Master. L2
ELL

Tie to Prior Knowledge

Review the characteristics and needs of living things. Elicit from volunteers their ideas on where organisms possessing such characteristics and needs came from.

✔ **Reading Check**

Answer from mud

Resource Manager

Chapter Resources Booklet
Transparency Activity, p. 46
Directed Reading for Content Mastery, p. 19

Section ✔*Assessment* Planner

PORTFOLIO
Reteach, p. 23

PERFORMANCE ASSESSMENT
Skill Builder Activities, p. 23
See page 36 for more options.

CONTENT ASSESSMENT
Section, p. 23
Challenge, p. 23
Chapter, pp. 36–37

Visualizing the Origins of Life

Have students examine the pictures and read the captions. Then ask the following questions.

What are the similarities of Spallanzani's and Redi's work? Students should note that both Spallanzani and Redi did experiments that questioned the idea of spontaneous generation.

What must have been present in the neck of the S-necked flasks used by Pasteur in his experiments? The necks of the S-neck flasks must have contained microorganisms, which contaminated the broth when the flask was tilted.

Activity

Students should work in small groups to create and play a matching game based on the scientists in the this feature and their work. In the game, points should be awarded for correctly matching a scientist with his work. Have students explain the rules of their game to the class.

Extension

Have interested students research other world events that occurred in the years the experiments shown in this feature took place. These students can construct an expanded time line showing these other events, and shared their findings with the class.

Figure 14

For centuries scientists have theorized about the origins of life. As shown on this timeline, some examined spontaneous generation—the idea that nonliving material can produce life. More recently, scientists have proposed theories about the origins of life on Earth by testing hypotheses about conditions on early Earth.

1668 Francesco Redi put decaying meat in some jars, then covered half of them. When fly maggots appeared only on the uncovered meat (see below, left), Redi concluded that they had hatched from fly eggs and had not come from the meat.

1745 John Needham heated broth in sealed flasks. When the broth became cloudy with microorganisms, he mistakenly concluded that they developed spontaneously from the broth.

1768 Lazzaro Spallanzani broiled broth in sealed flasks for a longer time than Needham did. Only the ones he opened became cloudy with contamination.

Not contaminated   Contaminated

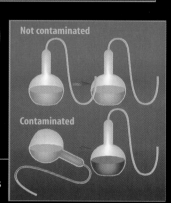

Not contaminated

Contaminated

1859 Louis Pasteur disproved spontaneous generation by boiling broth in S-necked flasks that were open to the air. The broth became cloudy (see above, bottom right) only when a flask was tilted and the broth was exposed to dust in the S-neck.

Gases of Earth's early atmosphere

Electric current

Oceanlike mixture forms

Cools

Materials in present-day cells

1924 Alexander Oparin hypothesized that energy from the Sun, lightning, and Earth's heat triggered chemical reactions early in Earth's history. The newly-formed molecules washed into Earth's ancient oceans and became a part of what is often called the primordial soup.

1953 Stanley Miller and Harold Urey sent electric currents through a mixture of gases like those thought to be in Earth's early atmosphere. When the gases cooled, they condensed to form an oceanlike liquid that contained materials such as amino acids, found in present-day cells.

22 ◆ A   CHAPTER 1 Exploring and Classifying Life

Resource Manager

Chapter Resources Booklet
Enrichment, p. 31
Reinforcement, p. 27

Earth Science Critical Thinking/Problem Solving, pp. 1, 12, 14

Visual Learning

Figure 14 Have students create a poster showing the progression of scientific thought on life origins, as evidenced by the experiments in this feature.

Life's Origins

Astronomy
INTEGRATION

If living things can come only from other living things, how did life on Earth begin? Some scientists hypothesize that about 5 billion years ago, Earth's solar system was a whirling mass of gas and dust. They hypothesize that the Sun and planets were formed from this mass. It is estimated that Earth is about 4.6 billion years old. Rocks found in Australia that are more than 3.5 billion years old contain fossils of once-living organisms. Where did these living organisms come from?

Oparin's Hypothesis In 1924, a Russian scientist named Alexander I. Oparin suggested that Earth's early atmosphere had no oxygen but was made up of the gases ammonia, hydrogen, methane, and water vapor. Oparin hypothesized that these gases could have combined to form the more complex compounds found in living things.

Using gases and conditions that Oparin described, American scientists Stanley L. Miller and Harold Urey set up an experiment to test Oparin's hypothesis in 1953. Although the Miller-Urey experiment showed that chemicals found in living things could be produced, it did not prove that life began in this way.

For many centuries, scientists have tried to find the origins of life, as shown in **Figure 14.** Although questions about spontaneous generation have been answered, some scientists still are investigating ideas about life's origins.

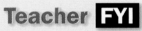

Earth Science
INTEGRATION

Scientists hypothesize that Earth's oceans originally formed when water vapor was released into the atmosphere from many volcanic eruptions. Once it cooled, rain fell and filled Earth's lowland areas. Identify five lowland areas on Earth that are now filled with water. Record your answer in your Science Journal.

Section ③ Assessment

1. Compare and contrast spontaneous generation and biogenesis.
2. Describe three controlled experiments that helped disprove the theory of spontaneous generation.
3. List one substance that was used in the Miller-Urey experiment.
4. What were the results of the Miller-Urey experiment?
5. **Think Critically** Why was Oparin's hypothesis about the origins of life important to Miller and Urey?

Skill Builder Activities

6. **Drawing Conclusions** It was thought that in the 1768 experiment some "vital force" in the broth was destroyed. Was it? Based on this experiment, what could have been concluded about where organisms come from? **For more help, refer to the** Science Skill Handbook.
7. **Using Percentages** Earth's age is estimated at 4.6 billion years old. It is estimated that life began 3.5 billion years ago. Life has been present for what percent of Earth's age? **For more help, refer to the** Math Skill Handbook.

Answers to Section Assessment

1. spontaneous generation: living things come from nonliving matter; biogenesis: living things come only from other living things of the same kind
2. Students should describe the experiments performed by Redi, Pasteur, and Spallanzani.
3. Possible answer: ammonia
4. The experiment showed that chemicals found in living things could be produced.
5. Miller and Urey used the chemicals suggested in Oparin's hypothesis.
6. By boiling the broth, the microorganisms present in it were destroyed. It could have been concluded that organisms come from the air.
7. 76%

② Teach

Life's Origins

Earth Science
INTEGRATION

Students may list any of the oceans and seas.

Teacher FYI

When Oparin first presented his hypotheses on the origins of life, they received a negative response. It was only after continued re-testing that his ideas began to be accepted.

③ Assess

Reteach

Have students make a three-column chart to summarize the experiments described in this section. Columns should be headed Experimenter, Summary of Experiment, and Conclusions.
L2 P

Challenge

How did Pasteur's experiments lead to the development of pasteurization? He showed that heating could kill bacteria that caused food to spoil.

✓Assessment

Performance Have students review the results of Redi's experiment and write their interpretation. The jars that were left open to the air attracted flies, and maggots appeared on the meat. Flies could not get to the meat in the jars that were covered, and no maggots appeared. Use **Performance Assessment in the Science Classroom,** p. 99.

How are living things classified?

SECTION

4

How are living things classified?

1 Motivate

Bellringer Transparency

Display the Section Focus Transparency for Section 4. Use the accompanying Transparency Activity Master. L2

ELL

Tie to Prior Knowledge

Ask students to identify real-life situations in which they need to classify a group of items. Possible responses may include organizing a collection of tapes or CDs, arranging canned goods in a pantry, and sorting beads used to make jewelry. Have volunteers explain the process they use in these instances.

Caption Answer

Figure 15 Possible answer: amphibians and all invertebrates

As You Read

What You'll Learn

- **Describe** how early scientists classified living things.
- **Explain** the system of binomial nomenclature.
- **Demonstrate** how to use a dichotomous key.

Vocabulary

phylogeny
kingdom
binomial nomenclature
genus

Why It's Important

Knowing how living things are classified will help you understand the relationships that exist among all living things.

Classification

If you go to a library to find a book about the life of Louis Pasteur, where do you look? Do you look for it among the mystery or sports books? You expect to find a book about Pasteur's life with other biography books. Libraries group similar types of books together. When you place similar items together, you classify them. Organisms also are classified into groups.

History of Classification When did people begin to group similar organisms together? Early classifications included grouping plants that were used in medicines. Animals were often given human traits that were used to classify them such as courageous—like lions—or wise—like owls.

More than 2,000 years ago, a Greek named Aristotle observed living things. He decided that any organism could be classified as either a plant or an animal. Then he broke these two groups into smaller groups. For example, animal categories included hair or no hair, four legs or fewer legs, and blood or no blood. **Figure 15** shows some of the organisms Aristotle would have grouped together. For hundreds of years after Aristotle, no one way of classifying was accepted by everyone.

Figure 15
According to Aristotle's classification system, all animals without hair would be grouped together. *What other animals without hair would Aristotle have put in this group?*

Section ✓ Assessment Planner

PORTFOLIO
Assessment, p. 28
PERFORMANCE ASSESSMENT
Try at Home MiniLAB, p. 27
Skill Builder Activities, p. 28
See page 36 for more options.

CONTENT ASSESSMENT
Section, p. 28
Challenge, p. 28
Chapter, pp. 36–37

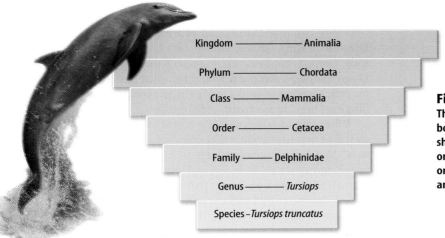

Kingdom ———————— Animalia

Phylum ———————— Chordata

Class ———————— Mammalia

Order ———————— Cetacea

Family ———————— Delphinidae

Genus ———————— *Tursiops*

Species – *Tursiops truncatus*

Figure 16
The classification of the bottle-nosed dolphin shows that it is in the order Cetacea. This order includes whales and porpoises.

Linnaeus In the late eighteenth century, Carolus Linnaeus, a Swedish naturalist, developed a new system of grouping organisms. His classification system was based on looking for organisms with similar structures. For example, plants that had similar flower structure were grouped together. Linnaeus's system eventually was accepted and used by most other scientists.

Modern Classification Like Linnaeus, modern scientists use similarities in structure to classify organisms. They also study fossils, hereditary information, and early stages of development. Scientists use all of this information to determine an organism's phylogeny. **Phylogeny** (fi LAH juh nee) is the evolutionary history of an organism, or how it has changed over time. Today, it is the basis for the classification of many organisms.

Reading Check *What information would a scientist use to determine an organism's phylogeny?*

A classification system commonly used today groups organisms into six kingdoms. A **kingdom** is the first and largest category. Refer to Student Resources, Diversity of Life at the back of your text to find characteristics that place organisms into kingdoms. Kingdoms can be divided into smaller groups. The smallest classification category is a species. Organisms that belong to the same species can mate and produce fertile offspring. To understand how an organism is classified, look at the classification of the bottle-nosed dolphin in **Figure 16.** Some scientists propose that before organisms are grouped into kingdoms, they should be placed in larger groups called domains. One proposed system groups all organisms into three domains.

SCIENCE Online

Data Update For an online update of domains, visit the Glencoe Science Web site at **science.glencoe.com** and select the appropriate chapter. Communicate to your class what you learn.

---

2 Teach

Classification

Quick Demo
Display a photo or an actual member of each of the six kingdoms to the class. Have students identify the kingdom each represents. L2 **Visual-Spatial**

Use Science Words
Word Meaning Have students compare the use of the word *kingdom* in the context of this chapter and in a Social Studies text. In science, a kingdom is the largest category of organisms. In social studies, it is a community or area governed by a king or queen. L2 **Linguistic**

Use an Analogy
Develop the idea that the classification system is similar to divisions that exist within your school. The entire school population is similar to all living things with each grade representing a kingdom, each classroom a phylum, and so on.

Reading Check

Answer similar structures, fossils, hereditary information, and early stages of development

Discussion
Which classification group has the most members? Which has the fewest? Kingdom has the most; species has the fewest.

Resource Manager

Chapter Resources Booklet
Transparency Activity, p. 47
Directed Reading for Content Mastery, pp. 19, 20

SCIENCE Online
Internet Addresses

_____

_____

_____

Explore the Glencoe Science Web site at **science.glencoe.com** to find out more about topics in this section.

Scientific Names

Quick Demo

Use a world map or globe to point out the Roman Empire. Tell students that Latin originated there thousands of years ago. Explain that Latin was the basis of the Romance languages—Spanish, French, Italian, and Portuguese.

Fun Fact

Scientists around the world may speak other languages but they all use Latin for scientific names.

Use an Analogy

The two-word naming system is similar to the structure of Chinese names. The first word in a Chinese name is that of the family and the second and third words are those of the individual. American and European names represent the same idea in reverse order.

Extension

Challenge students to identify an organism from its scientific name. Use *Musca domestica* (housefly), *Equus zebra* (zebra), and *Camelus dromedarius* (dromedary camel). Have students find other scientific names to present to their classmates.

Caption Answer

Figure 17B Possible answers: Sea horses are not horses that live in the sea; wolverines are not small wolves.

Scientific Names

Using common names can cause confusion. Suppose that Diego is visiting Jamaal. Jamaal asks Diego if he would like a soda. Diego is confused until Jamaal hands him a soft drink. At Diego's house, a soft drink would be called pop. Jamaal's grandmother, listening from the living room, thought that Jamaal was offering Diego an ice-cream soda.

What would happen if life scientists used only common names of organisms when they communicated with other scientists? Many misunderstandings would occur, and sometimes health and safety are involved. In **Figure 17,** you see examples of animals with common names that can be misleading. A naming system developed by Linnaeus helped solve this problem. It gave each species a unique, two-word scientific name.

Figure 17
Common names can be misleading.

A Sea lions are more closely related to seals than to lions.

Binomial Nomenclature The two-word naming system that Linnaeus used to name the various species is called **binomial nomenclature** (bi NOH mee ul • NOH mun klay chur). It is the system used by modern scientists to name organisms. The first word of the two-word name identifies the genus of the organism. A **genus** is a group of similar species. The second word of the name might tell you something about the organism—what it looks like, where it is found, or who discovered it.

In this system, the tree species commonly known as red maple has been given the name *Acer rubrum*. The maple genus is *Acer*. The word *rubrum* is Latin for red, which is the color of a red maple's leaves in the fall. The scientific name of another maple is *Acer saccharum*. The Latin word for sugar is *saccharum*. In the spring, the sap of this tree is sweet.

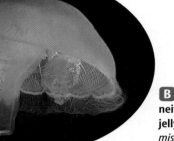

B Jellyfish are neither fish nor jelly. *Do you know a misleading common name?*

Curriculum Connection

Math Ask students to explain how numbers are classified. Answers may include real and imaginary, whole numbers and fractions, decimals and percents, and rational and irrational.

Teacher FYI

Aristotle's classification system remained in use for almost two thousand years. In the 16th and 17th centuries, there was renewed interest in classification when European explorers brought back unidentified plant and animal species from other lands. In the 17th century, John Ray classified plants according to the structure of their seeds.

A

Figure 18
These two lizards have the same common name, iguana, but are two different species.

B

Uses of Scientific Names Scientific names are used for four reasons. First, they help avoid mistakes. Both of the lizards shown in **Figure 18** have the name iguana. Using binomial nomenclature, the green iguana is named *Iguana iguana*. Someone who studied this iguana, shown in **Figure 18A,** would not be confused by information he or she read about *Dispsosaurus dorsalis,* the desert iguana, shown in **Figure 18B.** Second, organisms with similar evolutionary histories are classified together. Because of this, you know that organisms in the same genus are related. Third, scientific names give descriptive information about the species, like the maples mentioned earlier. Fourth, scientific names allow information about organisms to be organized easily and efficiently. Such information may be found in a book or a pamphlet that lists related organisms and gives their scientific names.

✓ **Reading Check**   *What are four functions of scientific names?*

Tools for Identifying Organisms

Tools used to identify organisms include field guides and dichotomous (di KAH toh mus) keys. Using these tools is one way you and scientists solve problems scientifically.

Many different field guides are available. You will find some field guides at the back of this book. Most have descriptions and illustrations of organisms and information about where each organism lives. You can identify species from around the world using the appropriate field guide.

SECTION 4   How are living things classified?   **A ◆ 27**

TRY AT HOME
Mini LAB

Communicating Ideas

Procedure
1. Find a **magazine picture of a piece of furniture** that can be used as a place to sit and to lie down.
2. Show the picture to ten people and ask them to tell you what word they use for this piece of furniture.
3. Keep a record of the answers in your **Science Journal.**

Analysis
1. In your Science Journal, infer how using common names can be confusing.
2. How do scientific names make communication among scientists easier?

Tools for Identifying Organisms, continued

Activity

Pass out taxonomic keys or field guides. Ask students to describe how these tools are used. Have them use the keys to identify a particular organism. Note that students may try to skip steps in keys. Point out that skipping steps often leads to the wrong identification. L2

Text Question Answer

Microtus pinetorum

3 Assess

Reteach

Develop understanding of modern classification by asking students to name the lowest taxonomic category for the organisms described. Ask: **Which level contains a spider plant?** species **Which level contains all willow trees?** genus **Which level contains all plants?** kingdom

Challenge

Why do organisms in the same classification group have characteristics that are similar? Many probably evolved from a common ancestor.

Performance Have students make a concept map to show how an address is like a classification system. The first step should be Country—United States. Use **Performance Assessment in the Science Classroom,** p. 161. P

Dichotomous Keys A dichotomous key is a detailed list of identifying characteristics that includes scientific names. Dichotomous keys are arranged in steps with two descriptive statements at each step. If you learn how to use a dichotomous key, you can identify and name a species.

Did you know many types of mice exist? You can use **Table 2** to find out what type of mouse is pictured to the left. Start by choosing between the first pair of descriptions. The mouse has hair on its tail, so you go to 2. The ears of the mouse are small, so you go on to 3. The tail of the mouse is less that 25 mm. What is the name of this mouse according to the key?

Table 2 Key to Some Mice of North America

1. Tail hair	**a.** no hair on tail; scales show plainly; house mouse, *Mus musculus*
	b. hair on tail, go to 2
2. Ear size	**a.** ears small and nearly hidden in fur, go to 3
	b. ears large and not hidden in fur, go to 4
3. Tail length	**a.** less than 25 mm; woodland vole, *Microtus pinetorum*
	b. more than 25 mm; prairie vole, *Microtus ochrogaster*
4. Tail coloration	**a.** sharply bicolor, white beneath and dark above; deer mouse, *Peromyscus maniculatus*
	b. darker above than below but not sharply bicolor; white-footed mouse, *Peromyscus leucopus*

Section 4 Assessment

1. What is the purpose of classification?
2. What were the contributions of Aristotle and Carolus Linnaeus to classification of living things?
3. How can you identify a species using a dichotomous key?
4. Why can common names cause confusion?
5. **Think Critically** Would you expect a field guide to have common names as well as scientific names? Why or why not?

Skill Builder Activities

6. **Classifying** Create a dichotomous key that identifies types of cars. **For more help, refer to the** Science Skill Handbook.
7. **Communicating** Select a field guide for trees, insects, or mammals. Select two organisms in the field guide that closely resemble each other. Use labeled diagrams to show how they are different. **For more help, refer to the** Science Skill Handbook.

Answers to Section Assessment

1. to arrange or group things according to similarities and differences
2. Aristotle—two kingdoms: plants and animals; Linnaeus—binomial nomenclature
3. A dichotomous key contains a detailed list of identifying characteristics for species.
4. Two different organisms may have the same common name.
5. A field guide does not give as much scientific information as a key. It has pictures and descriptions that help you identify what you see, and often includes common as well as scientific names.
6. Keys will vary, but should be structured like the key shown in **Table 2.**
7. Students should be able to identify two organisms and state how they differ.

Activity

Classifying Seeds

Scientists use classification systems to show how organisms are related. How do they determine which features to use to classify organisms? In this activity, you will observe seeds and use their features to classify them.

What You'll Investigate
How can the features of seeds be used to develop a key to identify the seed?

Materials
packets of seeds (10 different kinds)
hand lens
metric ruler

Goals
■ **Observe** the seeds and notice their features.
■ **Classify** seeds using these features.

Safety Precautions

Do not eat any seeds or put them in your mouth. Some may have been treated with chemicals.

Procedure

1. Copy the following data table in your Science Journal and record the features of each seed. Your table will have a column for each different type of seed you observe.

Seed Data

Feature	Type of Seed		
	corn	kidney bean	wheat
Color	yellow	dark brown	light brown
Length (mm)	10	17	5
Shape	triangle	oval	oval
Texture	smooth	smooth	smooth

2. Use the features to develop a key.

3. Exchange keys with another group. Can you use their key to identify seeds?

Conclude and Apply

1. How can different seeds be classified?

2. Which feature could you use to divide the seeds into two groups?

3. **Explain** how you would classify a seed you had not seen before using your data table.

4. Why is it an advantage for scientists to use a standardized system to classify organisms? What observations did you make to support your answer?

Communicating Your Data

Compare your conclusions with those of other students in your class. **For more help, refer to the** Science Skill Handbook.

Communicating Your Data

Comparisons may or may not result in agreement. If one group can use another group's key, the second group was successful.

Resource Manager

Chapter Resources Booklet
 Activity Worksheets, pp. 5–6, 7–8
 Lab Activity, pp. 11–13
Lab Management and Safety, p. 65

Activity

BENCH TESTED

Purpose Students observe seed features and then classify the seeds. L2 LS **Kinesthetic**

Process Skills observing and inferring, classifying, forming operational definitions, communicating, making and using tables, comparing and contrasting

Time Required 45 minutes

Alternate Materials Any objects may be used, but biological specimens should be used if possible.

Safety Precautions Use only edible seeds, not seeds that have been treated for planting.

Teaching Strategy Prepare packets of ten different kinds of easily classified seeds, such as black-eyed peas, squash, beans (lima, kidney, pinto, black), green peas, popcorn, seed corn, and sunflower.

Answers to Questions

1. color, shape, size, texture, how they are attached to the plant
2. Answers will vary; color, shape, size, and texture are possibilities.
3. You would use the data table to categorize identifying characteristics of seeds.
4. Different classification systems could result in confusion. Answers should be based on the observation that students classified the same seeds in different ways.

✓*Assessment*

Performance Give students photocopies of ten different leaves. Have them devise and describe a classification system for the leaves. Use **PASC,** p. 121.

Activity

Recognize the Problem

Purpose

Design and carry out an experiment using scientific methods to infer why brine shrimp live in the ocean. L1 COOP LEARN

IS **Interpersonal**

Process Skills

observing and inferring, comparing and contrasting, recognizing cause and effect, interpreting data, hypothesizing, communicating, making and using tables, making and using graphs, designing an experiment, separating and controlling variables, measuring in SI

Time Required

50 minutes on Day 1, 5 minutes a day for 3 days, 30 minutes to summarize

Materials

Purchase brine shrimp eggs from a pet store or a biological supply house. Do not place too many brine shrimp eggs in each container. Brine shrimp are orange-colored and swim with a jerking motion. To maintain the brine shrimp, add a pinch of yeast to the container two or three times a week.

Safety Precautions

Students should use care when working with live animals.

Form a Hypothesis

Possible Hypothesis

Brine shrimp will best grow in a strong salt solution.

Activity *Design Your Own Experiment*

Using Scientific Methods

Brine shrimp are relatives of lobsters, crabs, crayfish, and the shrimp eaten by humans. They are often raised as a live food source in aquariums. In nature, they live in the oceans where fish feed on them. They can hatch from eggs that have been stored in a dry condition for many years. In this investigation, you will use scientific methods to find what factors affect their hatching and growth.

Brine shrimp

Recognize the Problem

How can you use scientific methods to determine whether salt affects the hatching and growth of brine shrimp?

Form a Hypothesis

Based on your observations, state a hypothesis about how salt affects the hatching and growth of brine shrimp.

Goals
- ■ **Design** and carry out an experiment using scientific methods to infer why brine shrimp live in the ocean.
- ■ **Observe** the jars for one week and notice whether the brine shrimp eggs hatch.

Possible Materials
500-mL, widemouthed containers (3)
brine shrimp eggs
small, plastic spoon
distilled water (500 mL)
weak salt solution (500 mL)
strong salt solution (500 mL)
labels (3)
hand lens

Safety Precautions

Protect eyes and clothing. Be careful when working with live organisms.

Test Your Hypothesis

Possible Procedures

The same amount of brine shrimp eggs can be added to the three solutions and observed.

Inclusion Strategies

Visually Impaired Have sighted students make paper or clay models of brine shrimp that visually impaired students can touch. Estimate the number of times the model has been enlarged so visually impaired students can have some idea of the size of brine shrimp.

Test Your Hypothesis

Plan

1. As a group, agree upon the hypothesis and decide how you will test it. Identify what results will confirm the hypothesis.

2. **List** the steps that you need to test your hypothesis. Be specific. Describe exactly what you will do in each step.

3. **List** your materials.

4. **Prepare** a data table in your Science Journal to record your data.

5. Read over your entire experiment to make sure that all planned steps are in logical order.

6. **Identify** any constants, variables, and controls of the experiment.

Do

1. Make sure your teacher approves your plan before you start.

2. Carry out the experiment as planned by your group.

3. While doing the experiment, record any observations and complete the data table in your Science Journal.

4. Use a bar graph to plot your results.

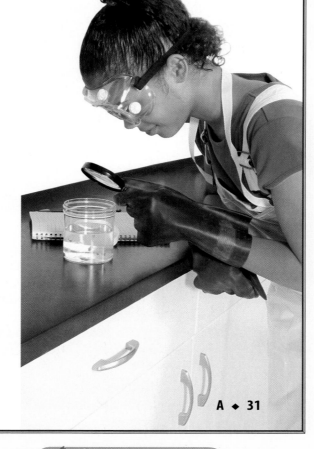

Analyze Your Data

1. **Describe** the contents of each jar after one week. Do they differ from one another? How?

2. What was your control in this experiment?

3. What were your variables?

Draw Conclusions

1. Did the results support your hypothesis? Explain.

2. **Predict** the effect that increasing the amount of salt in the water would have on the brine shrimp eggs.

3. **Compare** your results with those of other groups.

Communicating Your Data

Prepare a set of instructions on how to hatch brine shrimp to use to feed fish. Include diagrams and a step-by-step procedure.

A ◆ 31

Teaching Strategies

Prepare the solutions as follows:

- Dechlorinated water: Allow tap water to stand for 48 hours.
- Weak salt solution: Add 20 mL noniodized salt to 4 L dechlorinated water. Stir until dissolved.
- Strong salt solution: Add 75 mL noniodized salt to 4 L dechlorinated water. Stir until dissolved.

Expected Outcome

Most results will reflect that the brine shrimp grew best in the strong salt solution.

Analyze Your Data

1. There were no shrimp in the distilled water or weak salt solution. There were many shrimp in the strong salt solution.

2. The dechlorinated water without salt was the control.

3. The amount of salt in the water was the variable.

Error Analysis

Have students compare their results and their hypotheses and explain any differences.

Draw Conclusions

1. Answers will be determined by students' hypotheses.

2. Answers will vary. Some may predict that more brine shrimp will hatch.

3. Results will vary.

Communicating Your Data

Instructions should include information on the amount of salt to add to the water, light conditions, and so on. Students can use word-processing software programs to write their instructions.

✔ Assessment

Performance Have students design an experiment to determine how ocean currents affect brine shrimp. Use **Performance Assessment in the Science Classroom,** p. 95.

Content Background

The rain forests of the world are home to fifty percent of all species of plants and animals. Some insect species evolve and become extinct without ever having been seen alive by humans. This is partly a function of the fact that most rain forest species live in the forest canopy between about 18 to 46 meters (60–150 ft) above the ground. Observing wildlife in this environment is extremely difficult, particularly over long periods of time. The need for extensive study of the rain forest canopy becomes more pressing as logging and slash and burn agriculture destroys more of the forest habitat.

One method being attempted to halt the incursion of uncontrolled agriculture into sensitive areas is the development of ecotourism. Governments, corporations and environmental groups have fostered programs intended to preserve wild areas by attracting tourists. The idea is to build an economy based on service industries, thereby relieving some of the pressure to clear more land for farming. One widespread version of ecotourism is the canopy tour effected by means ranging from climbing harnesses to walkways and aerial tramways. One of the benefits of these operations is the establishment of permanent platforms from which canopy research can be conducted.

TIME SCIENCE AND Society

SCIENCE ISSUES THAT AFFECT YOU!

M

A marmoset stands in a tree. It is about the size of a squirrel.

Acari marmoset

Deep in the heart of the rain forest lives a small, furry animal. It swings from the trees, searches for food, and sleeps nestled high in the treetop canopy. What makes this animal unique is that it never had been seen by a human being. In fact, there is a whole world of creatures as yet undiscovered by humans. Many of them reside in the Amazon rain forest.

In 2000, a scientist from Brazil's Amazon National Research Institute came across two squirrel-sized monkeys in a remote and isolated corner of the rain forest, about 2,575 km from Rio de Janeiro.

It turns out that the monkeys had never been seen before, or even known to exist.

The new species were spotted by a scientist who named them after two nearby rivers where the animals were discovered, the Manicore and the Acari. Both animals are marmosets, which is a type of monkey found only in Central and South America. Marmosets have claws instead of nails, live in trees, and use their extraordinarily long tail like an extra arm or leg. Small and light, both marmosets measure about 23 cm in length with a 38 cm tail, and weigh no more than 0.4 kg.

The Manicore marmoset has a silvery-white upper body, a light-gray cap on its head, a yellow-orange underbody, and a black tail.

32 ◆ A

Resources for Teachers and Students

Tropical Rain Forest, by Arnold Newman, New York: Facts On File, Inc., 1990.

Rain Forests of the World: Water, Fire, Earth, Air, by Art Wolfe and Sir Ghillean Prance, New York: Crown Publishers, 1998.

"New study pinpoints rain-forest destruction" by Jeff Donn, The Associated Press, *Seattle Times,* Thursday, April 8, 1999.

Manicore marmoset

key BUSINESS

The Amazon rain forest is home to animals waiting to be discovered

The Acari marmoset's upper body is snowy white, its gray back sports a stripe running to the knee, and its black tail flashes a bright-orange tip.

Amazin' Amazon

The Amazon Basin is a treasure trove of unique species. The Amazon River is Earth's largest body of freshwater, with 1,100 smaller tributaries. And, more than half of the world's plant and animal species live in the rain forest ecosystems.

Many of these species are found nowhere else on Earth. Scientists believe that some animals, like the newly discovered marmosets, evolved differently from other marmosets because the rivers create natural barriers that separated the animals.

The discovery reminds people of how much we have to learn about Earth's diversity of life. Even among our closest relatives, the primates, there are still new species to be discovered.

CONNECTIONS Research and Report Working in small groups, find out more about the Amazon rain forest. Which plants and animals live there? What products come from the rain forest? How does what happens in the Amazon rain forest affect you? Prepare a multimedia presentation.

SCIENCE *Online*
For more information, visit science.glencoe.com

SCIENCE *Online*

Internet Addresses

_____

_____

_____

Explore the Glencoe Science Web site at **science.glencoe.com** to find out more about topics in this feature.

Chapter ① Study Guide

Reviewing Main Ideas

Preview

Students can answer the questions in their Science Journals. Discuss the answers as you go through the chapter. **LS** **Linguistic**

Review

Students can write their answers, then compare them with those of other students. **LS** **Interpersonal**

Reteach

Students can look at the illustrations and describe details that support the main ideas of the chapter. **LS** **Visual-Spatial**

Answers to Chapter Review

SECTION 1

1. Accept all reasonable answers.

SECTION 2

2. water

SECTION 3

2. from mosquitos

SECTION 4

4. It assigns a unique two-word name for every species of organism.

Reviewing Main Ideas

Section 1   What is science?

1. Scientists investigate observations about living and nonliving things with the help of problem-solving techniques. *What problem-solving methods would this scientist use to find out how dolphins learn?*

2. Scientists use SI measurements to gather measurable data.

3. Safe laboratory practices help you learn more about science.

Section 2   Living Things

1. Organisms are made of cells, use energy, reproduce, respond, grow, and develop.

2. Organisms need energy, water, food, and a place to live. *What raw material is limited for organisms living in a desert?*

Section 3   Where does life come from?

1. Controlled experiments over many years finally disproved the theory of spontaneous generation.

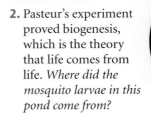

2. Pasteur's experiment proved biogenesis, which is the theory that life comes from life. *Where did the mosquito larvae in this pond come from?*

3. Oparin's hypothesis is one explanation of how life began on Earth.

Section 4   How are living things classified?

1. Classification is the grouping of ideas, information, or objects based on their similar characteristics.

2. Scientists today use phylogeny to group organisms into six kingdoms.

3. All organisms are given a two word scientific name using binomial nomenclature.

4. Dichotomous keys are used to identify specific organisms. *How would binomial nomenclature keep scientists from confusing these two beetles?*

FOLDABLES Reading & Study Skills   **After You Read**

Trade vocabulary study Foldables with a classmate and quiz each other to see how many words you can define without looking under the tabs.

FOLDABLES Reading & Study Skills   **After You Read**

After students have read the chapter and completed the Foldable described in Before You Read, have them do the activity on the student page.

Visualizing Main Ideas

Use the following terms to complete an events chain concept map showing the order in which you might use a scientific method: analyze data, perform an experiment, *and* form a hypothesis.

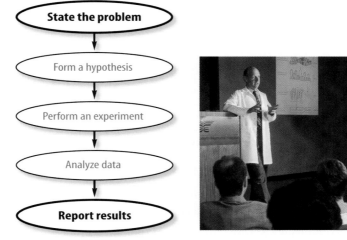

State the problem

↓

Form a hypothesis

↓

Perform an experiment

↓

Analyze data

↓

Report results

Vocabulary Review

Vocabulary Words

a. binomial nomenclature
b. biogenesis
c. cell
d. control
e. genus
f. homeostasis
g. hypothesis
h. kingdom
i. law
j. organism
k. phylogeny
l. scientific methods
m. spontaneous generation
n. theory
o. variable

THE PRINCETON REVIEW **Study Tip**

If you're not sure how terms in a question are related, try making a concept map of the terms. Ask your teacher to check your map.

Using Vocabulary

Explain the differences in the vocabulary words in each pair below. Then explain how they are related.

1. control, variable
2. law, theory
3. biogenesis, spontaneous generation
4. binomial nomenclature, phylogeny
5. organism, cell
6. kingdom, phylogeny
7. hypothesis, scientific methods
8. organism, homeostasis
9. kingdom, genus
10. theory, hypothesis

Visualizing Main Ideas

See student page.

Vocabulary Review

Using Vocabulary

1. variable—condition tested; control—standard used to compare with outcome of the test
2. Theory—explanation of things or events based on many observations; law—a statement about how things work in nature.
3. The theory of spontaneous generation (living things come from nonliving things) was replaced with the theory of biogenesis (living things come only from other living things).
4. Phylogeny is the evolutionary history of an organism; binomial nomenclature—a naming system based on phylogeny.
5. A cell is the smallest unit of an organism that carries out the functions of life. All organisms are made of cells.
6. Phylogeny is the basis for placing organisms into kingdoms.
7. Forming a hypothesis is an important part of solving a problem with scientific methods.
8. Homeostasis—keeping proper internal conditions no matter what external conditions are—is a trait of all organisms.
9. A genus is a subgroup of a kingdom.
10. If the results of repeated experiments always support the same hypothesis, the hypothesis may be called a theory.

IDENTIFYING Misconceptions

Assess

Use the assessment as follow-up to page 6F after students have completed the chapter.

Assessment Show students several pictures of living and nonliving things, and have them record whether they think each item is living or nonliving and their reason. When responses are recorded, list their ideas on the board and generate a list of characteristics that students think describe living things. Compare this list to the characteristics of life listed in **Section 2** and ask the class if they would like to make any changes in their list.

Expected Outcome Some students may persist in listing only animal-like characteristics, but most students should be forming a more sophisticated definition that includes the characteristics given in the text. They should begin to recognize that their favorite "characteristic," movement, is simply one way that some living organisms respond to the environment.

Checking Concepts

1. D
2. D
3. A
4. D
5. C
6. D
7. A
8. B
9. D
10. B

Thinking Critically

11. Scientists can compare and repeat experiments; they have a common tool for measurement.
12. A bird is made up of cells, uses energy to fly and breathe, moves, responds to the environment, maintains a constant body temperature, reproduces young that grow and develop, and has a life span.
13. Binomial nomenclature is a two-word naming system. It is important because scientists assign a unique name to an organism that may have many common names. This allows accurate communication between scientists and others.
14. Redis experiment used a variable and a control.
15. The name *odoratus* tells you that the sweet pea probably has an odor.

Checking Concepts

Choose the word or phrase that best answers the question.

1. What category of organisms can mate and produce fertile offspring?
   - A) family
   - B) class
   - C) genus
   - D) species

2. What is the closest relative of *Canis lupus*?
   - A) *Quercus alba*
   - B) *Equus zebra*
   - C) *Felis tigris*
   - D) *Canis familiaris*

3. What is the source of energy for plants?
   - A) the Sun
   - B) carbon dioxide
   - C) water
   - D) oxygen

4. What makes up more than 50 percent of all living things?
   - A) oxygen
   - B) carbon dioxide
   - C) minerals
   - D) water

5. Who finally disproved the theory of spontaneous generation?
   - A) Oparin
   - B) Aristotle
   - C) Pasteur
   - D) Miller

6. What gas do some scientists think was missing from Earth's early atmosphere?
   - A) ammonia
   - B) hydrogen
   - C) methane
   - D) oxygen

7. What is the length of time an organism is expected to live?
   - A) life span
   - B) stimulus
   - C) homeostasis
   - D) theory

8. What is the part of an experiment that can be changed called?
   - A) conclusion
   - B) variable
   - C) control
   - D) data

9. What does the first word in a two-word name of an organism identify?
   - A) kingdom
   - B) species
   - C) phylum
   - D) genus

10. What SI unit is used to measure the volume of liquids?
    - A) meter
    - B) liter
    - C) gram
    - D) degree

Thinking Critically

11. How does SI help scientists in different parts of the world?

12. Using a bird as an example, explain how it has all the traits of living things.

13. Explain what binomial nomenclature is and why it is important.

14. Explain how the experiment of 1668 correctly used scientific methods to test the theory of spontaneous generation.

15. What does *Lathyrus odoratus*, the name for a sweet pea, tell you about one of its characteristics?

Developing Skills

16. **Using and Manipulating Variables and Controls** Design an experiment to test the effects of fertilizer on growing plants. Identify scientific methods used in your experiment.

17. **Forming Hypotheses** A lima bean plant is placed under a green light, another is placed under a red light, and a third under a blue light. Their growth is measured for four weeks to determine which light is best for plant growth. What are the variables in this experiment? State a hypothesis for this experiment.

18. **Comparing and Contrasting** What characteristics do an icicle and a plant share? How can you tell that the plant is a living thing and the icicle is not?

Chapter ✓Assessment Planner

Portfolio Encourage students to place in their portfolios one or two items of what they consider to be their best work. Examples include:
- Science Journal, p. 9
- Curriculum Connection, p. 18
- Reteach, p. 23
- Assessment, p. 28

Performance Additional performance assessments, Performance Task Assessment Lists, and rubrics for evaluating these activities can be found in Glencoe's **Performance Assessment in the Science Classroom.**

19. Interpreting Data Read the following hypothesis: Babies with a birth weight of 2.5 kg have the best chance of survival. Do the data in the following graph support this hypothesis? Explain.

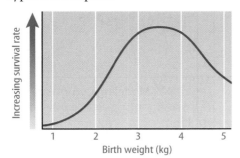

Increasing survival rate

Birth weight (kg)

20. Classifying Which of these metric units—meter, kilometer, kilogram, or liter—is the best one to use when measuring each of the following?
A) your height
B) distance between two cities
C) how much juice is in a pitcher
D) your mass

Performance Assessment

21. Bulletin Board Interview people in your community whose jobs require a knowledge of life science. Make a Life Science Careers bulletin board. Summarize each person's job and what he or she had to study to prepare for that job.

TECHNOLOGY

Go to the Glencoe Science Web site at **science.glencoe.com** or use the **Glencoe Science CD-ROM** for additional chapter assessment.

Test Practice

A science class was learning about how living things respond to stimuli. Their experiment about the response of plants to light is shown below.

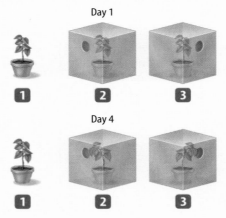

Day 1

Day 4

Study the experiment and answer the following questions.

1. Which hypothesis is probably being tested by this experiment?
   A) Plants grow better in full light.
   B) Plants prefer to grow in a box with one hole.
   C) Plants can grow in any direction.
   D) Plants grow toward the light.

2. After day 4, Fatima wanted to find out how plant 2 and plant 3 would grow in normal light. To do this, she would have to _____ .
   A) use all new plants and boxes without holes
   B) add water to all of the pots
   C) remove the boxes over plant 2 and plant 3
   D) put holes on all sides of the boxes

Test Practice

The Test-Taking Tip was written by The Princeton Review, the nation's leader in test preparation.
1. D
2. C

Developing Skills

16. An experiment should contain a hypothesis, observations, a variable, a control, and an interpretation of results.
17. Variables: the different colors of light; hypothesis might be that the green light will cause the most favorable plant growth.
18. Both respond to their surroundings and grow in size. Unlike a plant, an icicle is not made of cells and cannot take in and use energy or reproduce.
19. No; babies with a birth weight of approximately 3.5 kg have the best chance of survival.
20. a. meter b. kilometer c. liter d. kilogram

Performance Assessment

21. Careers could include farmers, produce clerks, florists, veterinary technicians, health care workers, and teachers. Use **PASC**, p. 131.

Resources

📁 **Reproducible Masters**

Chapter Resources Booklet
   Chapter Review, pp. 37–38
   Chapter Tests, pp. 39–42
   Assessment Transparency Activity, p. 51

Glencoe Science Web site
   Interactive Tutor
   Chapter Quizzes

Glencoe Technology
   🔦 Assessment Transparency
   💿 Interactive CD-ROM Chapter Quizzes
   💿 ExamView Pro Test Bank
   💿 Vocabulary PuzzleMaker Software
   📼 MindJogger Videoquiz DVD/VHS

Section/Objectives	Standards		Activities/Features
	National	**State/Local**	
Chapter Opener	See p. 6T for a Key to Standards.		**Explore Activity:** Measure a small object, p. 39 **Before You Read,** p. 39
Section 1 Cell Structure ⏱ 2 sessions 📦 1 block 1. **Identify** names and functions of each part of a cell. 2. **Explain** how important a nucleus is in a cell. 3. **Compare** tissues, organs, and organ systems.	National Content Standards: UCP1, UCP5, A1, C1		**MiniLAB:** Modeling Cytoplasm, p. 42 **Environmental Science Integration,** p. 46 **Math Skills Activity:** Calculate the Ratio of Surface Area to Volume of Cells, p. 46 **Activity:** Comparing Cells, p. 48
Section 2 Viewing Cells ⏱ 2 sessions 📦 1 block 1. **Compare** the differences between the compound light microscope and the electron microscope. 2. **Summarize** the discoveries that led to the development of the cell theory. 3. **Relate** the cell theory to modern biology.	National Content Standards: UCP1, A1, C1		**Visualizing Microscopes,** pp. 50–51 **MiniLAB:** Observing Magnified Objects, p. 52 **Physics Integration,** p. 52
Section 3 Viruses ⏱ 3 sessions 📦 1.5 blocks 1. **Explain** how a virus makes copies of itself. 2. **Identify** the benefits of vaccines. 3. **Investigate** some uses of viruses.	National Content Standards: UCP5, A1, C1, C2, E2, F1, G3		**Science Online,** p. 55 **Science Online,** p. 56 **Activity:** Comparing Light Microscopes, pp. 58–59 **Science and History:** Cobb Against Cancer, pp. 60–61

NATIONAL GEOGRAPHIC

Teacher's Corner

PRODUCTS AVAILABLE FROM GLENCOE
To order call 1-800-334-7344:
CD-ROM
NGS PictureShow: The Cell

Curriculm Kit
GeoKit: Cells and Microorganisms
Transparency Set
NGS PicturePack: The Cell

PRODUCTS AVAILABLE FROM NATIONAL GEOGRAPHIC SOCIETY
To order call 1-800-368-2728:
Videos
Discovering the Cell
Virus!

Activity Materials	Reproducible Resources	Section Assessment	Technology
Explore Activity: hand lens, metric ruler	**Chapter Resources Booklet** Foldables Worksheet, p. 17 Directed Reading Overview, p. 19 Note-taking Worksheets, pp. 33–35	GLENCOE'S **ASSESSMENT** ADVANTAGE	
MiniLAB: water, clear container, unflavored gelatin, flashlight **Activity:** microscope, microscope slide, coverslip, forceps, tap water, dropper, *Elodea* plant, prepared slide of human cheek cells	**Chapter Resources Booklet** Transparency Activity, p. 44 MiniLAB, p. 3 Enrichment, p. 30 Reinforcement, p. 27 Directed Reading, p. 20 Transparency Activity, pp. 47–48 Activity Worksheet, pp. 5–6 **Mathematics Skill Activities, p. 5**	Portfolio Visual Learning, p. 43 Performance MiniLAB, p. 42 Skill Builder Activities, p. 47 Content Section Assessment, p. 47	Section Focus Transparency Teaching Transparency Interactive CD-ROM/DVD Guided Reading Audio Program
MiniLAB: newspaper, clear empty glass, clear empty glass bowl, water, hand lens *Need materials?* **Contact Science Kit at 1-800-828-7777 or www.sciencekit.com on the Internet.**	**Chapter Resources Booklet** Transparency Activity, p. 45 MiniLAB, p. 4 Enrichment, p. 31 Reinforcement, p. 28 Directed Reading, p. 20 Lab Activity, pp. 9–12, 13–16 **Science Inquiry Labs, p. 3**	Portfolio Assessment, p. 53 Performance MiniLAB, p. 52 Skill Builder Activities, p. 53 Content Section Assessment, p. 53	Section Focus Transparency Interactive CD-ROM/DVD Guided Reading Audio Program
Activity: compound light microscope, stereomicroscope, 8 classroom items to view, microscope slides and coverslips, plastic petri dishes, distilled water, dropper	**Chapter Resources Booklet** Transparency Activity, p. 46 Enrichment, p. 32 Reinforcement, p. 28 Directed Reading, pp. 21, 22 Activity Worksheet, pp. 7–8 **Lab Management and Safety, p. 58** **Reading and Writing Skill Activities, p. 31**	Portfolio Extension, p. 56 Performance Skill Builder Activities, p. 57 Content Section Assessment, p. 57	Section Focus Transparency Interactive CD-ROM/DVD Guided Reading Audio Program

End of Chapter Assessment

GLENCOE'S **ASSESSMENT** ADVANTAGE

Blackline Masters	Technology	Professional Series
Chapter Resources Booklet Chapter Review, pp. 37–38 Chapter Tests, pp. 39–42 **Standardized Test Practice by The Princeton Review, pp. 11–14**	MindJogger Videoquiz CD-ROM Explorations and Quizzes Vocabulary Puzzle Makers ExamView Pro Test Bank Interactive Lesson Planner Interactive Teacher's Edition	Performance Assessment in the Science Classroom (PASC)

Transparencies

Section Focus

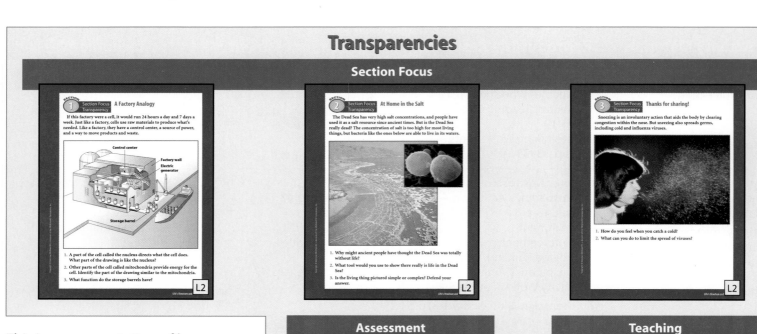

This is a representation of key blackline masters available in the Teacher Classroom Resources. See Resource Manager boxes within the chapter for additional information.

Assessment

Teaching

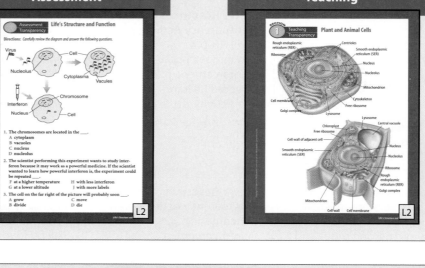

Key to Teaching Strategies

The following designations will help you decide which activities are appropriate for your students.

L1 Level 1 activities should be appropriate for students with learning difficulties.

L2 Level 2 activities should be within the ability range of all students.

L3 Level 3 activities are designed for above-average students.

ELL ELL activities should be within the ability range of English Language Learners.

COOP LEARN Cooperative Learning activities are designed for small group work.

LS Multiple Learning Styles logos are used throughout to indicate strategies that address different learning styles.

P These strategies represent student products that can be placed into a best-work portfolio.

Hands-on Activities

Activity Worksheets

Laboratory Activities

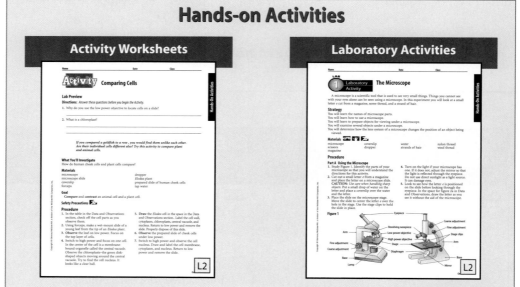

RESOURCE MANAGER

Meeting Different Ability Levels

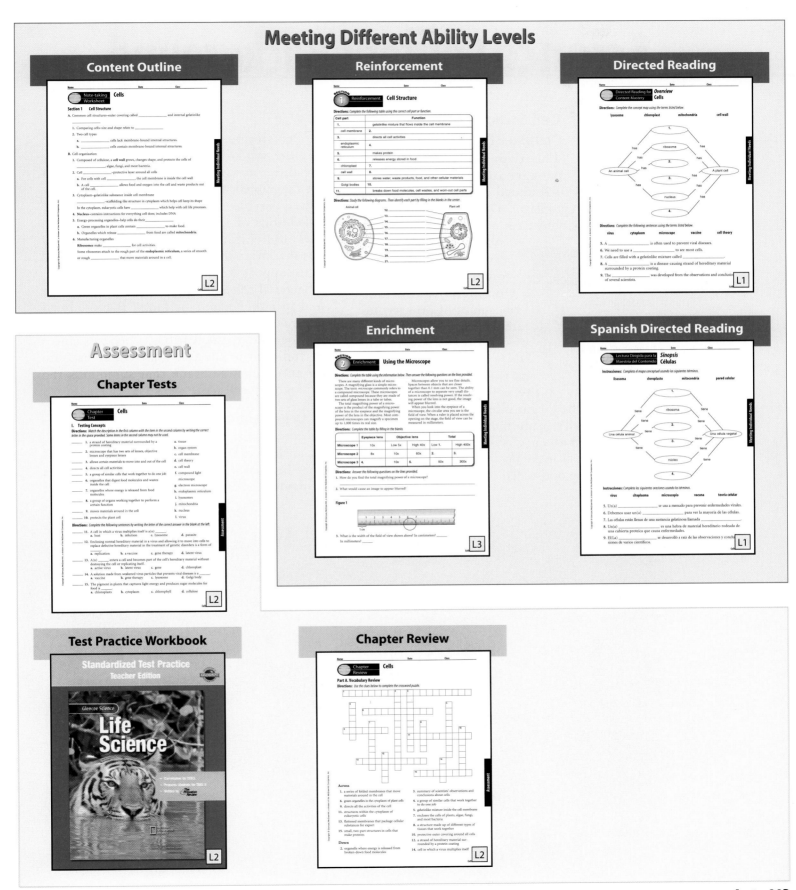

Content Outline
L2

Reinforcement
L2

Directed Reading
L1

Assessment

Chapter Tests
L2

Enrichment
L3

Spanish Directed Reading
L1

Test Practice Workbook
L2

Chapter Review
L2

Science Content Background

Cell Structure
Common Cell Traits

The two kinds of cells are prokaryotes and eukaryotes. Each type is surrounded by a cell membrane and contain cytoplasm, DNA, and ribosomes. Prokaryotes have a relatively uniform cytoplasm that is not divided into separate compartments by interior membranes. The ribosomes of prokaryotes are different from those of eukaryotes. Prokaryotic DNA is a single molecule and is found floating free in the cell's cytoplasm. The nucleus is the organelle that contains the eukaryotic cell's many molecules of DNA. All prokaryotic cells are one-celled organisms. Eukaryotic cells make up all many-celled organisms and some one-celled organisms.

Fun Fact

Scientists have found small sporelike cells in mammal tissues that are involved in tissue repair. They have been used to repair breaks in the spinal cords of rats.

Cell Wall

Although structurally they resemble plant cell walls, the walls of fungi cells are chemically quite different. Some contain cellulose, but most fungal cell walls are made up of chitin, a polysaccharide that also is found in the exoskeletons of insects. Just like cellulose in plants, the chitin is laid down in bundles of fibers that make the fungal cell walls tough and able to support the fungal body.

Bacterial cell walls are different from those found in either plants or fungi. Bacterial cell walls are composed in large part of a compound called peptidoglycan. Various other substances coat and bind to the cell wall. Other bacteria have an outer membrane that surrounds the peptidoglycan cell wall.

Cell Organization

The cytoskeleton, found only in eukaryotic cells, anchors cell organelles. This "scaffolding" cannot be seen with a normal light microscope but stands out clearly when special fluorescent

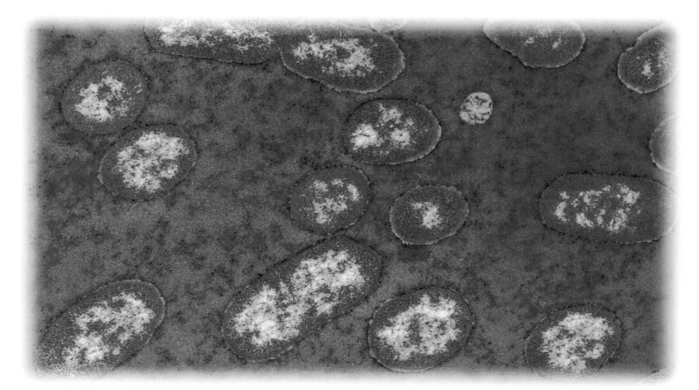

dyes are used on the cell. Three different kinds of protein fibers—microfilaments, microtubules, and intermediate fibers—make up the cytoskeleton.

SECTION 2 Viewing Cells

Magnifying Cells

Microscopes enlarge the image of an object and show its details. The change of an object's apparent size is magnification. The power to show details is resolution. The resolution power of light microscopes is limited by the wavelengths of visible light. Unless the wavelength of light can pass between two objects, the objects are seen as one unit, not two. The electron microscope allows for greater resolution because it uses a beam of electrons to generate an image of the specimen. Because they move in waves that have extremely short wavelengths, electron waves can easily pass through microscopic spaces that visible light cannot enter.

Fun Fact

Creatures 20–150 nanometers in length were found living in sandstone from the Australian seabed. They are smaller than any other known living organism. They contain DNA and distinct cell membranes and grow spontaneously.

Development of the Cell Theory

The cell theory is sometimes called the cell doctrine. Those scientists who use the term *cell doctrine* want to make it clear that extensive data support the cell theory and that it is universally accepted by biologists.

SECTION 3 Viruses

Living or Not?

To a biologist, living organisms are cellular and are able to grow and reproduce independently. The smallest organisms that satisfy these criteria are bacteria. Viruses do not meet most other criteria for being a living organism.

Telegraph Colour Library/FPG International

Viruses are segments of DNA or RNA wrapped in a protein coat. A membranous envelope surrounds many animal viruses. The lipids of the envelope are taken from the host cell, but the proteins are coded by the virus's genetic material. Viruses cannot reproduce on their own but reproduce only within host cells using the cellular machinery of the host cell. The host cells often are destroyed when viruses reproduce. For the host organism, infection by a virus may have a minor effect like a cold or may be devastating like AIDS. Several types of cancer, including some skin and cervical cancers, are now known to be caused by viruses. Viruses continue to have a major impact on the living world.

SCIENCE Online

For additional content background on this topic, go to the Glencoe Science Web site at science.glencoe.com.

Cells

Chapter Vocabulary

cell membrane
cytoplasm
cell wall
organelle
nucleus
chloroplast
mitochondrion
ribosome
endoplasmic reticulum
Golgi body
tissue
organ
cell theory
virus
host cell

What do you think?

Science Journal The photograph is of a virus attacking a bacterium.

CHAPTER 2

Cells

The world around you is filled with organisms that you could overlook, or even be unable to see. Some of these organisms are one-celled and some are many-celled. The monster in this photograph is a louse crawling across human skin. It can be seen in great detail with a microscope that is found in many classrooms. You can study the cells of smaller organisms with other kinds of microscopes.

What do you think?

Science Journal Look at the picture below with a classmate. Discuss what you think is happening. Here's a hint: *Not every battlefield is found on land or at sea.* Write your answer or best guess in your Science Journal.

Theme Connection

Scale and Structure The scale and structure of cells and viruses are compared and the parts of which they are composed are described.

EXPLORE ACTIVITY

If you look around your classroom, you can see many things of all sizes. With the aid of a hand lens, you can see more details. You might examine a speck of dust and discover that it is a living or dead insect. In the following activity, use a hand lens to search for the smallest thing you can find in the classroom.

Measure a small object

1. Obtain a hand lens from your teacher. Note its power (the number followed by ✕, shown somewhere on the lens frame or handle).

2. Using the hand lens, look around the room for the smallest object you can find.

3. Measure the size of the image as you see it with the hand lens. To estimate the real size of the object, divide that number by the power. For example, if it looks 2 cm long and the power is 10✕, the real length is about 0.2 cm.

Observe
In your Science Journal, describe what you observe. Did the details become clearer? Explain.

FOLDABLES
Reading & Study Skills

Before You Read

Making a Main Ideas Study Fold **Make the following Foldable to help you identify the main ideas or major topics on cells.**

1. Place a sheet of paper in front of you so the long side is at the top. Fold the paper in half from the left side to the right side. Then unfold.

2. Label the left side of the paper *Plant Cell.* Label the right side of the paper *Animal Cell,* as shown.

3. Before you read the chapter, draw a plant cell on the left side of the paper and an animal cell on the right side of the paper.

4. As you read the chapter, change and add to your drawings.

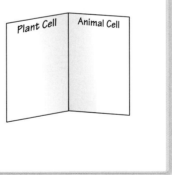

A ◆ 39

EXPLORE ACTIVITY

Purpose Students will use a hand lens to study very small objects. Students will calculate the actual size of the object from a measured size seen through the hand lens.

Preparation Obtain hand lenses and make sure the power is clearly visible on each one.

Materials hand lenses, rulers

Teaching Strategy Have some very small objects, such as grains of sand, salt, sugar, etc., available for students to study with their hand lenses.

Observe
Details of small objects will become larger and clearer when seen through a hand lens.

✓ *Assessment*

Oral Have students describe aloud additional features of small objects, such as sand, salt, sugar, dust particles, etc., that they can observe through a hand lens. Use **Performance Assessment in the Science Classroom,** p. 89.

FOLDABLES
Reading & Study Skills

Before You Read

Dinah Zike Study Fold

Purpose Students make and use a Foldable to diagram and collect information on plant and animal cells. Students use this information to compare and contrast these two types of cells and explain how the structure of each relates to its function.

📁 For additional help, see Foldables Worksheet, p. 17 in **Chapter Resources Booklet,** or go to the Glencoe Science Web site at **science.glencoe.com.** See After You Read in the Study Guide at the end of this chapter.

SECTION

1

Cell Structure

1 Motivate

Bellringer Transparency

Display the Section Focus Transparency for Section 1. Use the accompanying Transparency Activity Master. [L2]
ELL

SECTION 1 | Section Focus Transparency | A Factory Analogy

If this factory were a cell, it would run 24 hours a day and 7 days a week. Just like a factory, cells use raw materials to produce what's needed. Like a factory, they have a control center, a source of power, and a way to move products and waste.

Control center
Factory wall
Electric generator
Storage barrel

1. A part of the cell called the nucleus directs what the cell does. What part of the drawing is like the nucleus?
2. Other parts of the cell called mitochondria provide energy for the cell. Identify the part of the drawing similar to the mitochondria.
3. What function do the storage barrels have?

Life's Structure and Function

Tie to Prior Knowledge

Ask students what body systems they need to live. Write their responses on the board or overhead projector. Use this list to help students understand that the functions of life are carried out in the cell.

As You Read

What You'll Learn

Identify names and functions of each part of a cell.
Explain how important a nucleus is in a cell.
Compare tissues, organs, and organ systems.

Vocabulary

cell membrane	ribosome
cytoplasm	endoplasmic
cell wall	reticulum
organelle	Golgi body
nucleus	tissue
chloroplast	organ
mitochondrion	

Why It's Important

If you know how organelles function, it's easier to understand how cells survive.

Common Cell Traits

Living cells are dynamic and have several things in common. Cells are the smallest unit that is capable of performing life functions. All cells have an outer covering called a **cell membrane.** Inside every cell is a gelatinlike material called **cytoplasm** (SI toh plaz uhm). In the cytoplasm of every cell is hereditary material that controls the life of the cell.

Comparing Cells Cells come in many sizes. A nerve cell in your leg could be a meter long. A human egg cell is no bigger than the dot on this **i.** A human red blood cell is about one-tenth the size of a human egg cell. A bacterium is even smaller—8,000 of the smallest bacteria can fit inside one of your red blood cells.

A cell's shape might tell you something about its function. The nerve cell in **Figure 1** has many fine extensions that send and receive impulses to and from other cells. Though a nerve cell cannot change shape, muscle cells and some blood cells can. In plant stems, some cells are long and hollow and have openings at their ends. These cells carry food and water through the plant.

Figure 1
The shape of the cell can tell you something about its function. These cells are magnified 700 times their actual size.

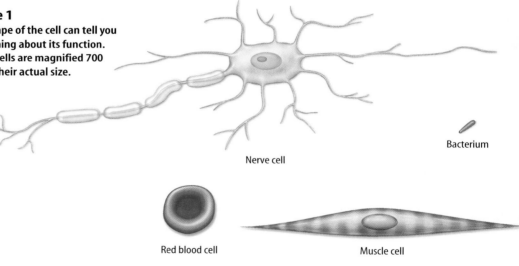

Bacterium

Nerve cell

Red blood cell

Muscle cell

Section ✔Assessment Planner

PORTFOLIO
Visual Learning, p. 43
PERFORMANCE ASSESSMENT
MiniLAB, p. 42
Skill Builder Activities, p. 47
See page 64 for more options.

CONTENT ASSESSMENT
Section, p. 47
Challenge, p. 47
Chapter, pp. 64–65

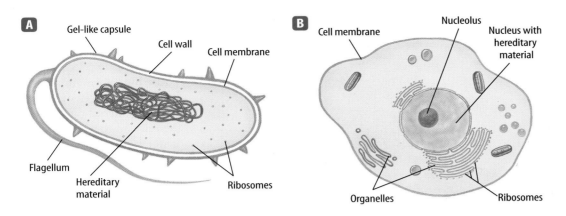

A
- Gel-like capsule
- Cell wall
- Cell membrane
- Flagellum
- Hereditary material
- Ribosomes

B
- Cell membrane
- Nucleolus
- Nucleus with hereditary material
- Organelles
- Ribosomes

Cell Types Scientists have found that cells can be separated into two groups. One group has no membrane-bound structures inside the cell and the other group does, as shown in **Figure 2.** Cells without membrane-bound structures are called prokaryotic (proh KAYR ee yah tihk) cells. Cells with membrane-bound structures are called eukaryotic (yew KAYR ee yah tihk) cells.

✔ **Reading Check** *Into what two groups can cells be separated?*

Cell Organization

Each cell in your body has a specific function. You might compare a cell to a busy delicatessen that is open 24 hours every day. Raw materials for the sandwiches are brought in often. Some food is eaten in the store, and some customers take their food with them. Sometimes food is prepared ahead of time for quick sale. Wastes are put into trash bags for removal or recycling. Similarly, your cells are taking in nutrients, secreting and storing chemicals, and breaking down substances 24 hours every day.

Cell Wall Just like a deli that is located inside the walls of a building, some cells are enclosed in a cell wall. The cells of plants, algae, fungi, and most bacteria are enclosed in a cell wall. **Cell walls** are tough, rigid outer coverings that protect the cell and give it shape.

A plant cell wall, as shown in **Figure 3,** mostly is made up of a carbohydrate called cellulose. The long, threadlike fibers of cellulose form a thick mesh that allows water and dissolved materials to pass through it. Cell walls also can contain pectin, which is used in jam and jelly, and lignin, which is a compound that makes cell walls rigid. Plant cells responsible for support have a lot of lignin in their walls.

Figure 2
Examine these drawings of cells.
A Prokaryotic cells are only found in one-celled organisms, such as bacteria. **B** Protists, fungi, plants and animals are made of eukaryotic cells. *What differences do you see between them?*

Figure 3
The protective cell wall of a plant cell is outside the cell membrane.

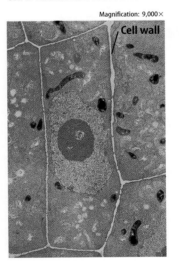

Magnification: 9,000×
Cell wall

SECTION 1 Cell Structure   **A ◆ 41**

Curriculum Connection

Health Cellulose, found in all plant cell walls, is not digestible by humans. However, it provides fiber, which is important because it helps in the elimination of wastes. Have students make a list of foods that contain fiber. Lists should include fruits, grains, and leafy vegetables. [L2]

Cell Organization, continued

Discussion

What would happen if the nucleus of a cell were damaged? The cell would no longer function correctly because the nucleus controls all the cell's activities. L2

Mini LAB

Purpose Students model cytoplasm. L1 ELL IS **Kinesthetic**

Materials 250 mL beaker, unflavored gelatin (one package per student group), water, flashlight, stirring rod

Teaching Strategy Be certain students stir the gelatin well before shining the light on the beaker.

Analysis
1. particles suspended in the gelatin, which represent organelles suspended in the cytoplasm
2. A model is a representation of an abstract object that is used to help visualize and better understand it.

✓ *Assessment*

Oral Have students infer how the chemical composition of cytoplasm compares to that of gelatin. Both are water-based suspensions. Cytoplasm is 80% water. Use **PASC**, p. 89.

Figure 4
The cell membrane is made up of a double layer of fatlike molecules.

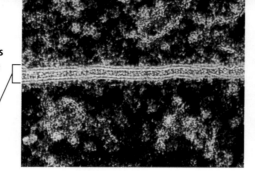

Cell membrane

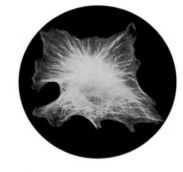

Figure 5
Cytoskeleton, a network of fibers in the cytoplasm, gives cells structure and helps them maintain shape.

Mini LAB

Modeling Cytoplasm

Procedure
1. Add 100 mL of **water** to a **clear container.**
2. Add **unflavored gelatin** and stir.
3. Shine a **flashlight** through the solution.

Analysis
1. Describe what you see.
2. How does a model help you understand what cytoplasm might be like?

Cell Membrane The protective layer around all cells is the cell membrane, as shown in **Figure 4.** If cells have cell walls, the cell membrane is inside of it. The cell membrane regulates interactions between the cell and the environment. Water is able to move freely into and out of the cell through the cell membrane. Food particles and some molecules enter and waste products leave through the cell membrane.

Cytoplasm Cells are filled with a gelatinlike substance called cytoplasm that constantly flows inside the cell membrane. Many important chemical reactions occur within the cytoplasm.

Throughout the cytoplasm is a framework called the cytoskeleton, which helps the cell maintain or change its shape. Cytoskeletons enable some cells to move. An amoeba, for example, moves by stretching and contracting its cytoskeleton. The cytoskeleton is made up of thin, hollow tubes of protein and thin, solid protein fibers, as shown in **Figure 5.** Proteins are organic molecules made up of amino acids.

☑ **Reading Check** *What is the function of the cytoskeleton?*

Most of a cell's life processes occur in the cytoplasm. Within the cytoplasm of eukaryotic cells are structures called **organelles.** Some organelles process energy and others manufacture substances needed by the cell or other cells. Certain organelles move materials, while others act as storage sites. Most organelles are surrounded by membranes. The nucleus is usually the largest organelle in a cell.

Nucleus The nucleus is like the deli manager who directs the store's daily operations and passes on information to employees. The **nucleus,** shown in **Figure 6,** directs all cell activities and is separated from the cytoplasm by a membrane. Materials enter and leave the nucleus through openings in the membrane. The nucleus contains the instructions for everything the cell does. These instructions are found on long, threadlike, hereditary material made of DNA. DNA is the chemical that contains the code for the cell's structure and activities. During cell division, the hereditary material coils tightly around proteins to form structures called chromosomes. A structure called a nucleolus also is found in the nucleus.

Teacher FYI

Before electron microscopes, scientists could only theorize about many cell structures and their makeups. Even the best compound microscope cannot reveal what can be seen with electron microscopes.

Curriculum Connection

Health Students may think that any cholesterol in the body presents a health risk. Cholesterol is an important component of the cell membrane. It creates a health risk only when it is present in high levels in the blood, where it builds up in arteries and obstructs blood flow. Ask students to investigate cholesterol to differentiate between blood cholesterol and dietary cholesterol. L3

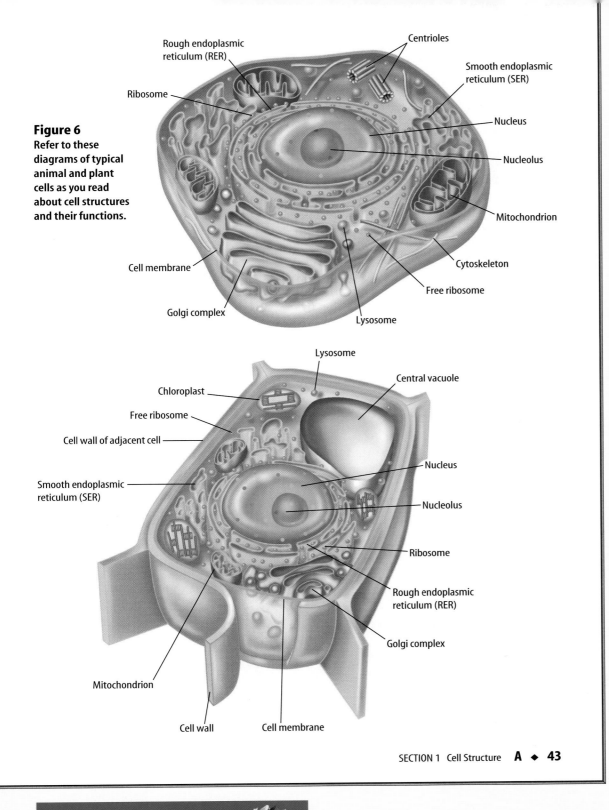

Figure 6
Refer to these diagrams of typical animal and plant cells as you read about cell structures and their functions.

Animal cell labels:
- Rough endoplasmic reticulum (RER)
- Centrioles
- Smooth endoplasmic reticulum (SER)
- Ribosome
- Nucleus
- Nucleolus
- Mitochondrion
- Cytoskeleton
- Cell membrane
- Free ribosome
- Golgi complex
- Lysosome

Plant cell labels:
- Lysosome
- Central vacuole
- Chloroplast
- Free ribosome
- Cell wall of adjacent cell
- Nucleus
- Smooth endoplasmic reticulum (SER)
- Nucleolus
- Ribosome
- Rough endoplasmic reticulum (RER)
- Golgi complex
- Mitochondrion
- Cell wall
- Cell membrane

Use an Analogy

Point out that just as each part of a machine performs a different function to enable the machine to work, each organelle performs a different function in the cell.

Use Science Words

Word Origin Greek and Latin words are used in naming cell parts. Have students make a list of cell parts and use a dictionary to find the origins of the words and their meanings. L2
LS **Linguistic**

Visual Learning

Figure 6 Have students create a network tree concept map comparing and contrasting plant and animal cells. Diagrams should make clear which organelles appear in both cells, and which are specific to only one type of cell. L2 **LS** **Visual-Spatial** P

IDENTIFYING Misconceptions

Students may think that cells are solid. Explain that almost 80% of a cell is water. The water is enclosed in a membrane that allows certain materials to enter and leave.

SECTION 1 Cell Structure **A** ◆ **43**

Resource Manager

Chapter Resources Booklet
MiniLAB, p. 3
Enrichment, p. 30

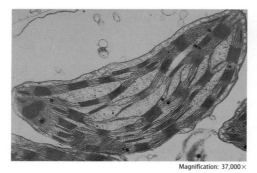

Magnification: 37,000×

Figure 7
Chloroplasts are organelles that use sunlight to make sugar from carbon dioxide and water. They contain chlorophyll, which gives most leaves and stems their green color.

Figure 8
Mitochondria are known as the powerhouses of the cell because they release energy that is needed by the cell from food.
What types of cells might contain many mitochondria?

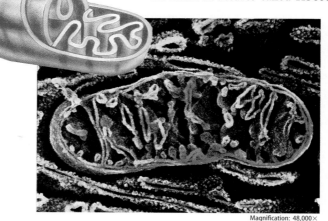

Magnification: 48,000×

Physics INTEGRATION

Energy-Processing Organelles To use food to make new substances and to communicate with each other, cells require a continuous supply of energy. In plant cells, food is made in green organelles in the cytoplasm called **chloroplasts** (KLOR uh plasts), as shown in **Figure 7.** Chloroplasts contain the green pigment chlorophyll, which gives leaves and stems their green color. Chlorophyll captures light energy and uses it to make a sugar called glucose. Glucose molecules store the captured light energy as chemical energy. Many cells, including animal cells, do not have chloroplasts for making food. They must get food from their environment.

The energy in food is stored until it is released by the mito-chondria. **Mitochondria** (mi tuh KAHN dree uh) (singular, *mitochondrion*), such as the one shown in **Figure 8,** are organelles where energy is released from breaking down food into carbon dioxide and water. Just as the gas or electric com-pany supplies fuel for the deli, a mitochondrion releases energy for use by the cell. Some types of cells, such as muscle cells, are more active than other cells. These cells have large numbers of mitochondria. Why would active cells have more or larger mitochondria?

Manufacturing Organelles One substance that takes part in nearly every cell activity is protein. Proteins are part of cell membranes. Other proteins are needed for chemical reactions that take place in the cytoplasm. Cells make their own proteins on small structures called **ribosomes.** Even though ribosomes are considered organelles, they are not membrane bound. Some ribosomes float freely in the cytoplasm; and others are attached to the endoplasmic reticulum. Ribosomes are made in the nucleolus and move out into the cytoplasm. Ribo-somes receive directions from the hereditary material in the nucleus on how, when, and in what order to make specific proteins.

Cultural Diversity

Ernest Everett Just, an African Ameri-can biologist in the early 1900s, studied cells and how they function. His research showed that all parts of the cell influence its activities, not just the nucleus, as scientists then believed. This idea changed scientific opinion concerning the basis of life. Discuss how Just's research is important to the study of cells today.

Inclusion Strategies

Learning Disabled Provide pairs of students with an unlabeled drawing of an animal cell. Have students print small stick-on labels and place them appropriately on the drawing. The labels can be folded to conceal the words and removed as the students learn the cell structures, then replaced for review. L1

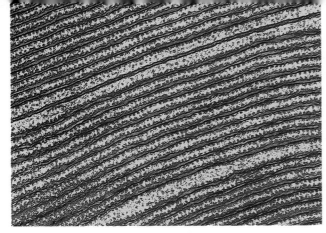

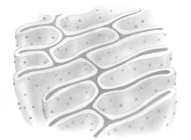

Figure 9
Endoplasmic reticulum (ER) is a complex series of membranes in the cytoplasm of the cell. *What would smooth ER look like?*

Processing, Transporting, and Storing Organelles

The **endoplasmic reticulum** (en duh PLAZ mihk • rih TIHK yuh lum) or ER, as shown in **Figure 9,** extends from the nucleus to the cell membrane. It is a series of folded membranes in which materials can be processed and moved around inside of the cell. The ER takes up a lot of space in some cells.

The endoplasmic reticulum may be "rough" or "smooth." ER that has no attached ribosomes is called smooth endoplasmic reticulum. This type of ER processes other cellular substances such as lipids that store energy. Ribosomes are attached to areas on the rough ER. There they carry out their job of making proteins that are moved out of the cell or used within the cell.

✓ Reading Check *What is the difference between rough ER and smooth ER?*

After proteins are made in a cell, they are transferred to another type of cell organelle called the Golgi (GAWL jee) bodies. The **Golgi bodies**, as shown ion **Figure 10,** are stacked, flattened membranes. The Golgi bodies sort proteins and other cellular substances and package them into membrane-bound structures called vesicles. The vesicles deliver cellular substances to areas inside the cell. They also carry cellular substances to the cell membrane where they are released to the outside of the cell.

Just as a deli has refrigerators for temporary storage of some its foods and ingredients, cells have membrane-bound spaces called vacuoles for the temporary storage of materials. A vacuole can store water, waste products, food, and other cellular materials. In plant cells, the vacuole may make up most of the cell's volume.

Figure 10
The Golgi body packages materials and moves them to the outside of the cell. *Why are materials removed from the cell?*

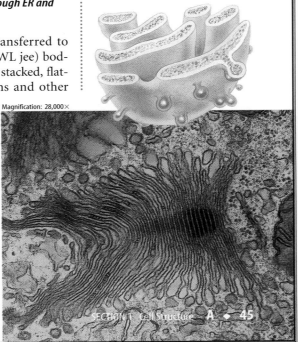

Magnification: 28,000×

SECTION 1 Cell Structure **A ◆ 45**

Cell Organization, continued

Environmental Science
INTEGRATION

Posters will vary.

✔ Reading Check

Answer to prevent digestive chemicals from leaking into the cytoplasm and destroying the cell

IDENTIFYING
Misconceptions

Students may assume that the larger an organism is, the larger its cells. Explain that while cells vary in shape and size, most are only about 0.0025 cm in diameter. The number of cells, not how large they are, determines an organism's size.

Math Skills Activity

National Math Standards

Correlation to Mathematics Objectives

1, 3, 4, 8, 9

Answers to Practice Problems

1. $A = 2\,cm \times 2\,cm \times 6 = 24\,cm^2$
   $V = 2\,cm \times 2\,cm \times 2\,cm = 8\,cm^3$
   $R = 24\,cm^2/8\,cm^3 = 3\,cm^2/cm^3$
   As the size of the cube decreases, the ratio increases.

2. $A = 8\,cm \times 8\,cm \times 6 = 384\,cm^2$
   $V = 8\,cm \times 8\,cm \times 8\,cm = 512\,cm^3$
   $R = 384\,cm^2/512\,cm^3 = 0.75\,cm^2/cm^3$
   As the size of the cube doubled, the ratio decreased by half.

Environmental Science
INTEGRATION

Just like a cell, you can recycle materials. Paper, plastics, aluminum, and glass are materials that can be recycled into usable items. Make a promotional poster to encourage others to recycle.

Recycling Organelles Active cells break down and recycle substances. Organelles called lysosomes (LI suh sohm) contain digestive chemicals that help break down food molecules, cell wastes, and worn-out cell parts. In a healthy cell, chemicals are released into vacuoles only when needed. The lysosome's membrane prevents the digestive chemicals inside from leaking into the cytoplasm and destroying the cell. When a cell dies, a lysosome's membrane disintegrates. This releases digestive chemicals that allow the quick breakdown of the cell's contents.

✔ Reading Check
What is the function of the lysosome's membrane?

Math Skills Activity

Calculate the Ratio of Surface Area to Volume of Cells

Example Problem

Assume that a cell is like a cube with six equal sides. Find the ratio of surface area to volume for a cube that is 4 cm high.

Solution

1 *This is what you know:* A cube has 6 equal sides of 4 cm × 4 cm.

2 *This is what you want to find:* the ratio (R) of surface area to volume for each cube

3 *These are the equations you use:* surface area (A) = width × length × 6
volume (V) = length × width × height
$R = (A)/(V)$

4 *Solve for surface area and volume, then solve for the ratio:* $A = 4\,cm \times 4\,cm \times 6 = 96\,cm^2$
$V = 4\,cm \times 4\,cm \times 4\,cm = 64\,cm^3$
$R = 96\,cm^2/64\,cm^3 = 1.5\,cm^2/cm^3$

Check your answer by multiplying the ratio by the volume. Do you calculate the surface area?

Practice Problems

1. Calculate the ratio of surface area to volume for a cube that is 2 cm high. What happens to this ratio as the size of the cube decreases?

2. If a 4-cm cube doubled just one of its dimensions—length, width, or height—what would happen to the ratio of surface area to volume?

For more help, refer to the Math Skills Handbook.

Resource Manager

Chapter Resources Booklet
  Activity Worksheet, pp. 5–6
  Reinforcement, p. 27
Mathematics Skill Activities, p. 5

✔ Active Reading

ReQuest To improve listening skills, have students listen carefully as you read an interesting article or story aloud. After the reading, have students construct discussion questions. Have students participate in a ReQuest with the chapter feature or another interesting article related to cell structure or function.

From Cell to Organism

Many one-celled organisms perform all their life functions by themselves. Cells in a many-celled organism, however, do not work alone. Each cell carries on its own life functions while depending in some way on other cells in the organism.

In **Figure 11,** you can see cardiac muscle cells grouped together to form a tissue. A **tissue** is a group of similar cells that work together to do one job. Each cell in a tissue does its part to keep the tissue alive.

Tissues are organized into organs. An **organ** is a structure made up of two or more different types of tissues that work together. Your heart is an organ made up of cardiac muscle tissue, nerve tissue, and blood tissues. The cardiac muscle tissue contracts, making the heart pump. The nerve tissue brings messages that tell the heart how fast to beat. The blood tissue is carried from the heart to other organs of the body.

✔ **Reading Check** *What type of tissues make up your heart?*

A group of organs working together to perform a certain function is an organ system. Your heart, arteries, veins, and capillaries make up your cardiovascular system. In a many-celled organism, several systems work together in order to perform life functions efficiently. Your nervous, circulatory, respiratory, muscular, and other systems work together to keep you alive.

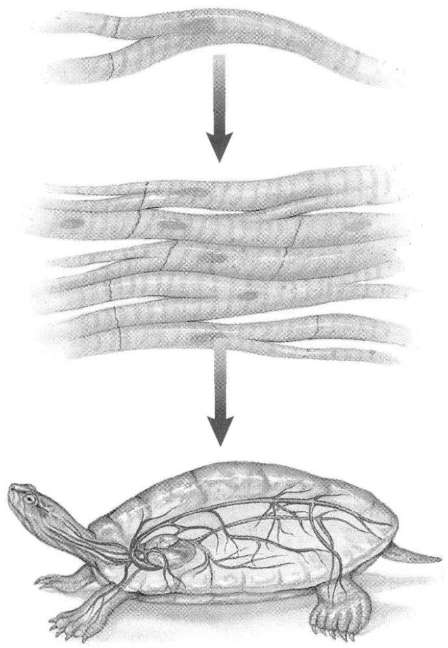

Figure 11
In many-celled organisms, cells are organized into tissues, tissues into organs, organs into systems, and systems into organisms.

Section 1 Assessment

1. Explain the important role of the nucleus in the life of a cell.

2. Compare and contrast the energy processing organelles.

3. Why are digestive enzymes in a cell enclosed in a membrane-bound organelle?

4. How are cells, tissues, organs, and organ systems related?

5. **Think Critically** How is the cell of a one-celled organism different from the cells in many-celled organisms?

Skill Builder Activities

6. **Interpreting Scientific Illustrations** Examine the illustrations of the animal cell and the plant cell in **Figure 6** and make a list of differences and similarities between them. **For more help, refer to the** Science Skill Handbook.

7. **Communicating** Your textbook compared some cell functions to that of a deli. In your Science Journal, write an essay that explains how a cell is like your school or town. **For more help, refer to the** Science Skill Handbook.

✔ **Reading Check**

Answer cardiac muscle tissue, nerve tissue, and blood tissue

③ Assess

Reteach
What are the differences between plant and animal cells? Most plant cells contain chloroplasts and cell walls; animal cells do not. **What is the difference between a prokaryotic and eukaryotic cell?** Eukaryotic cells have membrane-bound structures; prokaryotic cells do not.

Challenge
How do the cell walls, chloroplasts, and vacuoles of plant cells illustrate that cell structure is related to cell function? Cell walls, chloroplasts, and vacuoles provide the cell with protection, photosynthesis, and storage.

✔Assessment

Process To further assess students' abilities to compare and contrast different cell types, have them write statements in their Science Journals comparing animal and plant cells. Use **PASC,** p. 175.

Answers to Section Assessment

1. It directs the activities of the cell and stores hereditary information.
2. The chlorophyll in chloroplasts captures light energy and stores it as chemical energy in sugar molecules. Mitochondria release the energy stored in food.

3. It prevents the digestive chemicals inside from destroying the cell.
4. Organ systems are made of organs, which are made of tissues. Tissues are made of cells.
5. one-celled—performs all life functions; many-celled—cells depend on each other

6. Plant cells have chloroplasts and cell walls which animal cells do not have. Unlike plant cells, animal cells have centrioles.
7. A town or school has many parts. Different people supply services. Each person has a job. Each building has a function. All these things working

together make the town or school function properly. A cell has many parts. The different parts of a cell have jobs, and each part helps the cell carry out its life processes.

Activity

BENCH TESTED

Purpose Students identify and compare the parts of a plant and animal cell. [L2] [ELL]

LS Visual-Spatial

Process Skills observing, identifying, inferring, diagramming, comparing and contrasting, classifying

Time Required 45 minutes

Alternate Materials If *Elodea* is unavailable, cell parts can be seen in the thin, newest leaves of a coleus plant or similar houseplant.

Safety Precautions Caution students to use extreme care when working with a microscope and microscope slides.

Teaching Strategies

- Have students work in pairs. One student obtains and sets up the microscope while the other prepares the wet mount and obtains the cheek-cell slide. Both observe the slides and record data.

- Have students clean slides and coverslips after use.

Troubleshooting To see movement of cytoplasm, use only leaves from the tips of *Elodea*. Help students focus so they will see cell layers. Students may not be able to see the nucleus because most cell parts need to be stained to be visible. Many students may mistake the chloroplast for the cells, not realizing that the chloroplasts are *inside* the larger structure.

Answers to Questions

1. The *Elodea* cell is rectangular; the cheek cell is oval.
2. Only plant cells have a cell wall and chloroplasts.

Activity

Comparing Cells

If you compared a goldfish to a rose, you would find them unlike each other. Are their individual cells different also? Try this activity to compare plant and animal cells.

What You'll Investigate
How do human cheek cells and plant cells compare?

Materials
microscope	dropper
microscope slide	*Elodea* plant
coverslip	prepared slide of human
forceps	cheek cells
tap water	

Goal
- **Compare and contrast** an animal cell and a plant cell.

Safety Precautions

Procedure

1. Copy the data table in your Science Journal. Check off the cell parts as you observe them.

Cell Observations		
Cell Part	**Cheek**	***Elodea***
Cytoplasm	✔	✔
Nucleus	✔	✔
Chloroplasts		✔
Cell Wall		✔
Cell Membrane	✔	✔

2. Using forceps, make a wet-mount slide of a young leaf from the tip of an *Elodea* plant.

3. **Observe** the leaf on low power. Focus on the top layer of cells.

4. Switch to high power and focus on one cell. In the center of the cell is a membrane-bound organelle called the central vacuole. Observe the chloroplasts—the green, disk-shaped objects moving around the central vacuole. Try to find the cell nucleus. It looks like a clear ball.

5. **Draw** the *Elodea* cell. Label the cell wall, cytoplasm, chloroplasts, central vacuole, and nucleus. Return to low power and remove the slide. Properly dispose of the slide.

6. **Observe** the prepared slide of cheek cells under low power.

7. Switch to high power and observe the cell nucleus. Draw and label the cell membrane, cytoplasm, and nucleus. Return to low power and remove the slide.

Conclude and Apply

1. **Compare and contrast** the shapes of the cheek cell and the *Elodea* cell.

2. What can you conclude about the differences between plant and animal cells?

Communicating Your Data

Draw the two kinds of cells on one sheet of paper. Use a green pencil to label the organelles found only in plants, a red pencil to label the organelles found only in animals, and a blue pencil to label the organelles found in both. **For more help, refer to the Science Skill Handbook.**

✓Assessment

Performance To further assess students' abilities to compare plant and animal cells, have them examine cells from lettuce leaves and other types of animal cells on prepared slides. Use **Performance Assessment in the Science Classroom,** p. 97.

Communicating Your Data

Chloroplasts and cell walls should be labeled in green on the plant cell. No organelles visible are found only in animal cells. Cytoplasm, nuclei, and cell membranes should be labeled in blue, on both plant and animal cells.

Viewing Cells

Magnifying Cells

The number of living things in your environment that you can't see is much greater than the number that you can see. Many of the things that you cannot see are only one cell in size. To see most cells, you need to use a microscope.

Trying to see separate cells in a leaf, like the ones in **Figure 12,** is like trying to see individual photos in a photo mosaic picture that is on the wall across the room. As you walk toward the wall, it becomes easier to see the individual photos. When you get right up to the wall, you can see details of each small photo. A microscope has one or more lenses that enlarge the image of an object as though you are walking closer to it. Seen through these lenses, the leaf appears much closer to you, and you can see the individual cells that carry on life processes.

Early Microscopes In the late 1500s, the first microscope was made by a Dutch maker of reading glasses. He put two magnifying glasses together in a tube and got an image that was larger than the image that was made by either lens alone.

In the mid 1600s, Antonie van Leeuwenhoek, a Dutch fabric merchant, made a simple microscope with a tiny glass bead for a lens, as shown in **Figure 13.** With it, he reported seeing things in pond water that no one had ever imagined. His microscope could magnify up to 270 times. Another way to say this is that his microscope could make the image of an object 270 times larger than its actual size. Today you would say his lens had a power of 270×. Early compound microscopes were crude by today's standards. The lenses would make an image larger, but it wasn't always sharp or clear.

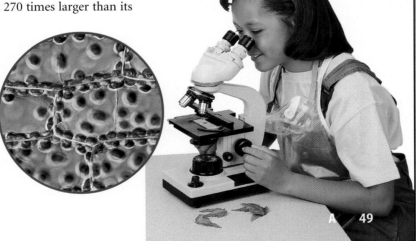

As You Read

What You'll Learn
Compare the differences between the compound light microscope and the electron microscope.
Summarize the discoveries that led to the development of the cell theory.
Relate the cell theory to modern biology.

Vocabulary
cell theory

Why It's Important
Humans are like other living things because they are all made of cells.

Figure 12
Individual cells become visible when a plant leaf is viewed using a microscope with enough magnifying power.

SECTION

Viewing Cells

Bellringer Transparency
Display the Section Focus Transparency for Section 2. Use the accompanying Transparency Activity Master. L2
ELL

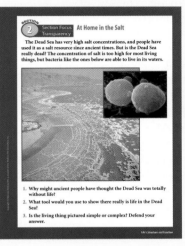

At Home in the Salt

The Dead Sea has very high salt concentrations, and people have used it as a salt resource since ancient times. But is the Dead Sea really dead? The concentration of salt is too high for most living things, but bacteria like the ones below are able to live in its waters.

1. Why might ancient people have thought the Dead Sea was totally without life?
2. What tool would you use to show there really is life in the Dead Sea?
3. Is the living thing pictured simple or complex? Defend your answer.

Tie to Prior Knowledge
Students may have used magnifying glasses and binoculars. Explain that a microscope magnifies in the same way.

Section ✓ *Assessment* Planner

PORTFOLIO
Assessment, p. 53
PERFORMANCE ASSESSMENT
Try at Home MiniLAB, p. 52
Skill Builder Activities, p. 53
See page 64 for more options.

CONTENT ASSESSMENT
Section, p. 53
Challenge, p. 53
Chapter, pp. 64–65

Resource Manager

Chapter Resources Booklet
Transparency Activities, p. 45
Directed Reading for Content Mastery, p. 20

Visualizing Microscopes

Have students examine the pictures and read the captions. Then ask the following questions.

What are the similarities and differences between a fluorescence microscope and a phase-contrast microscope? Possible answers: Both microscopes magnify up to 1500x. With the fluorescence microscope, the specimen must be stained and can be viewed through the scope directly. With the phase-contrast microscope, the specimen is not stained and can only be viewed on a monitor or in a photograph. Phase-contrast microscopes are good for viewing living things.

Compare and contrast the features of a TEM and an SEM. Possible answers: Both microscope use electrons to help produce the magnified image. Also, with both microscopes the specimen can only be viewed on a monitor or in a photograph. In a TEM the electrons go through the specimen and the magnification is up to 500,000x. With an SEM, the electrons sweep over the surface of the specimen and a three dimensional image is produced. The magnification of an SEM is only up to 200,000x.

Activity

Have students identify the type of microscope(s) they use in science class. Then have students view different slides under the microscope (e.g. onion slices, hair, sliver from a grass blade, comics color section of the newspaper). Have students draw what they observe. If possible, use several types of microscopes and a magnifying glass and have students compare how the same slide looks under each one. Ask students to list the similarities and differences between them, and hypothesize what accounts for these differences.

NATIONAL GEOGRAPHIC VISUALIZING MICROSCOPES

Figure 13

Microscopes give us a glimpse into a previously invisible world. Improvements have vastly increased their range of visibility, allowing researchers to study life at the molecular level. A selection of these powerful tools—and their magnification power—is shown here.

▶ **Up to 250x**

LEEUWENHOEK MICROSCOPE Held by a modern researcher, this historic microscope allowed Leeuwenhoek to see clear images of tiny freshwater organisms that he called "beasties."

▼ **Up to 1,500x** **BRIGHTFIELD / DARKFIELD MICROSCOPE** The light microscope is often called the brightfield microscope because the image is viewed against a bright background. A brightfield microscope is the tool most often used in laboratories to study cells. Placing a thin metal disc beneath the stage, between the light source and the objective lenses, converts a brightfield microscope to a darkfield microscope. The image seen using a darkfield microscope is bright against a dark background. This makes details more visible than with a brightfield microscope. Below are images of a *Paramecium* as seen using both processes.

Darkfield

Brightfield

▲ **Up to 1,500x** **FLUORESCENCE MICROSCOPE** This type of microscope requires that the specimen be treated with special fluorescent stains. When viewed through this microscope, certain cell structures or types of substances glow, as seen in the image of a *Paramecium* above.

50 ◆ A CHAPTER 2 Cells

Magnification Have students make a time line showing discoveries made with the light microscope, beginning with Robert Hooke (1665) identifying and drawing cells. L2

Teacher FYI

Any phenomena that occurs as a result of the fixing or staining procedure used to prepare a specimen to be viewed on a slide is called an artifact. An artifact is not a feature of the living organism. Sometimes an artifact can be a simple air bubble, other times the procedure can change the shape of a particular feature.

▶ **Up to 500,000x** TRANSMIS-
SION ELECTRON MICROSCOPE A TEM
aims a beam of electrons through
a specimen. Denser portions of the
specimen allow fewer electrons to
pass through and appear darker in
the image. Organisms, such as the
Paramecium at right, can only be seen
when the image is photographed or
shown on a monitor. A TEM can magnify hundreds of thousands of times.

▶ **Up to 1,500x** PHASE-CONTRAST MICROSCOPE
A phase-contrast microscope emphasizes slight
differences in a specimen's capacity to bend light
waves, thereby enhancing light and dark regions
without the use of stains. This type of microscope
is especially good for viewing living cells, like the
Paramecium above left. The images from a phase-
contrast microscope can only be seen when the
specimen is photographed or shown on a monitor.

▶ **Up to 200,000x** SCANNING ELECTRON
MICROSCOPE An SEM sweeps a beam of
electrons over a specimen's surface, causing
other electrons to be emitted from the
specimen. SEMs produce realistic, three-
dimensional images, which can only be
viewed as photographs or on a monitor,
as in the image of the *Paramecium* at
right. Here a researcher compares an
SEM picture to a computer monitor
showing an enhanced image.

SECTION 2 Viewing Cells **A ◆ 51**

NATIONAL GEOGRAPHIC

Visualizing Microscopes

Extension

Have students do a simple
experiment involving refraction.
Pour a quarter cup of water into a
clear glass jar or beaker. Place a
ruler in the beaker so that it is
leaning against the top rim. Gently pour in a quarter cup each of
cooking oil and rubbing alcohol
successively. Do not stir. Have
students record their observations regarding the appearance of
the ruler. Students should see refraction
of light as it passes through the different
mediums as evidenced by the ruler
appearing as though it is misshapen.
Have students look up the definition of refraction and relate it to
what they are seeing.

Content Background

Microscopes are used by many
different types of scientists
including, biologists, microbiologists, botanists, geologists, and
epidemiologists. In 1665, Robert
Hooke was the first person to
see cells through a microscope
of his creation. The idea of cell
theory-that all living things are
made of cells- was borne from
his discovery. Although Hooke
could see the individual cells
clearly, he did not stain any of
his specimens, therefore, he
would not have been able to see
other single-celled organisms
such as bacteria. It was Antoni
van Leeuwenhoek who first
examined living organisms
through a simple microscope in
the late seventeenth century. He
found organisms in the rain
water he collected, as well as in
the scrapings he took from the
surface of his teeth.

Resource Manager

Chapter Resources Booklet
Enrichment, p. 31
Lab Activity, pp. 9–12, 13–16
Science Inquiry Labs, p. 3

Visual Learning

Figure 13 Have students make a chart comparing
and contrasting the different types of microscopes in this figure. They should include
information on lenses and the uses of each. L2
LS Visual-Spatial

2 Teach

Magnifying Cells

TRY AT HOME
Mini LAB

Purpose Students discover objects that can be used to magnify. L2 ELL LS **Kinesthetic**
Materials clear drinking glass, clear glass bowl, water, magnifying glass, newspaper pages
Teaching Strategy Try this activity with the glasses students will use. Determine beforehand the amount of water that will be needed.
Analysis
Each of the objects magnifies the newsprint.

✓ Assessment

Performance Cover newsprint with clear plastic wrap. Place a drop of water on the plastic wrap. Have students explain what they see and why. The words appear magnified because the water drop acts like a convex lens. Use **Performance Assessment in the Science Classroom,** p. 97.

Physics INTEGRATION

A convex lens is thicker in the middle than at the edges. This causes the light rays to bend inward and meet at a point. Placing the object to be viewed a certain distance from the convex lens produces an enlarged image.

TRY AT HOME
Mini LAB

Observing Magnified Objects
Procedure
1. Look at a **newspaper** through the curved side and through the flat bottom of an **empty, clear glass.**
2. Look at the newspaper through a **clear glass bowl** filled with **water** and then with a **magnifying glass.**

Analysis
In your Science Journal, compare how well you can see the newspaper through each of the objects.

Physics INTEGRATION

A magnifying glass is a convex lens. All microscopes use one or more convex lenses. In your Science Journal, diagram a convex lens and describe its shape.

52 ◆ A CHAPTER 2 Cells

Modern Microscopes Scientists use a variety of microscopes to study organisms, cells, and cell parts that are too small to be seen with the human eye. Depending on how many lenses a microscope contains, it is called simple or compound. A simple microscope is similar to a magnifying glass. It has only one lens. A microscope's lens makes an enlarged image of an object and directs light toward your eye. The change in apparent size produced by a microscope is called magnification. Microscopes vary in powers of magnification. Some microscopes can make images of individual atoms.

The microscope you probably will use to study life science is a compound light microscope, similar to the one in the Reference Handbook at the back of this book. The compound light microscope has two sets of lenses—eyepiece lenses and objective lenses. The eyepiece lenses are mounted in one or two tubelike structures. Images of objects viewed through two eyepieces, or stereomicroscopes, are three-dimensional. Images of objects viewed through one eyepiece are not. Compound light microscopes usually have two to four movable objective lenses.

Magnification The powers of the eyepiece and objective lenses determine the total magnifications of a microscope. If the eyepiece lens has a power of 10× and the objective lens has a power of 43×, then the total magnification is 430× (10× times 43×). Some compound microscopes, like those in **Figure 13,** have more powerful lenses that can magnify an object up to 2,000 times its original size.

Electron Microscopes Things that are too small to be seen with other microscopes can be viewed with an electron microscope. Instead of using lenses to direct beams of light, an electron microscope uses a magnetic field in a vacuum to direct beams of electrons. Some electron microscopes can magnify images up to one million times. Electron microscope images must be photographed or electronically produced.

Several kinds of electron microscopes have been invented, as shown in **Figure 13.** Scanning electron microscopes (SEM) produce a realistic, three-dimensional image. Only the surface of the specimen can be observed using an SEM. Transmission electron microscopes (TEM) produce a two-dimensional image of a thinly-sliced specimen. Details of cell parts can be examined using a TEM. Scanning tunneling microscopes (STM) are able to show the arrangement of atoms on the surface of a molecule. A metal probe is placed near the surface of the specimen and electrons flow from the tip. The hills and valleys of the specimen's surface are mapped.

Curriculum Connection

Art Discuss the use of art in science before the camera was invented. Photocopy a picture of Hooke's drawing of cells for each student. Ask them to compare it with the photographs of cells throughout the chapter and write in their Science Journals their opinions of the advantages and disadvantages of using artwork and photography. L2 LS **Linguistic and Visual-Spatial**

Resource Manager

Chapter Resources Booklet
MiniLAB, p. 4
Reinforcement, p. 28

Development of the Cell Theory

During the seventeenth century, scientists used their new invention, the microscope, to explore the newly discovered microscopic world. They examined drops of blood, scrapings from their own teeth, and other small things. Cells weren't discovered until the microscope was improved. In 1665, Robert Hooke cut a thin slice of cork and looked at it under his microscope. To Hooke, the cork seemed to be made up of empty little boxes, which he named cells.

In the 1830s, Matthias Schleiden used a microscope to study plant parts. He concluded that all plants are made of cells. Theodor Schwann, after observing many different animal cells, concluded that all animals also are made up of cells. Eventually, they combined their ideas and became convinced that all living things are made of cells.

Several years later, Rudolf Virchow hypothesized that cells divide to form new cells. Virchow proposed that every cell came from a cell that already existed. His observations and conclusions and those of others are summarized in the **cell theory,** as described in **Table 1.**

Reading Check *Who made the conclusion that all animals are made of cells?*

Table 1 The Cell Theory

All organisms are made up of one or more cells.	An organism can be one cell or many cells like most plants and animals.
The cell is the basic unit of organization in organisms.	Even in complex organisms, the cell is the basic unit of structure and function.
All cells come from cells.	Most cells can divide to form two new, identical cells.

Section 2 Assessment

1. Explain why the invention of the microscope was important in the study of cells.
2. What is stated in the cell theory?
3. What is the difference between a simple and a compound light microscope?
4. What was Virchow's contribution to the cell theory?
5. **Think Critically** Why would it be better to look at living cells than at dead cells?

Skill Builder Activities

6. **Concept Mapping** Using a network tree concept map, compare a compound light microscope to an electron microscope. **For more help, refer to the** Science Skill Handbook.
7. **Solving One-Step Equations** Calculate the magnifications of a microscope that has an $8\times$ eyepiece, and $10\times$ and $40\times$ objectives. **For more help, refer to the** Math Skill Handbook.

SECTION 2 Viewing Cells **A ◆ 53**

Development of the Cell Theory

Teacher FYI

Hooke saw only cell walls. When plant cells die, the cell wall remains. Tree bark is dead tissue. The cork that Hooke examined comes from the bark of an oak tree.

✔ Reading Check

Answer Theodor Schwann

3 Assess

Reteach

Place a large drawing of a compound microscope on the bulletin board. Write the functions of each part on a 3 x 5 card. Have students select a card, name the part, and find it on the drawing. [L1] COOP LEARN [IS] **Visual-Spatial**

Challenge

How does the cell theory contradict the theory that living things come from nonliving things? It shows that cells are the basic units of life, all organisms are made of one or more cells, and all cells come from existing cells.

✔ Assessment

Portfolio Have students write a paragraph describing the limitations as they understand them of each microscope presented in this section. Use **PASC,** p. 157. [P]

Answers to Section Assessment

1. Microscopes made cells visible, which established them as a scientific fact. This led to the understanding that all living things are made of cells.
2. All organisms are made of one or more cells. The cell is the basic unit of organization in organisms. All cells come from other cells.
3. A simple light microscope has one lens. A compound light microscope has two or more lenses.
4. Virchow proposed that every cell came from a cell that already existed.
5. Possible answer: some cell parts disintegrate when the cell dies.
6. Map should include the following information: compound light microscopes—use light, magnify up to 2000$\times$; electron microscopes—use electrons, magnify up to 1,000,000$\times$.
7. The low-power magnification is $80\times = (8 \times 10)$ and the high-power magnification is $320\times = (8 \times 40)$.

SECTION

3

Viruses

1 Motivate

Bellringer Transparency

Display the Section Focus Transparency for Section 3. Use the accompanying Transparency Activity Master. L2 ELL

3 Section Focus Transparency

Thanks for sharing!

Sneezing is an involuntary action that aids the body by clearing congestion within the nose. But sneezing also spreads germs, including cold and influenza viruses.

1. How do you feel when you catch a cold?
2. What can you do to limit the spread of viruses?

Tie to Prior Knowledge

Most students will be familiar with at least one viral disease (chicken pox, cold sores, the common cold). Have them list its symptoms on the board.

SECTION

3 Viruses

As You Read

What You'll Learn
- **Explain** how a virus makes copies of itself.
- **Identify** the benefits of vaccines.
- **Investigate** some uses of viruses.

Vocabulary
virus
host cell

Why It's Important
Viruses infect nearly all organisms, usually affecting them negatively yet sometimes affecting them positively.

Figure 14
Viruses come in a variety of shapes.

What are viruses?

Cold sores, measles, chicken pox, colds, the flu, and AIDS are diseases caused by nonliving particles called viruses. A **virus** is a strand of hereditary material surrounded by a protein coating. Viruses don't have a nucleus or other organelles. They also lack a cell membrane. Viruses, as shown in **Figure 14,** have a variety of shapes. Because they are too small to be seen with a light microscope, they were discovered only after the electron microscope was invented. Before that time, scientists only hypothesized about viruses.

How do viruses multiply?

All viruses can do is make copies of themselves. However, they can't do that without the help of a living cell called a **host cell.** Crystalized forms of some viruses can be stored for years. Then, if they enter an organism, they can multiply quickly.

Once a virus is inside of a host cell, the virus can act in two ways. It can either be active or it can become latent, which is an inactive stage.

A Filoviruses do not have uniform shapes. Some of these *Ebola* viruses have a loop at one end.

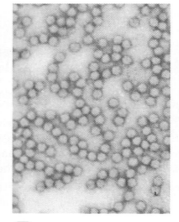

B The potato leafroll virus, *Polervirus,* damages potato crops worldwide.

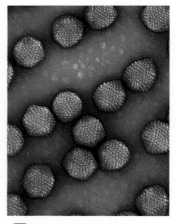

C This is just one of the many adenoviruses that can cause the common cold.

54 ◆ A CHAPTER 2 Cells

Section ✓Assessment Planner

PORTFOLIO
Extension, p. 56
PERFORMANCE ASSESSMENT
Skill Builder Activities, p. 57
See page 64 for more options.

CONTENT ASSESSMENT
Section, p. 57
Challenge, p. 57
Chapter, pp. 64–65

Figure 15
An active virus multiplies and destroys the host cell.
A The virus attaches to a specific host cell. **B** The virus's hereditary material enters the host cell. **C** The hereditary material of the virus causes the cell to make viral hereditary material and proteins. **D** New viruses form inside of the host cell. **E** New viruses are released as the host cell bursts open and is destroyed.

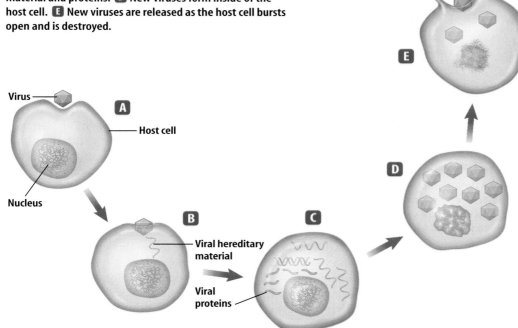

Virus
Host cell
Nucleus
Viral hereditary material
Viral proteins

2 Teach

How do viruses multiply?

Visual Learning

Figure 15 Have students make a concept map outlining the steps of viral infection and replication shown in this figure.

Active Viruses When a virus enters a cell and is active, it causes the host cell to make new viruses. This process destroys the host cell. Follow the steps in **Figure 15** to see one way that an active virus functions inside a cell.

Latent Viruses Some viruses can be latent. That means that after the virus enters a cell, its hereditary material can become part of the cell's hereditary material. It does not immediately make new viruses or destroy the cell. As the host cell reproduces, the viral DNA is copied. A virus can be latent for many years. Then, at any time, certain conditions, either inside or outside your body, can activate the virus.

If you have had a cold sore on your lip, a latent virus in your body has become active. The cold sore is a sign that the virus is active and destroying cells in your lip. When the cold sore disappears, the virus has become latent again. The virus is still in your body's cells, but it is hiding and doing no apparent harm.

SCIENCE *Online*

Research Visit the Glencoe Science Web site at **science.glencoe.com** for information on viruses. What environmental stimuli might activate a latent virus? Record your answer in your Science Journal.

SCIENCE *Online*
Internet Addresses
_____
_____
_____
_____

Explore the Glencoe Science Web site at **science.glencoe.com** to find out more about topics in this section.

Resource Manager

Chapter Resources Booklet
Transparency Activity, p. 46
Directed Reading for Content Mastery, pp. 20, 21
Enrichment, p. 32

SECTION 3 Viruses **A ◆ 55**

LAB DEMONSTRATION

Purpose to model two viruses
Materials bolt, 2 nuts to fit bolt, 2 pieces #22 gauge wire cut in 14-cm lengths, polystyrene ball 4.5 cm in diameter, craft sticks cut in 2-cm lengths
Preparation Prepare the materials and provide pictures of a bacteriophage and a flu virus.

Procedure Have students use the bacteriophage picture, the bolt, nuts, and wire to make a model bacteriophage. Have them use the polystyrene ball and craft sticks to make a model flu virus.

Expected Outcome Students should observe that different viruses have different structures.

Assessment

In a real virus, what would make up the threaded part of the bolt and the wires? protein If your flu virus were a real virus, what would you expect to find inside the ball? hereditary material

How do viruses affect organisms?

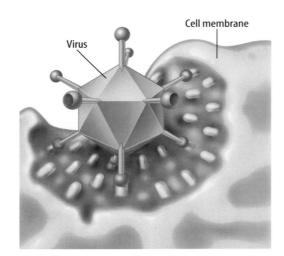

Figure 16
Viruses and the attachment sites of the host cell must match exactly. That's why most viruses infect only one kind of host cell.

SCIENCE *Online*

Collect Data Scientists have determined that *Marburg* virus, *Ebola zaire*, and *Ebola reston* all belong to the virus family Filoviridae. Visit the Glencoe Science Web site at **science.glencoe.com** for the latest information about these viruses. Share your results with your class.

How do viruses affect organisms?

Viruses attack animals, plants, fungi, protists, and all prokaryotes. Some viruses can infect only specific kinds of cells. For instance, many viruses, such as the potato leafroll virus, are limited to one host species or to one type of tissue within that species. A few viruses affect a broad range of hosts. An example of this is the rabies virus. Rabies can infect humans and many other animal hosts.

A virus cannot move by itself, but it can reach a host's body in several ways. For example, it can be carried onto a plant's surface by the wind or it can be inhaled by an animal. In a viral infection, the virus first attaches to the surface of the host cell. The virus and the place where it attaches must fit together exactly, as shown in **Figure 16.** Because of this, most viruses attack only one kind of host cell.

Viruses that infect bacteria are called bacteriophages (bak TIHR ee uh fay juhz). They differ from other kinds of viruses in the way that they enter bacteria and release their hereditary material. Bacteriophages attach to a bacterium and inject their hereditary material. The entire cycle takes about 20 min, and each virus-infected cell releases an average of 100 viruses.

Fighting Viruses

Vaccines are used to prevent disease. A vaccine is made from weakened virus particles that can't cause disease anymore. Vaccines have been made to prevent many diseases including measles, mumps, smallpox, chicken pox, polio, and rabies.

✔ Reading Check   *What is a vaccine?*

The First Vaccine Edward Jenner is credited with developing the first vaccine in 1796. He developed a vaccine for smallpox, a disease that was still feared in the early twentieth century. Jenner noticed that people who got a disease called cowpox didn't get smallpox. He prepared a vaccine from the sores of people who had cowpox. When injected into healthy people, the cowpox vaccine protected them from smallpox. Jenner didn't know he was fighting a virus. At that time, no one understood what caused disease or how the body fought disease.

Curriculum Connection

Math A common unit of measure for viruses is the nanometer (nm), which is 1,000 times smaller than a micrometer (µm) and 1 million times smaller than a millimeter. A typical virus is 20 nm in size. What part of a millimeter is that? 0.00002 mm A virus of 0.3 micrometers is how many nanometers? 300 nm
L2 LS **Logical-Mathematical**

Treating and Preventing Viral Diseases Antibiotics are used to treat bacterial infections. They are ineffective against any viral disease. One way your body can stop viral infections is by making interferons. Interferons are proteins that protect cells from viruses. These proteins are produced rapidly by infected cells and move to noninfected cells in the host. They cause the noninfected cells to produce protective substances.

Antiviral drugs can be given to infected patients to help fight a virus. A few drugs show some effectiveness against viruses but some have limited use because of their adverse side effects.

Public health measures for preventing viral diseases include vaccinating people, improving sanitary conditions, quarantining patients, and controlling animals that spread the disease. Yellow fever was wiped out completely in the United States through mosquito-control programs. Annual rabies vaccinations protect humans by keeping pets and farm animals free from infection. To control the spread of rabies in wild animals such as coyotes and wolves, wildlife workers place bait containing an oral rabies vaccine, as shown in **Figure 17,** where wild animals will find it.

Research with Viruses

You might think viruses are always harmful. However, through research, scientists are discovering helpful uses for some viruses. One use, called gene therapy, is being tried on cells with defective genes. Normal hereditary material is substituted for a cell's defective hereditary material. The normal material is enclosed in viruses. The viruses then "infect" targeted cells, taking the new hereditary material into the cells to replace the defective hereditary material. Using gene therapy, scientists hope to help people with genetic disorders and find a cure for cancer.

Figure 17
This oral rabies bait is being prepared for an aerial drop by the Texas Department of Health as part of their Oral Rabies Vaccination Program. This five-year program has prevented the expansion of rabies into Texas.

Section 3 Assessment

1. Describe the structure of viruses and explain how viruses multiply.
2. How are vaccines beneficial?
3. How might some viruses be helpful?
4. How might viral diseases be prevented?
5. **Think Critically** Explain why a doctor might not give you any medication if you have a viral disease.

Skill Builder Activities

6. **Concept Mapping** Make an events chain concept map to show what happens when a latent virus becomes active. **For more help, refer to the** Science Skill Handbook.
7. **Using a Word Processor** Make an outline of the cycle of an active virus. **For more help, refer to the** Technology Skill Handbook.

Answers to Section Assessment

1. A virus is a particle of hereditary material surrounded by protein. Viruses are reproduced only in a host cell. The host cell is destroyed when the viruses are released.
2. Vaccines, when properly administered, help prevent many viral infections.
3. They may be used to transfer normal DNA into a cell.
4. vaccinating people, improving sanitary conditions, quarantining patients, and controlling animals that spread disease
5. No medications cure a viral disease.
6. Maps should show the following:

latent virus enters cell; virus becomes part of cell's DNA; cell divides; virus reproduces as part of cell division; virus becomes active; virus forms new virus particles; cell is destroyed.
7. Outline should be similar to **Figure 15.**

BENCH TESTED

Recognize the Problem

Purpose
Students will design an experiment to compare uses of stereomicroscopes and compound light microscopes. L2

COOP LEARN

Logical-Mathematical

Process Skills
observing, identifying, recognizing and using spatial relationships, classifying, communicating

Time Required
15 minutes to plan the experiment and 45 minutes to do the experiment

Safety Precautions
Caution students to use care when working with microscope slides and coverslips. Remind them to carry microscopes with both hands. Have students wash the slides and coverslips when finished.

Form a Hypothesis

Possible Hypothesis
Students may hypothesize that large items can be viewed with the stereomicroscope and small objects can be viewed with the compound light microscope.

Test Your Hypothesis

Possible Procedures
Separate items into two groups: those that can be viewed with the stereomicroscope, and those that can be viewed with the light microscope.

Teaching Strategies
- Demonstrate how to make a wet-mount.
- If microscopes have mirrors, explain how to use them.

Activity · Design Your Own Experiment

Comparing Light Microscopes

You're a technician in a police forensic laboratory. You use a stereomicroscope and a compound light microscope in the laboratory. A detective just returned from a crime scene with bags of evidence. You must examine each piece of evidence under a microscope. How do you decide which microscope is the best tool to use?

Recognize the Problem
Will all of the evidence that you've collected be viewable through both microscopes?

Form a Hypothesis
Compare the items to be examined under the microscopes. Which microscope will be used for each item?

Possible Materials
compound light microscope
stereomicroscope
items from the classroom—include
    some living or once-living items (8)
microscope slides and coverslips
plastic petri dishes
distilled water
dropper

Goals
- **Learn** how to correctly use a stereomicroscope and a compound light microscope.
- **Compare** the uses of the stereomicroscope and compound light microscope.

Safety Precautions

Thoroughly wash your hands when you have completed this experiment.

58 ◆ A

Resource Manager

Chapter Resources Booklet
    Activity Worksheet, pp. 7–8
Home and Community Involvement, p. 26
Lab Management and Safety, p. 58

Test Your Hypothesis

Plan

1. As a group, decide how you will test your hypothesis.

2. **Describe** how you will carry out this experiment using a series of specific steps. Make sure the steps are in a logical order. Remember that you must place an item in the bottom of a plastic petri dish to examine it under the stereomicroscope and you must make a wet mount of any item to be examined under the compound light microscope. For more help, see the Reference Handbook.

3. If you need a data table or an observation table, design one in your Science Journal.

Do

1. Make sure your teacher approves the objects you'll examine, your plan, and your data table before you start.

2. Carry out the experiment.

3. While doing the experiment, record your observations and complete the data table.

Analyze Your Data

1. **Compare** the items you examined with those of your classmates.

2. Based on this experiment, classify the eight items you observed.

Draw Conclusions

1. **Infer** which microscope a scientist might use to examine a blood sample, fibers, and live snails.

2. **List** five careers that require people to use a stereomicroscope. List five careers that require people to use a compound light microscope. Enter the lists in your Science Journal.

3. If you examined an item under a compound light microscope and a stereomicroscope, how would the images differ?

4. Which microscope was better for looking at large, or possibly live items?

Communicating Your Data

In your Science Journal, **write** a short description of an imaginary crime scene and the evidence found there. **Sort** the evidence into two lists—items to be examined under a stereomicroscope and items to be examined under a compound light microscope. **For more help, refer to the Science Skill Handbook.**

Troubleshooting Place slides and coverslips for each group in a plastic petri dish to prevent breakage.

Expected Outcome

The stereomicroscope is used for items that are too large to fit under a coverslip on a slide. The compound light microscope reveals greater detail. Students should note that the image produced by the compound light microscope is upside down and reversed left to right.

Analyze Your Data

1. Answers will vary.
2. Large items should be classified together, and items small enough to fit on a slide should be grouped together.

Error Analysis

Have students compare their results and their hypotheses and explain why differences occurred.

Draw Conclusions

1. A scientist might use a stereomicroscope to examine live snails and a compound light microscope to examine blood and fibers.
2. Answers will vary, but may include lab technicians, forensic scientists, and cell biologists for the compound light microscope and surgeons, botanists, entomologists, geologists, and gemologists for the stereomicroscope.
3. The image under the compound light microscope will be magnified more and show greater detail.
4. stereomicroscope

Communicating Your Data

Items small enough to fit under a coverslip should be examined with a compound light microscope; larger items should be examined with a stereomicroscope.

✓ Assessment

Performance To further assess students' understanding of the differences in microscopes, provide other items and have students demonstrate how to use the appropriate microscope to view each item. Use **Performance Assessment in the Science Classroom,** p. 169.

Content Background

As a control, Cobb exposed cells from non-cancerous tissues to chemotherapy drugs. She hoped to discover if there was a particular drug or combination of drugs which would be effective in destroying specific types of cancer. She would also need to determine whether these drugs would also destroy healthy tissues.

Her results demonstrated that some drugs could stop the uncontrolled growth of certain types of cancer cells, but normal cells also were harmed. There were differences, however, as normal cells never showed the dramatic destruction produced in some cancer cells.

This suggested that chemotherapy was a viable approach to treatment of cancer.

Levy's research is one example of attempts to find ways to deliver high doses of cancer-killing drugs directly to a tumor while reducing the risk of damage to healthy cells.

TIME

SCIENCE AND HISTORY

SCIENCE CAN CHANGE THE COURSE OF HISTORY!

Magnification: 2,000×

This colored scanning electron micrograph (SEM) shows two breast cancer cells in the final stage of cell dvision.

Cobb Against Cancer

N ew York City, 1950. Jewel Plummer put yet another slide onto the stage of her microscope and clipped it into place. She switched to the high power objective, looked through the eyepiece, and turned the fine adjustment a tiny bit to bring her subject—cells from a cancerous tumor—into focus. She switched back to low power and removed the slide. She had found no change in the tumor cells. The drug that doctors had used wasn't killing or slowing the growth rate of those cancer cells. Sighing, she reached for the next slide. Maybe the slightly different drug they had used on that batch of cells would be the answer....

60 ◆ A

Resources for Teachers and Students

The National Cancer Institute
Public Inquiries Office
Building 31, Room 10A31
31 Center Drive
MSC 2580
Bethesda, MD 20892-2580 USA,
(301) 435-3848

Advancing Current Treatments for Cancer, by Samuel Hellman and Everett E. Vokes, Scientific American, September 1996.

How Cancer Arises, by Robert A. Weinberg, Scientific American, September 1996.

Jewel Plummer Cobb is a cell biologist who did important background research on the use of drugs against cancer. She removed cells from cancerous tumors and cultured them in the lab. Then, in a controlled study, she tried a series of different drugs against batches of the same cells. Her goal was to find the right drug to cure each patient's particular cancer. Cobb never met that goal, but her research laid the groundwork for modern chemotherapy—the use of chemicals to treat people with cancer.

Role Model

Jewel Cobb also influenced the course of science in a different way. She served as dean or president of several universities, retiring as president of the University of California at Fullerton. In her role as a college official, she was able to promote equal opportunity for students of all backgrounds, especially in the sciences.

Light Up a Cure

Vancouver, British Columbia, 2000. While Cobb herself was only able to infer what was going on inside a cell from its reactions to various drugs, her work has helped others go farther. Building on Cobb's work, Professor Julia Levy and her research team at the University of British Columbia actually go inside cells and even inside organelles to work against cancer. One technique they are pioneering is the use of light to guide cancer drugs to the right cells. First, the patient is given a chemotherapy drug that reacts to light. Next, a fiber optic tube is inserted into the tumor. Finally, laser light is passed through the tube. The light activates the light-sensitive drug—but only in the tumor itself. This technique keeps healthy cells healthy but kills sick cells on the spot.

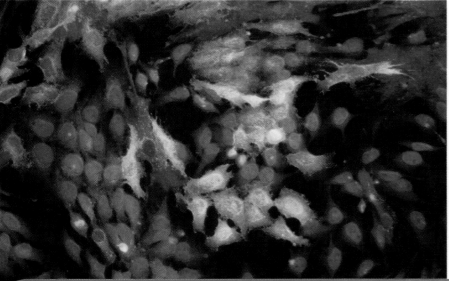

The image to the left shows human cervical cells magnified 125 times that have been attacked by cancer. The light blue areas at the center are keratin, a kind of protein. The cell nuclei are stained blue, and the red areas are fibroblasts, a kind of connective-tissue cell. These are the first human cells used to research cancer. This type of cell grows well in a lab, and is used in research worldwide.

CONNECTIONS Write Report on Cobb's experiments on cancer cells. What were her dependent and independent variables? What would she have used as a control? What sources of error did she have to guard against? Answer the same questions about Levy's work.

SCIENCE Online

For more information, visit science.glencoe.com

Discussion

Using Cobb's research as an example, discuss the value of experiments even if the results do not meet the researcher's specific goals. Possible answer: Science is a continuing process of discovery. Cobb's work is a necessary first step to new approaches to treatment like Levy's. **Chemotherapy treatments often result in discomfort and risk for cancer patients. Discuss why this is so.** Possible answer: All cells share the same genetic mechanisms. Treatments that affect DNA in one cell type will do so in others as well.

Historic Significance

The structure and function of DNA were not discovered until 1953. Cobb's research began shortly thereafter, long before the role of genes in the development of cancer was understood. Research like Cobb's leads to questions about how certain drugs can stop the unchecked growth of tumors. In combination with an increasing understanding of how genes work, these results allow scientists to refine the methods of administering treatments and to target the development of drugs specifically aimed at preventing the replication of DNA, a process that all cells require.

CONNECTIONS In Cobb's study the control group consisted of normal human cells that were exposed to the chemotherapeutic drugs. The independent variable was the specific drug administered to the cells. The dependent variable was the response of the cells to the treatment. Differences in these responses would allow conclusions about the effects of specific drugs, alone and in combination, on both cancerous and healthy cells.

SCIENCE Online

Internet Addresses

_____

_____

_____

_____

Explore the Glencoe Science Web site at **science.glencoe.com** to find out more about topics in this feature.

Reviewing Main Ideas

Preview

Students can answer the questions in their Science Journals. Discuss the answers as you go through the chapter. [IS] **Linguistic**

Review

Students can write their answers, then compare them with those of other students. [IS] **Interpersonal**

Reteach

Students can look at the illustrations and describe details that support the main ideas of the chapter. [IS] **Visual-Spatial**

Answers to Chapter Review

SECTION 1

6. temporarily stores cellular material

SECTION 2

4. The ant is dead because specimens are placed in a vacuum to be examined with an electron microscope.

SECTION 3

3. They can reproduce only within living cells. They do not have the cell components associated with living organisms.

Reviewing Main Ideas

Section 1 Cell Structure

1. There are two basic cell types. Cells without membrane-bound structures are called prokaryotic cells. Cells with membrane-bound structures are called eukaryotic cells.

2. Most of the life processes of a cell occur within the cytoplasm.

3. Cell functions are performed by organelles under the control of DNA in the nucleus.

4. Organelles such as mitochondria and chloroplasts process energy.

5. Proteins take part in nearly every cell activity.

6. Golgi bodies and vacuoles transport substances, rid the cell of wastes, and store cellular materials. *What does this organelle do?*

7. Most many-celled organisms are organized into tissues, organs, and organ systems that perform specific functions to keep an organism alive.

Section 2 Viewing Cells

1. A simple microscope has just one lens. A compound light microscope has eyepiece lenses and objective lenses.

2. To calculate the magnification of a microscope, multiply the power of the eyepiece by the power of the objective lens.

3. An electron microscope uses a beam of electrons instead of light to produce an image of an object.

4. Things that are too small to be viewed with a light microscope can be viewed with an electron microscope. This is an SEM of an ant. *How do you know if the ant is alive or dead?*

5. According to the cell theory, the cell is the basic unit of life. Organisms are made of one or more cells, and all cells come from other cells.

Section 3 Viruses

1. A virus is a structure containing hereditary material surrounded by a protein coating.

2. A virus can make copies of itself only when it is inside a living host cell.

3. Viruses cause diseases in animals, plants, fungi, and bacteria. *Why don't scientists consider viruses like these in the photo to be living organisms?*

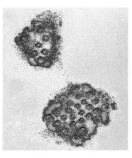

FOLDABLES
Reading & Study Skills

After You Read

On the inside of the Main Ideas Study Fold you made at the beginning of the chapter describe the characteristics of each type of cell.

FOLDABLES
Reading & Study Skills

After You Read

After students have read the chapter and completed the Foldable described in Before You Read, have them do the activity on the student page.

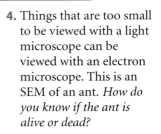

Dinah Zike

Visualizing Main Ideas

Complete the following concept map of the basic units of life.

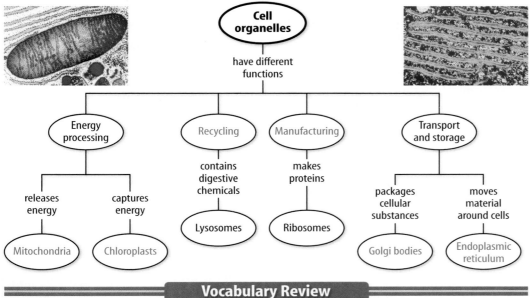

Cell organelles

have different functions

Energy processing — Recycling — Manufacturing — Transport and storage

Energy processing:
- releases energy → Mitochondria
- captures energy → Chloroplasts

Recycling: contains digestive chemicals → Lysosomes

Manufacturing: makes proteins → Ribosomes

Transport and storage:
- packages cellular substances → Golgi bodies
- moves material around cells → Endoplasmic reticulum

Vocabulary Review

Vocabulary Words

a. cell membrane
b. cell theory
c. cell wall
d. chloroplast
e. cytoplasm
f. endoplasmic reticulum
g. Golgi body
h. host cell
i. mitochondrion
j. nucleus
k. organ
l. organelle
m. ribosome
n. tissue
o. virus

Using Vocabulary

Using the vocabulary words, give an example of each of the following.

1. found in every organ
2. smaller than one cell
3. a plant-cell organelle
4. part of every cell
5. organelle having a double membrane
6. used by biologists
7. contains hereditary material
8. a structure that surrounds the cell
9. can be damaged by a virus
10. made up of cells

Visualizing Main Ideas

See student page.

Vocabulary Review

Using Vocabulary

1. n
2. d, f, g, i, j, l, m, o
3. d, e, f, g, j, m
4. a, e
5. i
6. b
7. e, j, o
8. a, c
9. h
10. k, n

Checking Concepts

1. B
2. A
3. D
4. A
5. C
6. B
7. B
8. C
9. A
10. A

Thinking Critically

11. Once a virus infects a cell, it uses the cell to produce more viruses. The immune system has to work to get rid of viruses because no drugs will kill them.

12. Answers may vary, but a stereomicroscope would enable you to view a large specimen as well as to look closely at the mold.

13. The plant cell would die or become dependent on other cells to provide its food.

14. No proteins could be made, and the animal cell would die.

15. If there is a cell wall and chloroplasts, it is a plant cell. A cell with no chloroplasts or cell wall is an animal cell. If no membrane-bound organelles are present, it is a bacterial cell.

Chapter 2 Assessment

Checking Concepts

Choose the word or phrase that best answers the question.

1. What structure allows only certain things to pass in and out of the cell?
   A) cytoplasm
   C) ribosomes
   B) cell membrane
   D) Golgi body

2. Which microscope uses lenses to magnify?
   A) compound light microscope
   B) scanning electron microscope
   C) transmission electron microscope
   D) atomic force microscope

3. What is made of folded membranes that move materials around inside the cell?
   A) nucleus
   B) cytoplasm
   C) Golgi body
   D) endoplasmic reticulum

4. Which scientist gave the name *cells* to structures he viewed?
   A) Hooke
   C) Schleiden
   B) Schwann
   D) Virchow

5. What organelle helps recycle old cell parts?
   A) chloroplast
   C) lysosome
   B) centriole
   D) cell wall

6. Which of the following is a viral disease?
   A) tuberculosis
   C) smallpox
   B) anthrax
   D) tetanus

7. What are structures in the cytoplasm of a eukaryotic cell called?
   A) organs
   C) organ systems
   B) organelles
   D) tissues

8. Which microscope magnifies up to a million times or more?
   A) compound light microscope
   B) stereomicroscope
   C) transmission electron microscope
   D) atomic force microscope

9. Which of the following is part of a bacterial cell?
   A) a cell wall
   C) mitochondria
   B) lysosomes
   D) a nucleus

10. Which of the following do groups of different tissues form?
    A) organ
    C) organ system
    B) organelle
    D) organism

Thinking Critically

11. Why is it difficult to treat a viral disease?

12. What type of microscope would be best to view a piece of moldy bread? Explain.

13. What would happen to a plant cell that suddenly lost its chloroplasts?

14. What would happen to this animal cell if it didn't have ribosomes?

15. How would you decide whether an unknown cell was an animal cell, a plant cell, or a bacterial cell?

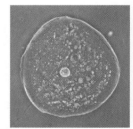

Developing Skills

16. **Sequencing** Sequence the following from simple to complex: *small intestine, circular muscle cell, human,* and *digestive system.*

17. **Interpreting Scientific Illustrations** Use the illustrations in **Figure 1** to describe how the shape of a cell is related to its function.

18. **Making and Using Graphs** Use a computer to make a line graph of the following data. At 37°C there are 1.0 million viruses; at, 37.5°C, 0.5 million; at 37.8°C, 0.25 million; at 38.3°C, 0.1 million; and at 38.9°C, 0.05 million.

Chapter ✓Assessment Planner

Portfolio Encourage students to place in their portfolios one or two items of what they consider to be their best work. Examples include:
• Visual Learning, p. 43
• Assessment, p. 53
• Extension, p. 56

Performance Additional performance assessments, Performance Task Assessment Lists, and rubrics for evaluating these activities can be found in Glencoe's **Performance Assessment in the Science Classroom.**

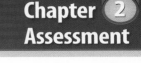
19. Comparing and Contrasting Complete the following table to compare and contrast the structures of a prokaryotic cell to those of a eukaryotic cell.

Cell Structures		
Structure	Prokaryotic Cell	Eukaryotic Cell
Cell Membrane	Yes	Yes
Cytoplasm	Yes	Yes
Nucleus	No	Yes
Endoplasmic Reticulum	No	Yes
Golgi Bodies	No	Yes

20. Making a Model Make and illustrate a time line to show the development of the cell theory. Begin with the development of the microscope and end with Virchow. Include the contributions of Leeuwenhoek, Hooke, Schleiden, and Schwann.

Performance Assessment

21. Model Use materials that resemble cell parts or that represent their functions to make a model of a plant cell or an animal cell. Make a key to the cell parts to explain your model.

22. Poster Research the history of vaccinations. Contact your local Health Department for current information. Display your results on a poster.

TECHNOLOGY

Go to the Glencoe Science Web site at **science.glencoe.com** or use the **Glencoe Science CD-ROM** for additional chapter assessment.

THE PRINCETON REVIEW **Test Practice**

A scientist is studying living cells. Below is an image of one of the cells that he is studying. This image represents what the scientist sees when he uses a tool in his laboratory.

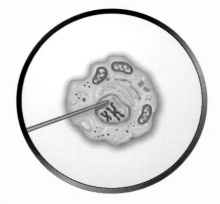

Closely examine the image above then answer the following questions.

1. If the pointer shown above with the cell is 10 micrometers in length, then about how wide is this cell?
A) 20 micrometers
B) 10 micrometers
C) 5 micrometers
D) 0.1 micrometers

2. Which of the following tools is the scientist probably using to view the living cell?
F) telescope
G) endoplasmic reticulum
H) compound light microscope
J) kaleidoscope

THE PRINCETON REVIEW **Test Practice**

The Test-Taking Tip was written by The Princeton Review, the nation's leader in test preparation.
1. B
2. H

Developing Skills

16. circular muscle cell, small intestine, digestive system, human
17. Answers will vary but should relate each shape to a function of the cell, such as the elongated shape of the nerve cell and its function in transmitting impulses.
18. Line graphs should show that, as temperature increases, the number of viruses decreases.
19. See student page.
20. The time line should have equal divisions of time and cover from the late 1500s to the late 1800s. Include these dates: late 1500s, microscope invented; late 1600s, Leeuwenhoek improves microscope; 1665, Hooke uses the word *cell;* 1830s, Schleiden discovers plants are made of cells; mid 1800s, Schwann discovers animals are made of cells; late 1800s, Virchow concludes that all cells come from cells.

Performance Assessment

21. Model should include cell parts and a key to identify them. Use **PASC,** p. 123.
22. Posters should correctly show the history of vaccinations. Use **PASC,** p. 145.

✔ Assessment Resources

📁 **Reproducible Masters**
Chapter Resources Booklet
Chapter Review, pp. 37–38
Chapter Tests, pp. 39–42
Assessment Transparency Activity, p. 49
Glencoe Science Web site
Interactive Tutor
Chapter Quizzes

Glencoe Technology
🔖 Assessment Transparency
💿 Interactive CD-ROM Chapter Quizzes
💿 ExamView Pro Test Bank
💿 Vocabulary PuzzleMaker Software
📺 MindJogger Videoquiz DVD/VHS

Section/Objectives	Standards		Activities/Features
	National	State/Local	
Chapter Opener	See p. 6T for a Key to Standards.		**Explore Activity:** Demonstrate why water leaves plant cells, p. 67 **Before You Read,** p. 67
Section 1 Chemistry of Life ⏱ 2 sessions 📦 1 block 1. **List** the differences among atoms, elements, molecules, and compounds. 2. **Explain** the relationship between chemistry and life science. 3. **Discuss** how organic compounds are different from inorganic compounds.	National Content Standards: UCP2, A1, B1, C1		**Science Online,** p. 72 **MiniLAB:** Determining How Enzymes Work, p. 73 **Math Skills Activity:** Calculating the Importance of Water, p. 74
Section 2 Moving Cellular Materials ⏱ 2 sessions 📦 1 block 1. **Describe** the function of a selectively permeable membrane. 2. **Explain** how the processes of diffusion and osmosis move molecules in living cells. 3. **Explain** how passive transport and active transport differ	National Content Standards: UCP4, A1, C1, C3		**MiniLAB:** Observing Diffusion, p. 77 **Health Integration,** p. 79 **Visualizing Cell Membrane Transport,** p. 81 **Activity:** Observing Osmosis, p. 82
Section 3 Energy for Life ⏱ 3 sessions 📦 1.5 blocks 1. **List** the differences between producers and consumers. 2. **Explain** how the processes of photosynthesis and respiration store and release energy. 3. **Describe** how cells get energy from glucose through fermentation.	National Content Standards: UCP1, A1, B3, C1, C4, G1		**Chemistry Integration,** p. 85 **Science Online,** p. 86 **Activity:** Photosynthesis and Respiration, pp. 88–89 **Science and Language Arts:** Tulip, pp. 90–91

NATIONAL GEOGRAPHIC

Teacher's Corner

PRODUCTS AVAILABLE FROM GLENCOE
To order call 1-800-334-7344:
CD-ROM's
NGS PictureShow: Looking at Living Things
Curriculum Kit
GeoKit: Cells and Microorganisms

Transparency Sets
NGS PicturePack: The Cell
NGS PicturePack: Looking At Living Things
PRODUCTS AVAILABLE FROM NATIONAL GEOGRAPHIC SOCIETY
To order call 1-800-368-2728:

Videos
Photosynthesis: Life Energy

INDEX TO NATIONAL GEOGRAPHIC SOCIETY
The following articles may be used for research relating to this chapter: "The Awesome Worlds Within a Cell," by Rick Gore, September 1976.

Activity Materials	Reproducible Resources	Section Assessment	Technology
Explore Activity: bowl, label, water (500 mL), salt (15 g), carrot sticks (6), watch or clock, beaker (250ml), balance, stirrer	**Chapter Resources Booklet** Foldables Worksheet, p. 15 Directed Reading Overview, p. 17 Note-taking Worksheets, pp. 31–33	GLENCOE'S ASSESSMENT ADVANTAGE	
MiniLAB: prepared gelatin, small cups, fresh pineapple pieces *Need materials?* Contact Science Kit at 1-800-828-7777 or www.sciencekit.com on the Internet.	**Chapter Resources Booklet** Transparency Activity, p. 42 MiniLAB, p. 3 Enrichment, p. 28 Reinforcement, p. 25 Directed Reading, p. 18 Transparency Activity, pp. 45–46 **Cultural Diversity,** p. 65	**Portfolio** Science Journal, p. 72 **Performance** MiniLAB, p. 73 Math Skills Activity, p. 74 Skill Builder Activities, p. 75 **Content** Section Assessment, p. 75	Section Focus Transparency Teaching Transparency Interactive CD-ROM/DVD Guided Reading Audio Program
MiniLAB: clean glasses (2 of equal size), labels, very warm water, cold water, food coloring, dropper, clock, marker or wax pencil **Activity:** unshelled egg, balance, spoon, distilled water (250 mL), light corn syrup (250 mL), 500-mL container	**Chapter Resources Booklet** Transparency Activity, p. 43 MiniLAB, p. 4 Enrichment, p. 29 Reinforcement, p. 26 Directed Reading, p. 18 Lab Activity, pp. 9–10 Activity Worksheet, pp. 5–6 **Home and Community Involvement,** p. 47	**Portfolio** Visual Learning, p. 81 **Performance** MiniLAB, p. 77 Skill Builder Activities, p. 80 **Content** Section Assessment, p. 80	Section Focus Transparency Interactive CD-ROM/DVD Guided Reading Audio Program
Activity: 16-mm test tubes (3), 150-mm test tubes with stoppers (4), test-tube rack, stirring rod, scissors, carbonated water (5 mL), bromothymol blue solution in dropper bottle, aged tap water (20 mL), sprig of *Elodea*	**Chapter Resources Booklet** Transparency Activity, p. 44 Enrichment, p. 30 Reinforcement, p. 27 Directed Reading, pp. 19, 20 Lab Activity, pp. 11–14 Activity Worksheet, pp. 7–8 **Lab Management and Safety,** p. 63	**Portfolio** Visual Learning, p. 87 **Performance** Skill Builder Activities, p. 87 **Content** Section Assessment, p. 87	Section Focus Transparency Interactive CD-ROM/DVD Guided Reading Audio Program

GLENCOE'S ASSESSMENT ADVANTAGE

End of Chapter Assessment

Blackline Masters	Technology	Professional Series
Chapter Resources Booklet Chapter Review, pp. 35–36 Chapter Tests, pp. 37–40 **Standardized Test Practice by The Princeton Review,** pp. 15–18	MindJogger Videoquiz CD-ROM Explorations and Quizzes Vocabulary Puzzle Makers ExamView Pro Test Bank Interactive Lesson Planner Interactive Teacher's Edition	Performance Assessment in the Science Classroom (PASC)

Transparencies

Section Focus

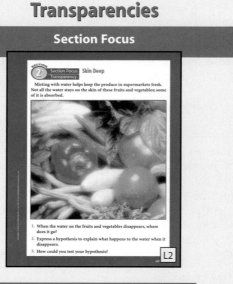

1 Section Focus Transparency — **Chemicals for Life**

Every living thing is made of organic compounds, which contain carbon and hydrogen. We need these compounds for energy, but not all organic compounds can be eaten.

1. Of the objects above, which contain organic compounds?
2. Which objects do not contain organic compounds?
3. Name four inorganic substances that your body needs to survive.

L2

2 Section Focus Transparency — **Skin Deep**

Misting with water helps keep the produce in supermarkets fresh. Not all the water stays on the skin of these fruits and vegetables; some of it is absorbed.

1. When the water on the fruits and vegetables disappears, where does it go?
2. Express a hypothesis to explain what happens to the water when it disappears.
3. How could you test your hypothesis?

L2

3 Section Focus Transparency — **What's for dinner?**

Some organisms don't need anyone to survive, but others need help to get by. In this picture, some of the living things shown can make their own food. They are called producers. Other living things, called consumers, depend on these producers for their survival.

1. Which things in the picture are producers? Consumers?
2. Explain whether you are a producer or consumer.
3. If all the plants died, what effect would it have on the animals?

L2

This is a representation of key blackline masters available in the Teacher Classroom Resources. See Resource Manager boxes within the chapter for additional information.

Assessment

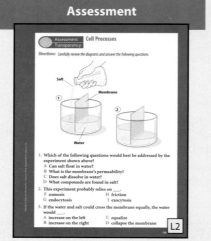

Assessment Transparency — **Cell Processes**

Directions: Carefully review the diagrams and answer the following questions.

1. Which of the following questions would best be addressed by the experiment shown above?
   A Can salt float in water?
   B What is the membrane's permeability?
   C Does salt dissolve in water?
   D What compounds are found in salt?
2. This experiment probably relies on ___.
   F osmosis   H friction
   G endocytosis   J exocytosis
3. If the water and salt could cross the membrane equally, the water would ___.
   A increase on the left   C equalize
   B increase on the right   D collapse the membrane

L2

Teaching

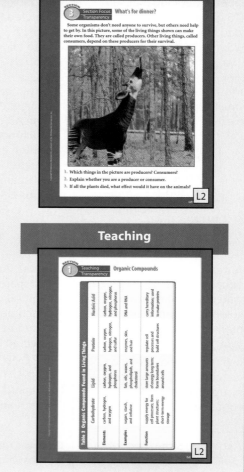

1 Teaching Transparency — **Organic Compounds**

Table 3 Organic Compounds Found in Living Things

L2

Key to Teaching Strategies

The following designations will help you decide which activities are appropriate for your students.

L1 **Level 1** activities should be appropriate for students with learning difficulties.

L2 **Level 2** activities should be within the ability range of all students.

L3 **Level 3** activities are designed for above-average students.

ELL **ELL** activities should be within the ability range of English Language Learners.

COOP LEARN **Cooperative Learning** activities are designed for small group work.

LS **Multiple Learning Styles** logos are used throughout to indicate strategies that address different learning styles.

P These strategies represent student products that can be placed into a best-work portfolio.

Hands-on Activities

Activity Worksheets

Activity — **Observing Osmosis**

Lab Preview
Directions: Answer these questions before you begin the Activity.
1. What safety symbols are associated with this activity?

2. What cell are you observing in this activity?

It is difficult to see osmosis occurring in cells because most cells are so small. However, a few cells can be seen without the aid of a microscope. Try this activity to see how osmosis occurs in a large cell.

What You'll Investigate
How does osmosis occur in an egg cell?

Materials
unboiled egg
balance
spoon
distilled water (250 mL)
light corn syrup (250 mL)
500-mL container

Goals
Observe osmosis in an egg cell.
Determine what affects osmosis.

Safety Precautions
Eggs may contain bacteria. Avoid touching your face. Wash your hands thoroughly when you are done.

Procedure
1. Use the table on the next page to record your data.
2. Obtain an unshelled egg from your teacher. Handle the egg gently. Use a balance to find its mass and record it in the table. Mark this beaker "salt."
3. Place the egg in the container and add enough distilled water to cover it.
4. **Observe** the egg after 30 min, one day, and two days. After each observation, record the egg's appearance in the table.
5. After day two, remove the egg with a spoon and allow it to drain. Find the egg's mass and record it in the table.
6. Empty the container, then put the egg back in. Now add enough corn syrup to cover it. Repeat steps 4 and 5.

L2

Laboratory Activities

Laboratory Activity — **Diffusion**

The more air you put into a tire, the larger and firmer the tire gets. If there is a leak, the tire may decrease in size and become soft. The same principle also applies to living cells. In cells, however, both water and material dissolved in water move into and out of the cells.

Strategy
You will observe carrots in salt water and freshwater.
You will determine if the carrots have lost or gained water after a 24-hour period.

Materials
CAUTION: Do not taste, eat, or drink any materials used in the lab.
2 beakers (500-mL)   salt   carrot
water   labels   thread
balance   scalpel   metric ruler

Procedure
1. Half fill two beakers with water.
2. Use a balance to measure 15 g salt and add it to one of the beakers. Mark this beaker "salt."
3. Cut a carrot in half as shown in Figure 1. **CAUTION:** Use care when cutting to avoid injury. Tightly tie a piece of thread 2 cm from the cut end of both parts.
4. Place one carrot half in the beaker of salt water with the cut end down. See Figure 2.
5. Place the other carrot half with the cut end down into the beaker of freshwater. Mark this beaker "fresh."
6. Allow the beakers to remain undisturbed for 24 hours. Remove the carrots and observe the tightness of the threads. Record your observations in Table 1 under Data and Observations.

Figure 1   Figure 2

L2

RESOURCE MANAGER

Meeting Different Ability Levels

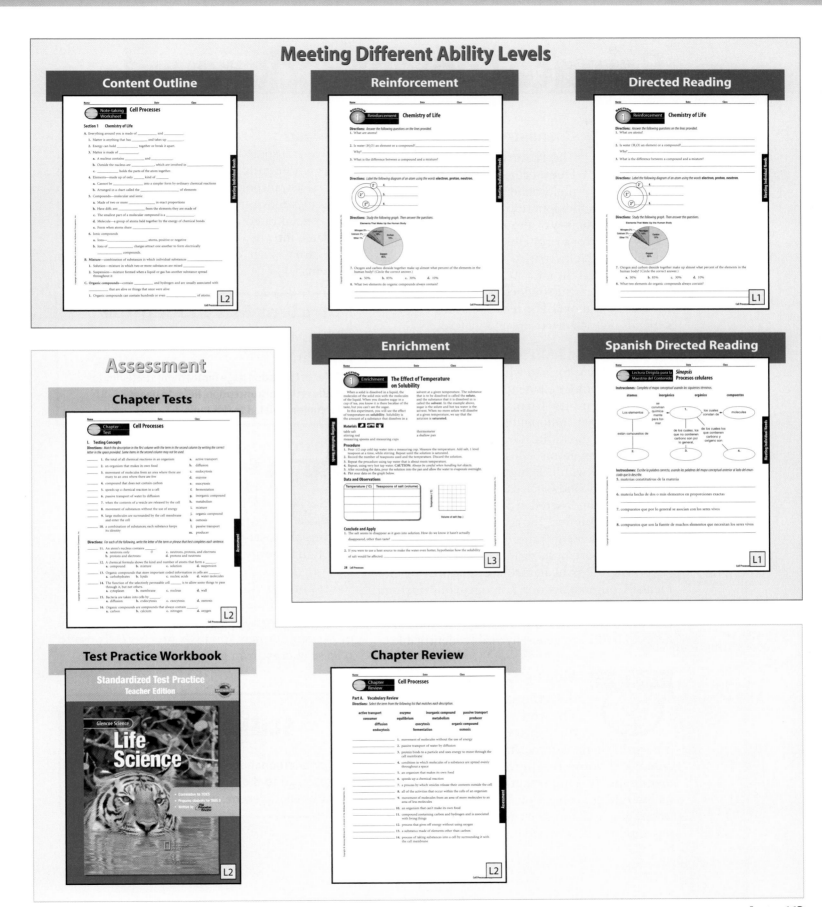

Content Outline

Cell Processes
Note-taking Worksheet

Section 1   Chemistry of Life

L2

Reinforcement

Chemistry of Life

L2

Directed Reading

Chemistry of Life

L1

Assessment

Chapter Tests

Cell Processes
Chapter Test

I. Testing Concepts

L2

Enrichment

The Effect of Temperature on Solubility

L3

Spanish Directed Reading

Sinopsis
Lectura Dirigida para la Maestría del Contenido
Procesos celulares

L1

Test Practice Workbook

Standardized Test Practice
Teacher Edition

Glencoe Science
Life Science

L2

Chapter Review

Cell Processes
Chapter Review

Part A. Vocabulary Review

L2

Science Content Background

Chemistry of Life
The Nature of Matter

Democrutis, an ancient Greek philosopher, proposed that atoms were small, solid spheres. From the late 1800s until recently, it was thought that negatively-charged electrons orbited the positively-charged nucleus in specific paths. Quantum mechanics provide us with the current model of a positively-charged nucleus surrounded by a region in which the electrons move. The location of the electrons depends on each electron's energy level.

Compounds and Mixtures

Compounds are formed when chemical reactions cause two or more elements to combine. Molecular components form when atoms share electrons. Ionic compounds form when negative and positive ions join. Organic compounds all contain carbon atoms. Most organic compounds are produced within living organisms. However, organic compounds such as plastics and synthetic fibers are constructed from organic materials such as petroleum. Inorganic compounds are made from elements other than carbon. Water is the most important inorganic compound.

Most things in nature are mixtures of elements. Components of a homogeneous mixture, such as solutions, cannot be distinguished from one another. The components of a heterogeneous mixture are generally visibly identifiable.

Moving Cellular Materials
Maintaining Balance

The cell membrane regulates what enters and leaves a cell. The size, shape, and electrical charge of molecules determine the permeability of the cell membrane. It is important for a cell to maintain its internal concentrations of substances such as water, glucose, and other nutrients while allowing elimination of waste products.

Transport

Passive transport—transport without the use of energy–depends on temperature. One form of passive transport, called diffusion, occurs when molecules move from a concentrated area into a less concentrated area. Osmosis is the diffusion of water into or out of a cell. Active transport, transport with energy, requires transport proteins.

Student Misconception

Plants do not use oxygen and do not release carbon dioxide.

Refer to the facing page for teaching strategies to address this misconception. Refer to pages 84–87 for content related to this topic.

Energy for Life
Photosynthesis, Respiration, and Fermentation

During photosynthesis, plants (producers) convert light energy to chemical energy to make carbohydrates (food). During respiration the food is broken down so the released energy can be used by other producers, consumers, and by the plants themselves. When there is a shortage of oxygen, fermentation is a process cells use to release energy from glucose.

For additional content background on this topic, go to the Glencoe Science Web site at science.glencoe.com.

IDENTIFYING Misconceptions

Find Out What Students Think

Students may think that . . .

• **Plants do not use oxygen and do not release carbon dioxide.**

Students do not completely understand the complementary nature of photosynthesis and respiration, especially with respect to exchange of gases.

Demonstration

Ask students to give the relationship between plants, animals, oxygen, and carbon dioxide. Summarize students' responses on the board. If students do not explicitly respond that plants also give off carbon dioxide, don't point it out at this time. Let that understanding come from the activities below.

Promote Understanding

Activity 1

Prepare a 0.1% solution of bromthymol blue.

• Have students blow through a straw into the bromthymol blue solution. The solution should turn yellow as the carbon dioxide from respiration dissolves in the solution (forming carbonic acid).

• Have students add drops of dilute ammonium hydroxide so that the solution again turns blue. Explain that the bromthymol blue is an indicator that turns yellow in an acidic solution and blue in a neutral or alkaline solution.

• Ask students what gas is given off in the process of respiration. (carbon dioxide) Explain that the carbon dioxide blown into the solution dissolves and makes the solution slightly acidic. Point out that adding the ammonium hydroxide made the solution slightly basic.

Activity 2

Have students slightly acidify a large test tube of bromthymol blue by blowing through a straw into the solution. Add a sprig of Elodea to the tube.

• Put the test tube in sunlight or under a bright light. The solution should begin to turn blue in 30 to 45 minutes. Have students record results.

• At the same time, have students put a sprig of Elodea in a test tube of bromthymol blue solution that is just very slightly alkaline and thus blue and place the tube in a dark area. Within 24 hours the color of the solution should change to a pale yellow as the plant respires and releases carbon dioxide. Again have students record their results.

Discussion

• Ask why the bromthymol blue solution turned blue in the light. Ask students what evidence supports their answer. Explicitly reinforce the fact the carbon dioxide was absorbed by the plant and used in the process of photosynthesis.

• Ask students whether they think carbon dioxide was given off by the Elodea kept in the dark. Although photosynthesis does continue in the dark, it does so at a lower rate than cell respiration, reversing the relative amounts of carbon dioxide produced and released. Stress that their results indicate that plants give off carbon dioxide during respiration. Point out that all living things must carry out some form of respiration.

Assess

After completing the chapter, see *Identifying Misconceptions* in the Study Guide.

Cell Processes

Chapter Vocabulary

mixture
organic compound
enzyme
inorganic compound
passive transport
diffusion
equilibrium
osmosis
active transport
endocytosis
exocytosis
metabolism
photosynthesis
respiration
fermentation

What do you think?

Science Journal The object in the picture is a mitochondrion, the place in a cell in which food molecules are broken down and their energy is released.

Cell Processes

The Sun is hot. Your back aches and your hands are sore. Weeding a garden is hard work. You are sweaty, tired, thirsty, and hungry. Are the weeds having the same reactions? You may know that plants don't sweat or get tired, but they do need water and food, just like you. How do plants take in and use water and food? In this chapter you'll find the answer to this question. You'll also find out how living things get the energy that they need to survive.

What do you think?

Science Journal Look at the picture below with a classmate. Discuss what this might be or what is happening. Here's a hint: *It's sometimes called the powerhouse of the cell.* Write your answer or best guess in your Science Journal.

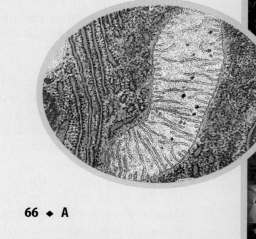

66 ◆ A

Theme Connection

Stability and Change Living things function as a result of chemical reactions in cells. The equilibrium maintained by cells results from their selectively permeable membranes. This is critical to the life of cells and the organism as a whole.

If you forget to water a plant, it will wilt. After you water the plant, it probably will straighten up and look healthier. Why does the plant straighten? In the following activity, find out about water entering and leaving plant cells.

Demonstrate why water leaves plant cells

1. Label a small bowl "salt water." Pour 250 mL of water into the bowl. Then add 15 g of salt to the water and stir.
2. Pour 250 mL of water into another small bowl.
3. Place two carrot sticks into each bowl. Also, place two carrot sticks on the lab table.
4. After 30 min, remove the carrot sticks from the bowls and keep them next to the bowl they came from. Examine all six carrot sticks then describe them in your Science Journal.

Observe

Predict what would happen if you moved the carrot sticks from the plain water to the lab table, the ones from the salt water into the plain water, and the ones from the lab table into the salt water. Now try it. Write your predictions and your results in your Science Journal.

Before You Read

FOLDABLES
Reading & Study Skills

Making a Vocabulary Study Fold To help you study cell processes, make the following vocabulary Foldable. Knowing the definition of vocabulary words in a chapter is a good way to ensure you have understood the content.

1. Place a sheet of notebook paper in front of you so the short side is at the top. Fold the paper in half from the left to the right side.
2. Through the top thickness of paper, cut along every third line from the outside edge to the center fold, forming ten tabs as shown.
3. On the front of each tab, write a vocabulary word listed on the first page of each section in this chapter. On the back of each tab, define the word.

A ◆ 67

Purpose Use the Explore Activity to show students that water moves into and out of carrot cells. Explain that the materials moving into and out of cells are atoms, molecules, and compounds. [L1] [LS] **Visual-Spatial**

Preparation Purchase carrots for the activity. Peel and cut the carrots into sticks.

Materials salt, 250-mL beaker, balance, 2 bowls, stirrer, 6 carrot sticks, water, label, watch or clock

Teaching Strategy Provide students with water at room temperature so the salt will dissolve more readily.

Observe

The carrot sticks in salt water and on the lab table were limp because water moved out of them. The carrot sticks in plain water were crisp because water moved into the cells that had less water. Students should predict that these conditions are reversible, depending on the relative amount of water inside and outside the carrot's cells.

Assessment

Oral Why does a wilted plant become rigid again after it has been watered? The water diffuses into the plant's cells. Use **Performance Assessment in the Science Classroom**, p. 89.

Before You Read

FOLDABLES
Reading & Study Skills

Dinah Zike Study Fold

Purpose Use this activity to expose students to the chapter's content and vocabulary before they read, and to encourage a search for terms and definitions as they read. The resulting Foldable can be used as an assessment tool and study guide before, during and after reading.

For additional help, see Foldables Worksheet, p. 15 in **Chapter Resources Booklet,** or go to the Glencoe Science Web site at **science.glencoe.com.** See After You Read in the Study Guide at the end of this chapter.

SECTION

1

Chemistry of Life

1 Motivate

Bellringer Transparency

Display the Section Focus Transparency for Section 1. Use the accompanying Transparency Activity Master. L2

ELL

Tie to Prior Knowledge

Bring in labels from foods and cleaning products. Have students use the periodic table to determine what elements are in the compounds contained in these products.

SECTION

1 Chemistry of Life

As You Read

What You'll Learn

- **List** the differences among atoms, elements, molecules, and compounds.
- **Explain** the relationship between chemistry and life science.
- **Discuss** how organic compounds are different from inorganic compounds.

Vocabulary

mixture
organic compound
enzyme
inorganic compound

Why It's Important

You grow because of chemical reactions in your body.

Figure 1
An oxygen atom model shows the placement of electrons, protons, and neutrons.

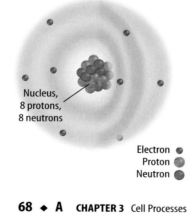

Oxygen atom

Nucleus,
8 protons,
8 neutrons

Electron
Proton
Neutron

The Nature of Matter

Think about everything that surrounds you—chairs, books, clothing, other students, and air. What are all these things made up of? You're right if you answer "matter and energy." Matter is anything that has mass and takes up space. Energy is anything that brings about change. Everything in your environment, including you, is made of matter. Energy can hold matter together or break it apart. For example, the food you eat is matter that is held together by chemical energy. When food is cooked, energy in the form of heat can break some of the bonds holding the matter in food together. **Table 1** compares matter and energy and gives some examples of each.

Atoms Whether it is solid, liquid, or gas, matter is made of atoms. **Figure 1** shows a model of an oxygen atom. At the center of an atom is a nucleus that contains protons and neutrons. Although they have nearly equal masses, a proton has a positive charge and a neutron has no charge. Outside the nucleus are electrons, each of which has a negative charge. It takes about 1,837 electrons to equal the mass of one proton. Electrons are important because they are the part of the atom that is involved in chemical reactions. Look at **Figure 1** again and you will see that an atom is mostly empty space. Energy holds the parts of an atom together.

Table 1 Matter and Energy		
	Definition	**Examples**
Matter	anything that has mass and takes up space	atoms, electrons, protons, and neutrons, living things, rocks, soil, and air
Energy	ability to cause change	sunlight, electricity, heat, chemical energy

---

Section ✓ Assessment Planner

PORTFOLIO
Science Journal, p. 72
PERFORMANCE ASSESSMENT
MiniLAB, p. 73
Math Skills Activity, p. 74
Skill Builder Activities, p. 75
See page 94 for more options.

CONTENT ASSESSMENT
Section, p. 75
Challenge, p. 75
Chapter, pp. 94–95

Table 2 Elements That Make Up the Human Body		
Symbol	Element	Percent
O	Oxygen	65.0
C	Carbon	18.5
H	Hydrogen	9.5
N	Nitrogen	3.2
Ca	Calcium	1.5
P	Phosphorus	1.0
K	Potassium	0.4
S	Sulfur	0.3
Na	Sodium	0.2
Cl	Chlorine	0.2
Mg	Magnesium	0.1
	Other elements	0.1

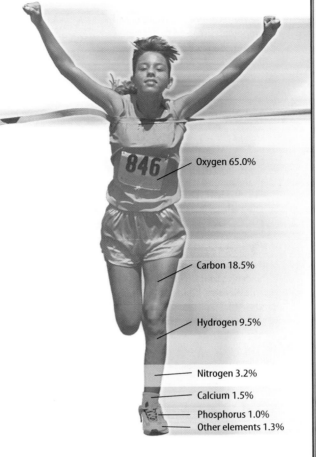

Oxygen 65.0%

Carbon 18.5%

Hydrogen 9.5%

Nitrogen 3.2%

Calcium 1.5%

Phosphorus 1.0%

Other elements 1.3%

Elements When something is made up of only one kind of atom, it is called an element. An element can't be broken down into a simpler form by ordinary chemical reactions. The element oxygen is made up of only oxygen atoms, and hydrogen is made up of only hydrogen atoms. Scientists have given each element its own one- or two-letter symbol.

All elements are arranged in a chart known as the periodic table of elements. You can find this table at the back of this book. The table provides information about each element including its mass, how many protons it has, and its symbol.

Everything is made up of elements. Most things, including all living things, are made up of a combination of elements. Few things exist as pure elements. **Table 2** lists elements that are in the human body. What two elements make up most of your body?

✔ **Reading Check** *What types of things are made up of elements?*

Six of the elements listed in the table are important because they make up about 99 percent of living matter. The symbols for these elements are S, P, O, N, C, and H. Use **Table 2** to find the names of these elements.

The Nature of Matter

Teacher FYI

Elements are often given names by their discoverers. An element's name may reflect a property of the element. For example, chlorine, a greenish gas, comes from the Greek word *chloros*, which means "green." Some elements, such as ytterbium—discovered in Ytterby, Sweden—are named for the place where they were discovered. Other elements are named to honor someone. Einsteinium is named in honor of Albert Einstein, fermium for Enrico Fermi, and curium for Marie and Pierre Curie.

Activity

Play Tom Lehrer's *Elements Song*, which lists the elements. Have students listen to see how many elements they recognize.

Fun Fact

The symbols of many elements are derived from the first one or two letters of the Greek, Latin, or English name of the elements. Scientists worldwide use these symbols.

Text Question Answer

oxygen and carbon

✔ **Reading Check**

Answer Everything is made up of elements or a combination of elements.

Resource Manager

Chapter Resources Booklet

Transparency Activity, p. 42

Directed Reading for Content Mastery, pp. 17, 18

Note-taking Worksheets, pp. 31–33

Inclusion Strategies

Visually Impaired To help visually impaired students understand the structure of an atom, make a model of an atom. Outline the nucleus and energy levels by gluing yarn to cardboard. Use marshmallows for protons, gumdrops for neutrons, and red hots for electrons. Have students feel the model to compare the sizes of the different parts. **Kinesthetic**

The Nature of Matter,
continued

Caption Answer

Figure 2 A molecule, the smallest part of a molecular compound, is a group of atoms held together by chemical bonds.

Quick Demo

To demonstrate attraction between opposite charges, run a comb through your hair. Then bring the comb close to your hair without touching it. The hair is attracted to the comb because the negative charges on the comb are attracted to the positive charges of the hair.

Discussion

Have students predict what might happen when a negatively charged ion comes in contact with a positively charged ion. The two ions may bond to form an electrically neutral compound.

Figure 2
The words *atoms, molecules,* and *compounds* are used to describe substances. *How are they related to each other?*

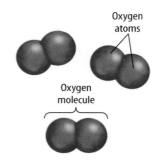

Oxygen atoms

Oxygen molecule

A Some elements, like oxygen, occur as molecules. These molecules contain atoms of the same element bonded together.

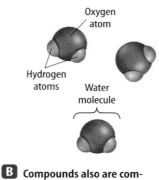

Oxygen atom

Hydrogen atoms

Water molecule

B Compounds also are composed of molecules. Molecules of compounds contain atoms of two or more different elements bonded together, as shown by these water molecules.

Compounds and Molecules

Suppose you make a pitcher of lemonade using a powdered mix and water. The water and the lemonade mix, which is mostly sugar, contain the elements oxygen and hydrogen. Yet, in one, they are part of a nearly tasteless liquid—water. In the other they are part of a sweet solid—sugar. How can the same elements be part of two materials that are so different? Water and sugar are compounds. Compounds are made up of two or more elements in exact proportions. For example, pure water, whether one milliliter of it or one million liters, is always made up of hydrogen atoms bonded to oxygen atoms in a ratio of two hydrogen atoms to one oxygen atom. Compounds have properties different from the elements they are made of. There are two types of compounds—molecular compounds and ionic compounds.

Molecular Compounds The smallest part of a molecular compound is a molecule. A molecule is a group of atoms held together by the energy of chemical bonds, as shown in **Figure 2.** When chemical reactions occur, chemical bonds break, new bonds form, and atoms are rearranged. The molecules produced are different from those that began the chemical reaction.

Molecular compounds form when different atoms share their outermost electrons. For example, two atoms of hydrogen can each share one electron with one atom of oxygen to form one molecule of water, as shown in **Figure 2B.** Water does not have the same properties as oxygen and hydrogen. Under normal conditions on Earth, oxygen and hydrogen are gases. Yet, water can be a liquid, a solid, or a gas. When hydrogen and oxygen combine, changes occur and a new substance forms.

Ions Atoms also combine because they've become positively or negatively charged. Atoms are usually neutral—they have no overall electric charge. When an atom loses an electron, it has more protons than electrons, so it becomes positively charged. When an atom gains an electron, it has more electrons than protons, so it becomes negatively charged. Electrically charged atoms—positive or negative—are called ions.

Inclusion Strategies

Hearing Impaired Provide discussion questions to hearing-impaired students before discussion. Assign another student to record the answers to the questions when they are given. L2
IS Auditory-Musical

Curriculum Connection

History Have students research alchemy. During the Middle Ages, alchemists searched for a way to turn common metals into gold. Though unsuccessful, they were precursors to modern chemists. Much of alchemy was based on Aristotle's idea that matter tries to reach perfection. Alchemists concluded that there must be a way to turn other metals into gold, since it was the "perfect" metal. L3 **IS Linguistic**

Ionic Compounds Ions of opposite charges attract one another to form electrically neutral compounds called ionic compounds. Table salt is made of sodium (Na) and chlorine (Cl) ions, as shown in **Figure 3.** When they combine, a chlorine atom gains an electron from a sodium atom. The chlorine becomes a negatively charged ion, and the sodium becomes a positively charged ion. These oppositely charged ions are attracted to each other and form the ionic compound sodium chloride, NaCl.

Ions are important in many life processes that take place in your body and in other organisms. For example, messages are sent along your nerves as potassium and sodium ions move in and out of nerve cells. Calcium ions are important in causing your muscles to contract. Ions also are involved in the transport of oxygen by your blood. The movement of some substances into and out of a cell would not be possible without ions.

Mixtures

Some substances, such as a combination of sugar and salt, can't change each other or combine chemically. A **mixture** is a combination of substances in which individual substances retain their own properties. Mixtures can be solids, liquids, gases, or any combination of them.

✔ **Reading Check** *Why is a combination of sugar and salt said to be a mixture?*

Most chemical reactions in living organisms take place in mixtures called solutions. You've probably noticed the taste of salt when you perspire. Sweat is a solution of salt and water. In a solution, two or more substances are mixed evenly. A cell's cytoplasm is a solution of dissolved molecules and ions.

Living things also contain mixtures called suspensions. A suspension is formed when a liquid or a gas has another substance evenly spread throughout it. Unlike solutions, the substances in a suspension eventually sink to the bottom. If blood, shown in **Figure 4,** is left undisturbed, the red blood cells and white blood cells will sink gradually to the bottom. However, the pumping action of your heart constantly moves your blood and the blood cells remain suspended.

Magnification: 8×

A Magnified crystals of salt look like this.

B The salt crystal is held together by the attraction between sodium ions and chlorine ions.

Figure 3
Table salt, or sodium chloride (NaCl), is a crystal composed of sodium ions and chlorine ions held together by ionic bonds.

Figure 4
When a test tube of whole blood is left standing, the blood cells sink in the watery plasma.

Teacher
The two most common bonds in compounds are covalent and ionic. In covalent bonds, atoms share outermost electrons. In ionic bonds, one atom loses electrons, while the other atom gains electrons.

Mixtures

Quick Demo

Demonstrate mixtures and compounds. Mix baking soda with darker sand. Point out the different, distinct parts of the mixture. Then mix baking soda with vinegar in a clear container. The bubbles indicate that a new compound—carbon dioxide—has formed. **NOTE:** Make sure students understand that formation of bubbles does not *always* indicate that a chemical reaction has taken place. For example, the bubbles in soda indicate carbon dioxide is coming out of the mixture, not that a new substance is being formed.

✔ **Reading Check**

Answer It is a combination of two substances, each of which retains its own properties when combined with the other.

Visual Learning

Figure 4 Have students identify the visibly separate parts in the test tube. **What is the transparent substance in the tube?** plasma **What is the concentrated substance at the bottom of the tube?** red and white blood cells **Describe what would happen if the tube was shaken.** The blood cells and plasma would mix, forming a suspension. This suspension is blood.

Resource Manager

Chapter Resources Booklet
Enrichment, p. 28

Inclusion Strategies

Gifted Mark lines on a glass jar with a glass-marking pen, indicating the one-cup and two-cup levels. Pour 1 cup of hot water into the jar. Add 1 cup of sugar. Stir until the sugar dissolves. Ask why there are not two cups of solution. The sugar takes up the spaces between the particles of water. L3 **IN Logical-Mathematical**

Organic Compounds

IDENTIFYING Misconceptions

Student awareness of the emphasis on maintaining a "low-fat" diet may lead them to believe that all lipids (fats) are harmful. Explain that fats have many useful functions in living organisms, such as energy storage, and are a vital component of cell membranes.

Activity

Display a Food Guide Pyramid and discuss the types of organic compounds represented by foods in each group. Ask students to use this information to create a bulletin board display of foods rich in carbohydrates, lipids, and proteins. Have students illustrate the display with pictures of the foods.

Fun Fact

A paste made of meat tenderizer and water is often used to treat bee and jellyfish stings. An enzyme in the meat tenderizer helps to break down the proteins in the venom, making the area less painful.

Table 3 Organic Compounds Found in Living Things

	Carbohydrate	Lipid	Protein	Nucleic Acid
Elements	carbon, hydrogen, and oxygen	carbon, oxygen, hydrogen, and phosphorus	carbon, oxygen, hydrogen, nitrogen, and sulfur	carbon, oxygen, hydrogen, nitrogen, and phosphorus
Examples	sugars, starch, and cellulose	fats, oils, waxes, phospholipids, and cholesterol	enzymes, skin, and hair	DNA and RNA
Function	supply energy for cell processes; form plant structures; short-term energy storage	store large amounts of energy long term; form boundaries around cells	regulate cell processes and build cell structures	carry hereditary information; used to make proteins

SCIENCE Online

Research Air is a mixture of many things. Weather forecasts often include information about air quality. Visit the Glencoe Science Web site at **science.glencoe.com** for more information about air quality. In your Science Journal list some things that may be measured when testing air quality.

Organic Compounds

You and all living things are made up of compounds that are classified as organic or inorganic. Rocks and other nonliving things contain inorganic compounds, but most do not contain large amounts of organic compounds. **Organic compounds** always contain carbon and hydrogen and usually are associated with living things. One exception would be nonliving things that are products of living things. For example, coal contains organic compounds because it forms from dead and decaying plants. Organic molecules can contain hundreds or even thousands of atoms that can be arranged in many ways. **Table 3** compares the four groups of organic compounds that make up all living things—carbohydrates, lipids, proteins, and nucleic acids.

Carbohydrates Carbohydrates are organic molecules that supply energy for cell processes. Sugars and starches are carbohydrates that cells use for energy. Some carbohydrates also are important parts of cell structures. For example, a carbohydrate called cellulose is an important part of plant cells.

Lipids Another type of organic compound found in living things is a lipid. Lipids do not mix with water. Lipids such as fats and oils store and release even larger amounts of energy than carbohydrates do. One type of lipid, the phospholipid, is a major part of cell membranes.

Science Journal

CFCs Have students research and summarize in their Science Journals the organic compounds known as chlorofluorocarbons (CFCs). Summaries should include a description of the composition of these compounds, their use as refrigerants, and a description of how the use of these substances has impacted the environment. P

SCIENCE Online

Internet Addresses

_____

_____

_____

Explore the Glencoe Science Web site at **science.glencoe.com** to find out more about topics in this section.

Proteins Organic compounds called proteins have many important functions in living organisms. They are made up of smaller molecules called amino acids. Proteins are the building blocks of many structures in organisms. Your muscles contain large amounts of protein. Proteins are scattered throughout cell membranes. Certain proteins called **enzymes** regulate nearly all chemical reactions in cells.

Nucleic Acids Large organic molecules that store important coded information in cells are called nucleic acids. One nucleic acid, deoxyribonucleic acid, or DNA—called genetic material—is found in all cells. It carries information that directs each cell's activities. Another nucleic acid, ribonucleic acid, or RNA, is needed to make enzymes and other proteins.

Inorganic Compounds

Most **inorganic compounds** are made from elements other than carbon. Generally, inorganic molecules contain fewer atoms than organic molecules. Inorganic compounds are the source for many elements needed by living things. For example, plants take up inorganic compounds from the soil. These inorganic compounds can contain the elements nitrogen, phosphorus, and sulfur. Many foods that you eat contain inorganic compounds. **Table 4** shows some of the inorganic compounds that are important to you. One of the most important inorganic compounds for living things is water.

Table 4 Some Inorganic Compounds Important in Humans	
Compound	**Use in Body**
Water	makes up most of the blood; most chemical reactions occur in water
Calcium phosphate	gives strength to bones
Hydrochloric acid	breaks down foods in the stomach
Sodium bicarbonate	helps the digestion of food to occur
Salts containing sodium, chlorine, and potassium	important in sending messages along nerves

Determining How Enzymes Work

Procedure
1. Get two small cups of **prepared gelatin** from your teacher. Do not eat or drink anything in lab.
2. On the gelatin in one of the cups, place a piece of **fresh pineapple.**
3. Let both cups stand undisturbed during your class period. Wash your hands when you are done.
4. Observe what happens to the gelatin.

Analysis
1. What effect did the piece of fresh pineapple have on the gelatin?
2. What does fresh pineapple contain that caused it to have the effect on the gelatin you observed?
3. Why do the preparation directions on a box of gelatin dessert tell you not to mix it with fresh pineapple?

Purpose to observe how enzymes affect gelatin L1

Ⓘ **Visual-Spatial**

Materials two small cups of prepared gelatin, 1 slice of fresh pineapple

Teaching Strategies
• To prepare gelatin, add only half the amount of water indicated on the gelatin package.
• After students add pineapple to one cup, allow both cups of gelatin to sit overnight.

Analysis
1. The gelatin under the fresh pineapple turned to a liquid.
2. an enzyme
3. The gelatin would not solidify if in contact with fresh pineapple.

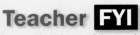

Performance Have students design an experiment to show conclusively that fresh pineapple contains enzymes that keep gelatin from becoming solid. They can repeat the experiment using canned pineapple. Use **PASC,** p. 95.

Inorganic Compounds

Teacher FYI

Life on Earth could not have evolved without water. Wherever life is found, water is found. Life is found in water at all temperatures. Bacteria can live under snow and in the near-boiling water of hot springs.

Resource Manager

Chapter Resources Booklet
MiniLAB, p. 3
Reinforcement, p. 25

Curriculum Connection

Health Provide students with copies of the periodic table. Ask them to research which elements are important for good health. They can find this information on food labels, in reference books, and on the Internet. Ask students to shade each element they discover on the table and to share their results with the class. L2

Ⓘ **Interpersonal**

Inorganic Compounds, continued

Quick Demo

Display different liquids, such as a glass of fruit juice, a jar of paint, a bottle of oil, a beaker of alcohol, and a glass of water. Ask which substance is the most unique. Explain that water is the most unique, as it contains chemical and physical properties seen in no other substance. It is liquid at temperatures found on most of Earth's surface. Unlike most other substances, water expands when it freezes. In addition, water is the most common solvent in the world.
LS Visual-Spatial

Make a Model

Have students make a model of a water molecule. They may use foam balls or colored marshmallows to represent the atoms, and toothpicks to hold them together. **L2** **LS Kinesthetic**

Math Skills Activity

National Math Standards

Correlation to Mathematics Objectives
1,2,6,9

Answer to Practice Problem

Calculate the infant's water weight and the adult's water weight, then subtract to find the difference.
Infant: $78/100 = x \div 3.2$ kg
$x = (78 \times 3.2) \div 100$
$x = 2.496$ kg of water:
Adult: $60 \div 100 = x \div 95$ kg
$x = (60 \times 95) \div 100$
$x = 57$ kg of water;
Difference: 57 kg $- 2.496$ kg
$= 54.504$

Importance of Water Some scientists hypothesize that life began in the water of Earth's ancient oceans. Chemical reactions may have occurred that produced organic molecules. Similar chemical reactions can take place in cells in your body.

Living things are composed of more than 50 percent water and depend on water to survive. You can live for weeks without food but only for a few days without water. **Figure 5** shows where water is found in your body. Although seeds and spores of plants, fungi, and bacteria can exist without water, they must have water if they are to grow and reproduce. All the chemical reactions in living things take place in water solutions, and most organisms use water to transport materials through their bodies. For example, many animals have blood that is mostly water to move materials. Plants use water to move minerals and sugars between the roots and leaves.

Math Skills Activity

Calculating the Importance of Water

All life on Earth depends on water for survival. Water is the most vital part of humans and other animals. It is required for all of the chemical processes that keep us alive.

Example Problem

At least 60% of an adult human body consists of water. If an adult man weighs 90 kg, how many kilograms of water does his body contain?

Solution

1 *This is what you know:*   adult human body = 60% water
    man = 90 kg

2 *This is what you want to find:*   60% of 90 kg

3 *This is the equation you need to use:* $60/100 = x/90$

4 *Solve the equation for* x: $x = (60 \times 90)/100$
    $x = 54$ kg

Check your answer by dividing your answer by 90, then multiplying by 100. Do you get 60%?

Practice Problem

A human body at birth consists of 78% water. This percent gradually decreases to 60% in an adult. Assume a baby weighed 3.2 kg at birth, and grew into an adult weighing 95 kg. Calculate the approximate number of kilograms of water the human gained.

For more help, refer to the Math Skill Handbook.

74 ◆ A   **CHAPTER 3** Cell Processes

Resource Manager

Chapter Resources Booklet
    Transparency Activity, pp. 45–46
Mathematics Skill Activities, p. 5
Science Inquiry Labs, pp. 43, 47

Curriculum Connection

Art Have students cut out pictures from magazines that illustrate water use by organisms, in industry, and in the environment. Then, have each student make a water collage using the pictures they chose. Display collages in the classroom. **L1** **LS Visual-Spatial**

Characteristics of Water

The atoms of a water molecule are arranged in such a way that the molecule has areas with different charges. Water molecules are like magnets. Just like magnets have north and south poles that are attracted to each other, the positive part of one water molecule attracts the negative part of another water molecule, causing them to stick together. At the surface of water, molecules form a film. The film is strong enough to support small insects because the attraction between water molecules is greater than the attraction between the insect and gravity.

When heat is added to any substance, its molecules begin to move faster. Because water molecules are so strongly attracted to each other, water resists changes in temperature. The large percentage of water in living things acts like an insulator. The water in a cell helps to keep its temperature constant, which allows life-sustaining chemical reactions to take place.

You've seen ice floating on water. When water freezes, ice crystals form. In the crystals, each water molecule is spaced at a certain distance from all the others. Because this distance is greater in frozen water than in liquid water, ice floats on water. Bodies of water freeze from the top down. The floating ice provides insulation from extremely cold temperatures and allows living things to survive in the cold water under the ice.

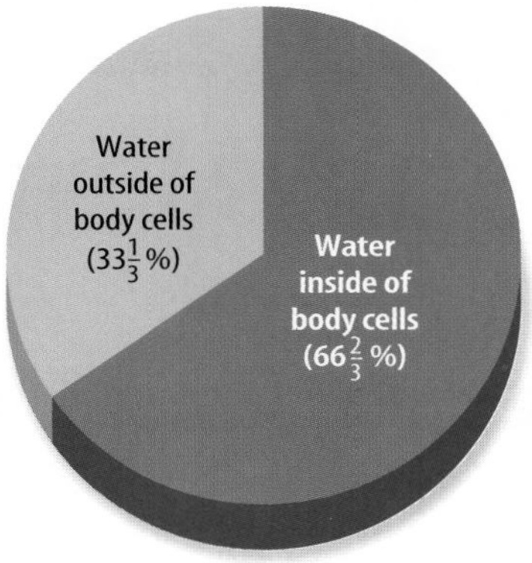

Figure 5
About two thirds of your body's water is located within your body's cells. Water helps maintain the cells' shapes and sizes. One third of your body's water is outside of your body's cells.

Water outside of body cells ($33\frac{1}{3}$ %)

Water inside of body cells ($66\frac{2}{3}$ %)

Section 1 Assessment

1. What are the similarities and differences between atoms and molecules?

2. What is the difference between organic and inorganic compounds? Give an example of each type of compound.

3. What are the four types of organic compounds found in all living things?

4. Why does life as we know it depend on water?

5. **Think Critically** If you mix salt, sand, and sugar with water in a small jar, will the resulting mixture be a suspension, a solution, or both?

Skill Builder Activities

6. **Interpreting Scientific Illustrations**
Carefully observe **Figure 1** and determine how many protons, neutrons, and electrons an atom of oxygen has. **For more help, refer to the** Science Skill Handbook.

7. **Using an Electronic Spreadsheet**
Research to find the percentage of elements that make up Earth's crust. Make a spreadsheet that includes this information and the information in **Table 2.** Create a circle graph for each set of percentages. **For more help, refer to the** Technology Skill Handbook.

SECTION 1 Chemistry of Life **A** ◆ **75**

Answers to Section Assessment

1. Atoms are the basic units of matter and are made of protons, neutrons, and electrons; molecules are made up of 2 or more atoms.

2. Organic compounds, such as lipids, contain carbon; most inorganic compounds, such as water, do not.

3. lipids, carbohydrates, proteins, and nucleic acids

4. Most life processes can occur only in water solutions.

5. Salt and sugar dissolve in water forming a solution; sand will sink to the bottom of the solution; if shaken, sand will spread throughout the solution and form a suspension.

6. 8 protons, 8 neutrons, and 8 electrons

7. Human body graph: 65% oxygen, 18.5% carbon, 9.5% hydrogen, 3.3% nitrogen, 1.5% calcium, and 2.2% other elements; Earth's crust graph: 46.6% oxygen, 27.7% silicon, 8.1% aluminum, 5.0% iron, 3.6% calcium, 2.8% sodium, 2.6% potassium, 2.1% magnesium, 1.5% all other elements

① Motivate

Bellringer Transparency

Display the Section Focus Transparency for Section 2. Use the accompanying Transparency Activity Master. L2 ELL

Section Focus Transparency — Skin Deep

Misting with water helps keep the produce in supermarkets fresh. Not all the water stays on the skin of these fruits and vegetables; some of it is absorbed.

1. When the water on the fruits and vegetables disappears, where does it go?
2. Express a hypothesis to explain what happens to the water when it disappears.
3. How could you test your hypothesis?

Cell Processes

Tie to Prior Knowledge

Use an overhead transparency to review the parts of a cell. Point out that the cell membrane helps a cell maintain a balance between the cell and materials, such as water, salt, and sugars, in its environment.

Moving Cellular Materials

As You Read

What You'll Learn

- **Describe** the function of a selectively permeable membrane.
- **Explain** how the processes of diffusion and osmosis move molecules in living cells.
- **Explain** how passive transport and active transport differ.

Vocabulary

passive transport	active transport
diffusion	endocytosis
equilibrium	exocytosis
osmosis	

Why It's Important

Cell membranes control the substances that enter and leave the cells in your body.

Passive Transport

"Close that window. Do you want to let in all the bugs and leaves?" How do you prevent unwanted things from coming through the window? As seen in **Figure 6,** a window screen provides the protection needed to keep unwanted things outside. It also allows some things to pass into or out of the room like air, unpleasant odors, or smoke.

Cells take in food, oxygen, and other substances from their environments. They also release waste materials into their environments. A cell has a membrane around it that works for a cell like a window screen does for a room. A cell's membrane is selectively permeable (PUR mee uh bul). It allows some things to enter or leave the cell while keeping other things outside or inside the cell. The window screen also is selectively permeable based on the size of its openings.

Things can pass through a cell membrane in several ways. Which way things move depends on the size of the molecules or particles, the path taken through the membrane, and whether or not energy is used. The movement of substances through the cell membrane without the use of energy is called **passive transport.** Cells use three types of passive transport. Which one is used depends on what is moving through the cell membrane.

Figure 6
A cell membrane, like a screen, will let some things through more easily than others. Air gets through a screen, but insects are kept out.

76 ◆ A   CHAPTER 3 Cell Processes

Section ✓*Assessment* Planner

PORTFOLIO
Visual Learning, p. 81
PERFORMANCE ASSESSMENT
Try at Home MiniLAB, p. 77
Skill Builder Activities, p. 80
See page 94 for more options.

CONTENT ASSESSMENT
Section, p. 80
Challenge, p. 80
Chapter, pp. 94–95

Figure 7
Like all other cells in your body, cells in your toes need oxygen.

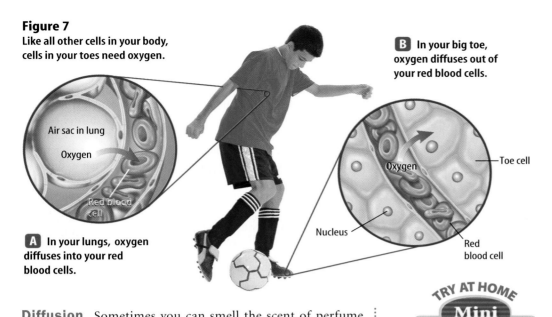

B In your big toe, oxygen diffuses out of your red blood cells.

Air sac in lung

Oxygen

Red blood cell

Oxygen

Toe cell

Nucleus

Red blood cell

A In your lungs, oxygen diffuses into your red blood cells.

Diffusion Sometimes you can smell the scent of perfume when you sit near someone in a room, on a bus, or as you walk past him or her. When that happens, you are experiencing the effects of diffusion. When some molecules move away from areas where there are more of them into areas where there are fewer of them, it is called **diffusion.** Diffusion is one type of passive transport that takes place in cells. Molecules in solids, liquids, and gases constantly and randomly move. Random movement of molecules is why diffusion occurs. When the molecules of one substance are spread evenly throughout another substance, **equilibrium** occurs and diffusion stops. When equilibrium is reached, molecules continue to move and maintain equilibrium.

✔ **Reading Check** *What is equilibrium?*

Every cell in your body, including those in your big toe, needs oxygen. When you breathe, how does oxygen get from your lungs to cells in your big toe? Oxygen is carried throughout your body in your blood by the red blood cells. When your blood is pumped from your heart to your lungs, your red blood cells do not contain much oxygen. However, your lungs have more oxygen molecules than your red blood cells do, so the oxygen molecules diffuse into your red blood cells, as shown in **Figure 7A.** When the blood reaches your big toe, there are more oxygen molecules in your red blood cells than in your big toe cells. The oxygen diffuses out of your red blood cells and into your big toe cells, as shown in **Figure 7B.**

TRY AT HOME
Mini LAB

Observing Diffusion
Procedure 🥽 🧤 👕
1. Use **two clean glasses** of equal size. Label one "hot," then fill it until half full with **very warm water.** Label the other "cold," then fill it until half full with **cold water. WARNING:** *Do not use boiling hot water.*
2. Add one drop of **food coloring** to each glass. Carefully release the drop just at the water's surface to avoid splashing the water.
3. Observe the glasses. Record your observations immediately and again after 15 min.

Analysis
1. Describe what happens when food coloring is added to each glass.
2. How does temperature affect the rate of diffusion?

Teacher FYI
A permeable membrane allows all molecules to pass through. An impermeable membrane doesn't allow any to pass. Only some molecules can pass through a semi-permeable membrane—usually only small molecules that can pass through quickly.

2 Teach

Passive Transport

TRY AT HOME
Mini LAB

Purpose to investigate the effect of temperature on diffusion rate [L1] [ELL] [COOP LEARN]
🔢 **Logical-Mathematical**
Materials 2 clean glasses, hot water, cold water, food coloring, dropper, marker or wax pencil, clock, labels

Teaching Strategies
• Have students record how long it takes the food coloring to diffuse evenly throughout each beaker.
• Caution students not to move the water-filled beakers.

Analysis
1. The food coloring spreads throughout the water; it spreads faster in the hot water.
2. Heat increases the rate of diffusion.

✔ Assessment

Performance To further assess understanding of the effect of temperature on diffusion, have students repeat the activity using ice water instead of hot water. Use **PASC,** p. 105.

✔ **Reading Check**

Answer when the molecules of one substance are spread evenly throughout another substance

Passive Transport, continued

Quick Demo

To demonstrate a selectively permeable membrane, pour different substances (i.e. sand, salt, marbles, water) through a kitchen strainer. Select some substances that will pass through the strainer, and some that will not. LS **Visual-Spatial**

Discussion

Why do salty foods make you thirsty? The salt present in the food causes water to leave your cells; therefore, your body needs water to replace what your cells have lost.

Extension

Fertilizers contain chemical salts. If fertilizers are placed on plants and it doesn't rain soon after, the plants may die. Have students investigate and report on the use of fertilizers by interviewing farmers or lawn-maintenance workers. L2
LS **Interpersonal**

✔ Reading Check

Answer Because there are relatively fewer water molecules in the salt solution around the carrot cells than inside the carrot cells, water leaves the carrot and moves into the salt solution.

Osmosis—The Diffusion of Water Remember that water makes up a large part of living matter. Cells contain water and are surrounded by water. Water molecules move by diffusion into and out of cells. The diffusion of water through a cell membrane is called **osmosis.**

If cells weren't surrounded by water that contains few dissolved substances, water inside the cells would diffuse out of them. This is why water left the carrot cells in this chapter's Explore Activity. Because there were relatively fewer water molecules in the salt solution around the carrot cells than in the carrot cells, water moved out of the cells and into the salt solution.

Losing water from inside a plant cell causes the cell membrane to come away from the cell wall, as shown in **Figure 8A.** This reduces the pressure against the cell wall, and the plant cell becomes limp. If the carrot sticks were taken out of the salt water and put in pure water, the water around the cells would move into the cells. The cells would fill with water and their cell membranes would press against their cell walls, as shown in **Figure 8B.** Pressure would increase and the plant cells would become firm. That is why the carrot sticks would be crisp again.

✔ Reading Check   *Why do carrots in salt water become limp?*

Osmosis also takes place in animal cells. If animal cells were placed in pure water, they too would swell up. However, animal cells have no cell walls. Just like an overfilled water balloon, they will burst if too much water enters the cell.

Figure 8
Cells respond to differences between the amount of water inside and outside the cell.

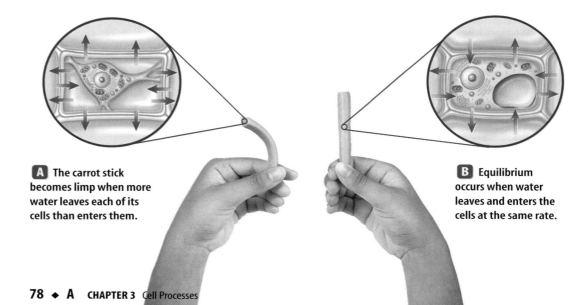

A The carrot stick becomes limp when more water leaves each of its cells than enters them.

B Equilibrium occurs when water leaves and enters the cells at the same rate.

🔷 LAB DEMONSTRATION

Purpose to observe diffusion
Materials self-sealing plastic sandwich bag, cooked rice, tincture of iodine, 8-oz. clear plastic cups, tablespoon
Preparation Half-fill the plastic cups with water and add 6 drops of tincture of iodine. Cook rice.

Procedure Seal a sandwich bag containing 2 tablespoons of rice, and place it into the water that contains iodine. Observe after 10 minutes.

Expected Outcome Iodine molecules will move through the plastic bag, turning the rice blue-black. Iodine always turns blue-black in the presence of starch.

✔ *Assessment*

What did you observe? The rice inside the plastic bag turned blue-black. **Explain what occurred.** Iodine molecules diffused from an area where there was a large number of iodine molecules (outside the bag) to an area where there were few iodine molecules (inside the bag).

Facilitated Diffusion Cells take in many substances. Some substances pass easily through the cell membrane by diffusion. Other substances, such as glucose molecules, are so large that they can enter the cell only with the help of molecules in the cell membrane called transport proteins. This process, a type of passive transport, is known as facilitated diffusion. Have you ever used the drive through at a fast-food restaurant to get your meal? The transport proteins in the cell membrane are like the drive-through window at the restaurant. The window lets you get food out of the restaurant and put money into the restaurant. Similarly, transport proteins are used to move substances into and out of the cell.

Active Transport

Imagine that a football game is over and you leave the stadium. As soon as you get outside of the stadium, you remember that you left your jacket on your seat. Now you have to move against the crowd coming out of the stadium to get back in to get your jacket. Which required more energy—leaving the stadium with the crowd or going back to get your jacket? Something similar to this happens in cells.

Sometimes, a substance is needed inside a cell even though the amount of that substance inside the cell is already greater than the amount outside the cell. For example, root cells require minerals from the soil. The roots of the plant in **Figure 9** already may contain more of those mineral molecules than the surrounding soil does. The tendency is for mineral molecules to move out of the root by diffusion or facilitated diffusion. But the cell needs to move them back across the cell membrane and into the cell just like you had to move back into the stadium. To do this, energy is used. When energy is required to move materials through a cell membrane, **active transport** takes place.

Active transport involves transport proteins, just as facilitated diffusion does. In active transport, a transport protein binds with the needed particle and uses cellular energy to move it through the cell membrane. When the particle is released, the transport protein is ready to move another needed particle through the membrane.

Figure 9
Some root cells have extensions called root hairs that may be 5 mm to 8 mm long. Minerals are taken in by active transport through the cell membranes of root hairs.

Labels on figure: Higher mineral levels · Lower mineral levels · Minerals · Active transport · Soil particles · Root hair

Health INTEGRATION

Transport proteins are important to your health. Sometimes transport proteins are missing or do not function correctly. What would happen if proteins that transport cholesterol across membranes were missing? Cholesterol is an important lipid used by your cells. Write your ideas in your Science Journal.

Active Transport

Use an Analogy

Have students compare active and passive transport with the energy they must exert to get a bicycle to the top of a hill and then ride it back down. Students must exert energy to get the bicycle up the hill. In the same way, the cell uses energy to move substances from areas of low concentration to areas of high concentration. Students do not need to exert energy to ride the bicycle down the hill. In passive transport, cells do not have to use energy to move substances from areas of high concentration to areas of low concentration.
LS Logical-Mathematical

Text Question Answer

going back for the jacket

Teacher FYI

Cell membranes contain spaces through which some substances (water molecules, mineral ions, sugar molecules) can easily pass. The spaces are too small for most proteins and other large molecules to pass through. Some ions cannot pass through membranes due to their charge. These move into a cell via channels or active transport.

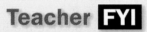

Health INTEGRATION

Cholesterol would not be transported to different areas of the body. Without cholesterol, the body could not synthesize bile acids, steroid hormones, or Vitamin D.

Cultural **Diversity**

Preserving Foods A practical use of osmosis is the drying and salting of food. Have students report on the processes and uses of dried and salted foods in Native American and other cultures. For example, the French developed a vegetable dehydrator in 1795. Both processes remove water from cells in order to preserve the food. In drying, water evaporates. In salting, a salt solution is used to remove water from cells.

Resource Manager

Chapter Resources Booklet
Enrichment, p. 29
Reinforcement, p. 26
Lab Activity, pp. 9–10

Endocytosis and Exocytosis

Use Science Words

Word Meaning Have students use a dictionary to find the meanings of the prefixes *endo-* and *exo-* (*taking in* and *turning out*). Ask them to find examples of other words that make use of these prefixes, and to explain how the meaning of the prefix relates to the meaning of the word. Possible answers: endoskeleton, a skeleton that is inside the body; exoskeleton, a skeleton that is outside the body.

③ Assess

Reteach

Place two or three drops of vanilla extract inside a balloon. Blow up the balloon and tie it. Have students observe the balloon until they can smell the vanilla. Then have them explain why they smell the vanilla outside the balloon. Diffusion has taken place across the membrane.

Challenge

Have students research selectively permeable membranes. Ask them to explain why some substances but not others can pass through the cell membrane. Molecules pass through selectively permeable membranes depending upon size, chemical composition, and how quickly they can be transported.

Oral Would a cell placed in syrup lose or gain water? Explain. It would lose water; water molecules move by diffusion from areas of high concentration to areas of low concentration. Use **Performance Assessment in the Science Classroom,** p. 93.

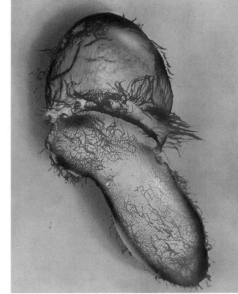

Magnification: 1400×

Figure 10
One-celled organisms like this egg-shaped one can take in other one-celled organisms using endocytosis.

Endocytosis and Exocytosis

Some molecules and particles are too large to move by diffusion or to use the cell membrane's transport proteins. Large protein molecules and bacteria, for example, can enter a cell when they are surrounded by the cell membrane. The cell membrane folds in on itself, enclosing the item in a sphere called a vesicle. Vesicles are transport and storage structures in a cell's cytoplasm. The sphere pinches off, and the resulting vesicle enters the cytoplasm. A similar thing happens when you poke your finger into a partially inflated balloon. Your finger is surrounded by the balloon in much the same way that the protein molecule is surrounded by the cell membrane. This process of taking substances into a cell by surrounding it with the cell membrane is called **endocytosis** (en duh si TOH sus). Some one-celled organisms, as shown in **Figure 10,** take in food this way.

The contents of a vesicle may be released by the cell using a process called **exocytosis** (ek soh si TOH sus). Exocytosis occurs in the opposite way that endocytosis does. The membrane of the vesicle fuses with the cell's membrane, and the vesicle's contents are released. Cells in your stomach use this process to release chemicals that help digest food. The different ways that materials may enter or leave a cell are summarized in **Figure 11.**

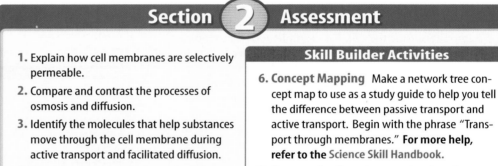

Section ② Assessment

1. Explain how cell membranes are selectively permeable.
2. Compare and contrast the processes of osmosis and diffusion.
3. Identify the molecules that help substances move through the cell membrane during active transport and facilitated diffusion.
4. Why are endocytosis and exocytosis important processes to cells?
5. **Think Critically** Why are fresh fruits and vegetables sprinkled with water at produce markets?

Skill Builder Activities

6. **Concept Mapping** Make a network tree concept map to use as a study guide to help you tell the difference between passive transport and active transport. Begin with the phrase "Transport through membranes." **For more help, refer to the** Science Skill Handbook.
7. **Communicating** Seawater is saltier than tap water. In your Science Journal, explain why drinking large amounts of seawater would be dangerous to humans. **For more help, refer to the** Science Skill Handbook.

Answers to Section Assessment

1. They allow some molecules to pass through, but not others.
2. In both, molecules move from areas with many molecules to areas with few molecules. Osmosis is the diffusion of water across a cell membrane; diffusion can apply to any form of matter.
3. transport proteins

4. Molecules and particles that are too large to move by diffusion or by the cell's transport proteins can move into and out of cells using endocytosis and exocytosis.
5. Water will diffuse into the fruits and vegetables and keep them crisp.
6. Check student concept maps for accuracy.

7. The high levels of salt in seawater would cause water to move out of the cells, resulting in dehydration.

Figure 11

A flexible yet strong layer, the cell membrane is built of two layers of lipids (gold) pierced by protein "passageways" (purple). Molecules can enter or exit the cell by slipping between the lipids or through the protein passageways. Substances that cannot enter or exit the cell in these ways may be surrounded by the membrane and drawn into or expelled from the cell.

Outside cell

Active Transport

Inside cell

Cell membrane

DIFFUSION AND OSMOSIS Small molecules such as oxygen, carbon dioxide, and water can move between the lipids into or out of the cell.

FACILITATED DIFFUSION Larger molecules such as glucose also diffuse through the membrane —but only with the help of transport proteins.

ACTIVE TRANSPORT Cellular energy is used to move some molecules through protein passageways. The protein binds to the molecule on one side of the membrane and then releases the molecule on the other side.

ENDOCYTOSIS AND EXOCYTOSIS In endocytosis, part of the cell membrane wraps around a particle and engulfs it in a vesicle. During exocytosis, a vesicle filled with molecules bound for export moves to the cell membrane, fuses with it, and the contents are released to the outside.

Endocytosis

Exocytosis

Nucleolus **Nucleus**

A ◆ 81

Visualizing Cell Membrane Transport

Have students examine the pictures and read the captions. Then ask the following questions.

Why do some substances move through the cell membrane through exocytosis and endocytosis instead of one of the other transport methods? These substances, which include proteins and nucleic acids, are too large to use the other methods. For example, cholesterol enters by endocytosis; neurotransmitters exit by exocytosis.

Which transport method(s) is like floating downstream? Which is like paddling upstream? Why? In diffusion (osmosis and facilitated diffusion), a substance moves from an area of higher concentration to an area of lower concentration. This does not require energy because it goes with the flow, like floating downstream. In active transport, the substance must go against the concentration gradient which, like paddling upstream, requires energy.

Activity

Have students make a model of a cell that illustrates one type of cell membrane transport. **IS Kinesthetic**

Extension

Challenge students to investigate transport proteins and the substances each transports. Have students make a card game to teach other students what they learned. **IS Logical-Mathematical**

<u>Visual</u>Learning

Figure 11 Have students make an outline from this figure of the steps a transport protein goes through to move substances into and out of cells. L2 **IS Visual-Spatial** P

Resource Manager

Life Science Critical Thinking/Problem Solving, p. 15

BENCH TESTED

Purpose to observe and measure the amount of water diffusing through an egg membrane [L2]

[IS] **Logical-Mathematical**

Process Skills observing and inferring, measuring, communicating, recognizing cause and effect, forming operational definitions

Time Required 50 minutes to set up, 5 minutes each day to observe, 15 minutes to summarize

Alternate Materials Clean, empty food containers with lids may be used to hold the de-shelled egg.

Teaching Strategy Cover raw eggs with vinegar. Leave undisturbed for two or three days until the shells dissolve.

Troubleshooting

• Remind students to handle de-shelled eggs carefully to avoid breaking membranes.

• Thick syrup works better than thin syrup.

• Make sure students replace lids on containers when not in use.

Answers to Questions

1. water— increased in size; corn syrup—decreased in size
2. about 30 mL of water entered; about 40 mL of water left
3. The eggshell is not permeable to water and syrup.
4. cell membrane

Assessment

Performance Have students place ten dried beans in water and let them remain overnight. Direct them to explain their observations. Use **PASC**, p. 97.

Activity

Observing Osmosis

It is difficult to see osmosis occurring in cells because most cells are so small. However, a few cells can be seen without the aid of a microscope. Try this activity to see how osmosis occurs in a large cell.

What You'll Investigate
How does osmosis occur in an egg cell?

Materials
unshelled egg	distilled water (250 mL)
balance	light corn syrup (250 mL)
spoon	500-mL container

Goals
■ **Observe** osmosis in an egg cell.
■ **Determine** what affects osmosis.

Safety Precautions

Eggs may contain bacteria. Avoid touching your face. Wash your hands thoroughly when you are done.

Procedure

1. Copy the table below into your Science Journal and use it to record your data.

Egg Mass Data

	Beginning Egg Mass	Egg Mass After Two Days
Distilled water	Answers may vary.	Answers may vary.
Corn syrup	Answers may vary.	Answers may vary.

2. Obtain an unshelled egg from your teacher. Handle the egg gently. Use a balance to find the egg's mass and record it in the table.

3. Place the egg in the container and add enough distilled water to cover it.

4. **Observe** the egg after 30 min, one day, and two days. After each observation, record the egg's appearance in your Science Journal.

5. After day two, remove the egg with a spoon and allow it to drain. Find the egg's mass and record it in the table.

6. Empty the container, then put the egg back in. Now add enough corn syrup to cover it. Repeat steps 4 and 5.

Conclude and Apply

1. **Explain** the difference between what happened to the egg in water and in corn syrup.

2. **Calculate** the mass of water that moved into and out of the egg.

3. **Hypothesize** why you used an unshelled egg for this investigation.

4. **Infer** what part of the egg controlled water's movement into and out of the egg.

Communicating
Your Data

Compare your conclusions with those of other students in your class. **For more help, refer to the** Science Skill Handbook.

Resource Manager

Chapter Resources Booklet
  Activity Worksheet, pp. 5–6

Communicating
Your Data

Students should discuss why their conclusions did or did not agree with those of other students.

Energy for Life

Trapping and Using Energy

Think of all the energy that players use in a basketball game. Where does the energy come from? The simplest answer is "from the food they eat." The chemical energy stored in food is changed in cells into forms needed to perform all the activities necessary for life. In every cell, these changes involve chemical reactions. All of the activities of an organism involve chemical reactions in some way. The total of all chemical reactions in an organism is called **metabolism.**

The chemical reactions of metabolism need enzymes. What do enzymes do? Suppose you are hungry and decide to open a can of spaghetti. You use a can opener to open the can. Without a can opener, the spaghetti is unusable. The can of spaghetti changed because of the can opener, but the can opener did not change. The can opener can be used again later to open more cans of spaghetti. Enzymes in cells work something like can openers, as shown in **Figure 12.** The enzyme, like the can opener, causes a change, but it is not changed and is reusable. Unlike the can opener, which can only break things apart, enzymes also can cause molecules to join. Without the right enzymes, chemical reactions in cells cannot take place.

As You Read

What You'll Learn
- **List** the differences between producers and consumers.
- **Explain** how the processes of photosynthesis and respiration store and release energy.
- **Describe** how cells get energy from glucose through fermentation.

Vocabulary
metabolism   respiration
photosynthesis   fermentation

Why It's Important
Because of photosynthesis and respiration, you use the Sun's energy.

Enzyme

A

Large
molecule

B

Enzyme

Small
molecules

Figure 12
Enzymes are needed for most chemical reactions that take place in cells. **A** The enzyme attaches to the large molecule it will help change. **B** The enzyme causes the larger molecule to break down into two smaller molecules. Like the can opener, the enzyme is not changed and can be used again.

Energy for Life

1 Motivate

Bellringer Transparency
Display the Section Focus Transparency for Section 3. Use the accompanying Transparency Activity Master. [L2] ELL

Section Focus Transparency

What's for dinner?

Some organisms don't need anyone to survive, but others need help to get by. In this picture, some of the living things shown can make their own food. They are called producers. Other living things, called consumers, depend on these producers for their survival.

1. Which things in the picture are producers? Consumers?
2. Explain whether you are a producer or consumer.
3. If all the plants died, what effect would it have on the animals?

Tie to Prior Knowledge
Display pictures of people using energy—playing sports, gardening, working, and so on. Ask students to identify the source of this energy. chemicals food Then ask where the energy in the food came from. It was derived from plants that captured Sun's energy.

Section ✓*Assessment* Planner

PORTFOLIO
Visual Learning, p. 87
PERFORMANCE ASSESSMENT
Skill Builder Activities, p. 87
See page 94 for more options.

CONTENT ASSESSMENT
Section, p. 87
Challenge, p. 87
Chapter, pp. 94–95

Trapping and Using Energy

Activity

Pick a leaf from a plant that has been exposed to sunlight for a few hours. Submerge it in water. Observe the surface of the leaf. **What forms on the leaf? Why?** Bubbles; the leaf is giving off oxygen.

Use an Analogy

Compare the construction of a house to photosynthesis. Building a house is a physical process that requires the putting together of raw materials. Photosynthesis is a chemical process of putting raw materials together. They both require raw materials and result in a usable product. [N] **Logical-Mathematical**

Caption Answer

Figure 13 carbon dioxide, water, sunlight, and chlorophyll

IDENTIFYING sconceptions

tudents may think that
obtain food from the
ts take in a variety of
and other substances
oil, but these are not
od. They are dis-
ater and absorbed
lant's roots. Once
are transported
in the plant
needed. The
—glucose—is
plant from
water, and
the chloro-

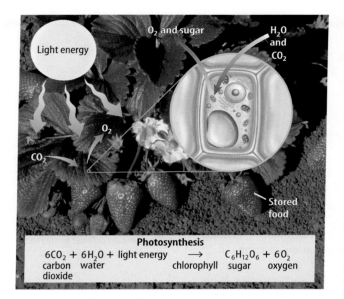

Figure 13
Plants use photosynthesis to make food. *According to the chemical equation, what raw materials would the plant pictured need for photosynthesis?*

Photosynthesis
$$6CO_2 + 6H_2O + \text{light energy} \xrightarrow{\text{chlorophyll}} C_6H_{12}O_6 + 6O_2$$
carbon dioxide   water   chlorophyll   sugar   oxygen

Photosynthesis Living things are divided into two groups—producers and consumers—based on how they obtain their food. Organisms that make their own food, such as plants, are called producers. Organisms that cannot make their own food are called consumers.

If you have ever walked barefoot across a sidewalk on a sunny summer day, you probably moved quickly because the sidewalk was hot. Sunlight energy was converted into thermal energy and heated the sidewalk. Plants and many other producers can convert sunlight energy into another kind of energy—chemical energy. The process they use is called photosynthesis. During **photosynthesis,** producers use light energy to make sugars, which can be used as food.

Producing Carbohydrates Producers that use photosynthesis are usually green because they contain a green pigment called chlorophyll (KLOR uh fihl). Chlorophyll and other pigments are used in photosynthesis to capture sunlight energy. In plant cells, these pigments are found in chloroplasts.

The captured sunlight energy is used to drive chemical reactions during which the raw materials, carbon dioxide and water, are used to produce sugar and oxygen. For plants, the raw materials come from air and soil. Some of the captured sunlight energy is stored in the chemical bonds that hold the sugar molecules together. **Figure 13** shows what happens during photosynthesis in a plant. Enzymes also are needed before these reactions can occur.

Storing Carbohydrates Plants make more sugar during photosynthesis than they need for survival. Excess sugar is changed and stored as starches or used to make other carbohydrates. Plants use these carbohydrates as food for growth, maintenance, and reproduction.

Why is photosynthesis important to consumers? Do you eat apples? Apple trees use photosynthesis to produce apples. Do you like cheese? Some cheese comes from milk, which is produced by cows that eat plants. Consumers take in food by eating producers or other consumers. No matter what you eat, photosynthesis was involved directly or indirectly in its production.

84 ◆ A   CHAPTER 3 Cell Processes

Inclusion Strategies

Gifted There are certain plants such as the Indian pipe (*Monotropa uniflora*) and dodder (*Cuscuta*) that lack chlorophyll. Have students research these plants and report to the class how they obtain food. Indian pipe is a saprophyte; it lives on the remains of dead organisms. Dodder is a parasite; it absorbs nourishment from a host plant. [L3]

Science Journal

Energy and Photosynthesis In their Science Journals, have students list all the foods they eat in one day. Have them to divide the list into two groups: (1) foods formed directly by photosynthesis, (2) foods not formed directly by photosynthesis. Use the lists to help students see that all food energy comes from photosynthesis, whether directly or indirectly.

Respiration Imagine that you get up late for school. You dress quickly, then run three blocks to school. When you get to school, you feel hot and are breathing fast. Why? Your muscle cells need a lot of energy to help you run. To get this energy, muscle cells must break down food. Some of the energy from the food allows your muscles to move and some of it becomes thermal energy, which is why you get hot. Most cells also need oxygen to break down food. You were breathing fast because your body was working to get oxygen to your muscles. Your muscle cells were using the process of respiration. During **respiration** chemical reactions occur that break down food molecules into simpler substances and release their stored energy. Just as in photosynthesis, enzymes are needed before the chemical reactions of respiration can occur.

✓ Reading Check *What must happen to food molecules for respiration to take place?*

Breaking Down Carbohydrates The type of food that is most easily broken down by cells is carbohydrates. Respiration of carbohydrates begins in the cytoplasm of the cell. The carbohydrates are broken down into glucose molecules. Each glucose molecule is broken down further into two simpler molecules. As the glucose molecules are broken down, energy is released.

The two simpler molecules are broken down again. This breakdown occurs in the mitochondria of the cells of plants, animals, fungi, and many other organisms. This process uses oxygen, releases much more energy, and produces carbon dioxide and water as wastes. When you exhale, you breathe out carbon dioxide and some of the water.

Respiration occurs in the cells of all living things. **Figure 14** shows how respiration occurs in one consumer. As you are reading this section of the chapter, millions of cells in your body are breaking down glucose, releasing energy, and producing carbon dioxide and water.

Chemistry
INTEGRATION

Compounds often are represented by a chemical formula. The chemical formula shows how many and what type of atoms are found in one molecule of the compound. For example, the sugar glucose has the chemical formula $C_6H_{12}O_6$. What is the total number of atoms in one glucose molecule?

Figure 14
Producers and consumers use respiration to release energy from their foods.

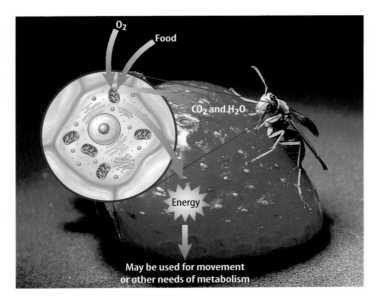

O₂

Food

CO₂ and H₂O

Energy

May be used for movement or other needs of metabolism

Chemistry
INTEGRATION

There are 24 atoms in one glucose molecule.

Use Science Words

Word Origin Have students study the parts of the word *photosynthesis*. It comes from the Greek *photo*, *syn-*, and *thesis*. Have them find the meaning of these words and word parts and describe how the word is defined. Photo: "light;" syn-: "together;" thesis: "to place;" photosynthesis uses light to place compounds together.

✓ Reading Check

Answer They are broken down into simpler substances and their stored energy is released.

IDENTIFYING
Misconceptions

Students often think that plants do not use oxygen, only that they produce oxygen and use carbon dioxide during photosynthesis. See page 66F for teaching strategies that address this misconception.

Resource Manager

Chapter Resources Booklet

Transparency Activity, p. 44

Directed Reading for Content Mastery, pp. 19, 20

Lab Activity, pp. 11–14

✓ Active Reading

Buddy Interviews This strategy helps students understand and clarify the reading. Have students interview one another to find out what helps them to understand what they are reading, how they find answers, and how they assimilate new vocabulary terms. Have students use Buddy Interviews to help them master photosynthesis and respiration. L2

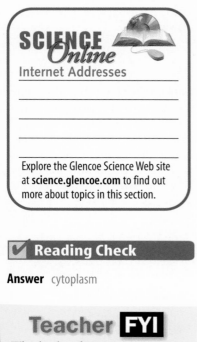
☑ **Reading Check**

Answer cytoplasm

Teacher FYI

The body of an average person running a 100-yard dash in 12 seconds would require 6 L (1.6 gal.) of air. The person's lungs could supply only about 1.2 L of air. As a result, oxygen debt would occur, and the muscles would produce lactic acid. Most athletes take in at least 10 percent more oxygen than the average person; trained marathon runners take in up to 45 percent more oxygen. They have more efficient respiratory and circulatory systems and can exert greater effort without incurring oxygen debt.

Discussion

Why do bakers use yeast for breadmaking? Yeast carry out processes that release energy in the absence of oxygen and produce carbon dioxide, which causes bread to rise.

Fermentation Remember imagining you were late and had to run to school? During your run, your muscle cells might not have received enough oxygen, even though you were breathing rapidly. When cells do not have enough oxygen for respiration, they use a process called **fermentation** to release some of the energy stored in glucose molecules.

Like respiration, fermentation begins in the cytoplasm. Again, as the glucose molecules are broken down, energy is released. But, the simple molecules from the breakdown of glucose do not move into the mitochondria. Instead, more chemical reactions occur in the cytoplasm. These reactions release some energy and produce wastes. The wastes may be lactic acid, alcohol, and carbon dioxide, as shown in **Figure 15.** Your muscle cells can use fermentation to change the simple molecules into lactic acid while releasing energy. The presence of lactic acid is why your muscle cells might feel stiff and sore after you run to school.

☑ **Reading Check** *Where in a cell does fermentation take place?*

Some microscopic organisms, such as bacteria, carry out fermentation and make lactic acid. Some of these organisms are used to produce yogurt and some cheeses. These organisms break down a sugar in milk to release energy. The lactic acid produced causes the milk to become more solid and gives these foods some of their flavor.

Have you ever used yeast to make bread? Yeasts are one-celled living organisms. Yeast cells use fermentation to break down sugar in bread dough. They produce alcohol and carbon dioxide as wastes. The carbon dioxide waste is a gas that makes bread dough rise before it is baked. The alcohol is lost as the bread bakes.

Figure 15
Organisms that use fermentation produce several different wastes.

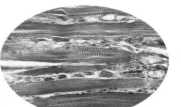

Fermentation → Carbon dioxide and alcohol

Fermentation → Lactic acid

A Yeast cells produce carbon dioxide and alcohol as wastes when they use fermentation.

B Your muscle cells produce lactic acid as a waste when they use fermentation.

Resource Manager

Chapter Resources Booklet
   Enrichment, p. 30
   Reinforcement, p. 27
Life Science Critical Thinking/Problem
   Solving, p. 5

Cultural Diversity

Fermenting Food Lactic acid fermentation by bacteria is responsible for a number of foods from different cultures. Have students research these foods and report their findings to the class in oral reports. Possible topics: Hawaiian *poi*, Japanese soy sauce, Korean *kimchi*, German sauerkraut, yogurt. [L2]

CO₂, H₂O

Photosynthesis (producers)

Respiration (all living things)

Sugars, O₂

Figure 16
The chemical reactions of photosynthesis and respiration could not take place without each other.

Related Processes How are photosynthesis, respiration, and fermentation related? Some producers use photosynthesis to make food. All living things use respiration or fermentation to release energy stored in food. If you think carefully about what happens during photosynthesis and respiration, you will see that what is produced in one is used in the other, as shown in **Figure 16.** These two processes are almost the opposite of each other. Photosynthesis produces sugars and oxygen, and respiration uses these products. The carbon dioxide and water produced during respiration are used during photosynthesis. Most life would not be possible without these important chemical reactions.

Section 3 Assessment

1. Explain the difference between producers and consumers and give three examples of each.

2. Explain how the energy used by many living things on Earth can be traced back to sunlight.

3. Compare and contrast respiration and fermentation.

4. What condition must exist in cells for fermentation to occur?

5. **Think Critically** How can some indoor plants help improve the quality of air in a room?

Skill Builder Activities

6. **Identifying and Manipulating Variables and Controls** Design an experiment to show what happens to a plant when you limit sunlight or one of the raw materials for photosynthesis. Identify the control. **For more help, refer to the** Science Skill Handbook.

7. **Solving One-Step Equations** Refer to the chemical equation for photosynthesis. Calculate then compare the number of carbon, hydrogen, and oxygen atoms before and after photosynthesis. **For more help, refer to the** Math Skill Handbook.

Answers to Section Assessment

1. Producers make food. Consumers get energy by eating producers, food made by producers, or other consumers. Examples will vary.

2. Producers change light energy from the Sun into the chemical energy used by all living things.

3. The amount of energy released by fermentation is less than that released by respiration. Both are processes that release the energy stored in food.

4. When cells do not have enough oxygen for respiration, fermentation occurs.

5. Plants remove carbon dioxide from the air, use it in photosynthesis, and produce oxygen.

6. Experimental designs should include a control and a variable for light, water, or carbon dioxide.

7. The number of atoms is the same before and after respiration; C = 6, H = 12, O = 18.

Quick Demo

Prepare a sugar solution by mixing 1 tablespoon of sugar with 1 cup of warm water in a jar. Add some yeast to the solution a few hours before class and cover it. Have students note the odor of alcohol and the bubbles of carbon dioxide. Point out that these products result from alcoholic fermentation. [L1]
IS Logical-Mathematical

Visual Learning

Figure 16 Have students create an events chain concept map to illustrate what is occurring in each of these pictures. Producer takes in carbon dioxide and water, goes through the process of photosynthesis, and produces oxygen and sugars; other living organisms take in oxygen and sugars, go through the process of respiration, and give off carbon dioxide and water. **IS Visual-Spatial** [P]

3 Assess

Reteach

Have students identify organisms that photosynthesize and those that respire. Only organisms with chlorophyll photosynthesize; all organisms respire.

Challenge

Have students compare photosynthesis and respiration in regard to energy. Photosynthesis stores energy; respiration releases energy.

Assessment

Content Have students make a table to compare and contrast photosynthesis and respiration. Use **Performance Assessment in the Science Classroom,** p. 109.

Activity

BENCH TESTED

What You'll Investigate

Purpose

Students observe photosynthesis and respiration in plants and infer whether the processes occur in light or darkness. L2

ELL   COOP LEARN   IS Visual-Spatial

Process Skills

measuring, observing, inferring, communicating, comparing and contrasting, recognizing cause and effect, separating and controlling variables, interpreting data

Time Required

50 minutes (leave overnight if using artificial light)

Safety Precautions

Students should use care when working with chemicals.

Procedure

Teaching Strategy

Tie to Prior Knowledge Most students are aware that plants use sunlight to make food and that photosynthesis will occur in the tube placed near the light.

Activity

Photosynthesis and Respiration

Every living cell carries on many chemical processes. Two important chemical processes are respiration and photosynthesis. All cells, including the ones in your body, carry on respiration. However, some plant cells can carry on both processes. In this experiment you will investigate when these processes occur in plant cells. How could you find out when plants were using these processes? Are the products of photosynthesis and respiration the same?

What You'll Investigate

When do plants carry on photosynthesis and respiration?

Materials

16-mm test tube (3)
150-mm test tube with stopper (4)
*small, clear-glass baby food jar with lid (4)
test-tube rack
stirring rod
scissors
carbonated water (5 mL)
bromothymol blue solution in dropper bottle
aged tap water (20 mL)
*distilled water (20 mL)
sprig of *Elodea* (2)
*other water plants
*Alternate materials

Goals

■ **Observe** green water plants in the light and dark.
■ **Determine** whether plants carry on photosynthesis and respiration.

Safety Precautions

Wear splash-proof safety goggles to protect eyes from hazardous chemicals. Wash hands thoroughly after the activity.

Inclusion Strategies

Visually Impaired Pair students who are visually impaired with those who can describe to them the colors in the test tubes, both before and after the experiment. L2

Resource Manager

Chapter Resources Booklet
   Activity Worksheet, pp. 7–8
Lab Management and Safety, p. 63

Procedure

1. Label each test tube using the numbers 1, 2, 3, and 4. Pour 5 mL of aged tap water into each test tube.

2. Add 10 drops of carbonated water to test tubes 1 and 2.

3. Add 10 drops of bromothymol blue to all of the test tubes. Bromothymol blue turns green to yellow in the presence of an acid.

4. Cut two 10-cm sprigs of *Elodea.* Place one sprig in test tube 1 and one sprig in test tube 3. Stopper all test tubes.

5. In your Science Journal, copy and complete the test-tube data table.

6. Place test tubes 1 and 2 in bright light. Place tubes 3 and 4 in the dark. Observe the test tubes for 30 min or until the color changes. Record the color of each of the four test tubes.

Test Tube Data		
Test Tube	Color at Start	Color After 30 Minutes
1	yellow	blue
2	yellow	yellow
3	blue	yellow
4	blue	blue

Conclude and Apply

1. What is indicated by the color of the water in all four test tubes at the start of the activity?

2. **Infer** what process occurred in the test tube or tubes that changed color after 30 min.

3. **Describe** the purpose of test tubes 2 and 4 in this experiment.

4. Do the results of this experiment show that photosynthesis and respiration occur in plants? Explain.

*C*ommunicating Your Data

Choose one of the following activities to **communicate** your data. Prepare an oral presentation that explains how the experiment showed the differences between products of photosynthesis and respiration. Draw a cartoon strip to **explain** what you did in this experiment. Use each panel to show a different step. **For more help, refer to the Science Skill Handbook.**

ACTIVITY A ◆ 89

*C*ommunicating Your Data

Students should use data from the experiment for the presentation or cartoon.

Troubleshooting

Elodea should be kept in the dark for two days before the activity. Use sharp scissors to make a clean diagonal cut at the bottom of each stem.

Expected Outcome

Most results will reflect that plants used carbon dioxide in the light and gave off carbon dioxide in the dark.

Conclude and Apply

1. Test tubes 1 and 2 contain carbon dioxide. Tubes 3 and 4 do not.

2. They underwent photosynthesis or respiration.

3. Tubes 2 and 4 were controls.

4. Yes, the experimental results showed that both processes happen in plant cells. In test tube 1, the green plant used carbon dioxide for photosynthesis. In test tube 3, the green plant gave off carbon dioxide as a result of respiration.

Error Analysis

Have students compare their results and explain why any differences occurred.

✓*Assessment*

Oral How are fermentation and respiration similar? Both processes release energy through the breakdown of other substances. Use **Performance Assessment in the Science Classroom,** p. 99.

Science and Language Arts

Science and Language Arts

"Tulip"
by Penny Harter

✓ Pre-Reading Activity

This activity should help students think about the power of nature. Collect photographs that show both the beauty and the harshness of nature. Photographs by Edward Weston and Ansel Adams are good sources of these types of images. Have students work in small groups to discuss one photograph and consider what they learn about the natural world from the image.

Respond to the Reading

Active Reading Strategies

Predict At certain points in the poem, stop and have students consider what the flower might look like as it grows and whether or not they think the plant will survive. **What gives the flower the strength to break through the rubble?**

Visualize Suggest that students keep the tulip and construction site in their minds' eye as they read. Encourage them to form a mental image of the tulip as it first sprouts, and then to imagine its growth as it fights the debris. **How do you picture the contrast between the flower and the rubble?**

Answers to Questions
1. Possible answers: The tulip bulb is buried deep in the ground; the tulip is a hardy plant.
2. Possible answer: The tulip represents the rebirth of spring. The narrator herself may be experiencing a rebirth or renewal.
3. part of the bud of the tulip

Respond to the Reading

1. Why do you suppose the tulip survived the builders' abuse?
2. The poet chooses to write about a tulip rather than another kind of flower. Why do you think that is?
3. What is the yellow throat that the narrator is staring into?

I watched its first green push
  through bare dirt, where the builders
  had dropped boards, shingles,
plaster—
killing everything.
I could not recall what grew
  there,
what returned each spring,
but the leaves looked tulip,
and one morning it arrived,
a scarlet slash against the
aluminum siding.

Mornings, on the way to
  my car,
I bow to the still bell
of its closed petals; evenings
it greets me, light ringing at
the end of my driveway.

Sometimes I kneel
to stare into the yellow
  throat . . .
It opens and closes my days.
It has made me weak with
  love. . . .

Reading Further

Other sources on this topic include:

Tulipa: A Photographer's Botonical, by Christopher Baker (Photographer), Willem Lemmers, Emma Sweeny, and Michael Pollan, Artisan, 1999.

Methods in Plant Cell Biology, by Editors David W. Galbreth, Hans J. Bohnert, and Leslie Wilson, Academic Press, 1995.

Photosynthesis, by Krishna Rao and David O. Hall, Cambridge University Press, 1999.

Plant Identification Terminology: An Illustrated Glossary, by James G. Harris and Melinda Woolf Harris, Spring Lake Publishers, 2001.

Guide to Flowering Plant Families, by Wendy B. Zomlefer, University of North Carolina, 1995.

American Society for Microbiology, Office of Education, 1325 Massachusetts Avenue, NW, Washington, DC 20005-4171.

Understanding Literature

Personification Using human traits or emotions to describe an idea, animal, or inanimate object is called personification. When the poet writes that the tulip has a "yellow throat," she uses personification. This can make the reader think of the tulip as more than just an inanimate object. The poet also uses of personification when she states that the tulip inspires love.

Science Connection Living things are made of more than 50 percent water and depend on it for their survival. Because chemical reactions almost always require water to take place, plants must have water in order to grow. In the poem, the tulip only pushes up through the ground in the spring when the tulip's underground bulb and roots absorb enough water. The water carries nutrients and minerals from the soil into the plant.

The process of active transport allows needed nutrients to enter the roots. The cell membranes of root cells contain proteins that bind with the needed nutrients. Cellular energy is used to move these nutrients through the cell membrane.

You also learned about photosynthesis in this chapter. From reading the poem, how would you know that photosynthesis had taken place?

Linking Science and Writing

Gardener's Journal Select a plant to observe. It could be a plant that you, your family, or one of your classmates grows. Depending on the season, it could be a plant growing on the grounds of your school or in a public park. Keep a gardener's observation journal of the plant for a month. Write weekly entries in your journal, describing the plant's condition, size, health, color, and other physical qualities.

Career Connection

Microbiologist

Dr. Harold Amos is a biologist who has studied cell processes in bacteria and mammals over the course of his career. He studied the way that sugar is transported in normal cells and cancer cells. Dr. Amos has a medical degree and a doctorate in bacteriology and immunology, which deals with the immune system and its interaction with diseases. He also has received many awards for his scientific work and his contributions to the careers of other scientists.

SCIENCE *Online* Visit the Glencoe Science Web site at **science.glencoe.com** to learn more about careers in microbiology.

Understanding Literature

Science Connection

Plant stems play a part in the transport of materials from roots to leaves. Stems vary greatly in size and shape from one plant species to another. Some grow entirely underground. All plant stems have two functions: they hold leaves up in the sunlight and they conduct various substances between roots and leaves. Some stems also may store water and nutrients. Plants often store food in their stems during their growth period. When a plant's growth stops, this stored food enables them to survive dormancy. Dormancy occurs during a cold winter or a long dry period. The dormant plant uses the stored food to begin growing when conditions again become favorable.

Linking Science and Writing

Writing Strategies

Divide the class into groups. Have each group pick a readily-available flower to study. Make study guides and plant books available for use in identification and research. Students should bring in a sample of their chosen flower, and draw a picture of it in their Science Journals. Then by carefully pulling the flower apart, they can identify, sketch and label the petals, stamens, sepals, and carpal. As they study the flower, the group should discuss and record the role each part plays in the plant's reproduction.

Career Connection

Students interested in a career in biology should study sciences, math and Latin. Taking courses that require laboratory and field work is also advisable. A bachelor's degree is required to work in this field. For the highest professional status, a doctorate is necessary. Microbiologists study organisms of microscopic or submicroscopic size. Other scientists work to diagnose, treat, and prevent diseases.

SCIENCE Online
Internet Addresses

_____

_____

_____

Explore the Glencoe Science Web site at **science.glencoe.com** to find out more about topics in this feature.

Chapter 3 Study Guide

Preview

Students can answer the questions in their Science Journals. Discuss the answers as you go through the chapter. **LS Linguistic**

Review

Students can write their answers, then compare them with those of other students. **LS Interpersonal**

Reteach

Students can look at the illustrations and describe details that support the main ideas of the chapter. **LS Visual-Spatial**

Answers to Chapter Review

SECTION 1

4. carbohydrates, lipids, proteins, and nucleic acids

SECTION 2

2. Osmosis moves water into the plant's cells.

SECTION 3

1. Their cells do not have the chlorophyll needed to capture sunlight.

Reviewing Main Ideas

Section 1 Chemistry of Life

1. Matter is anything that has mass and takes up space.

2. Energy in matter is in the chemical bonds that hold matter together.

3. All organic compounds contain the elements hydrogen and carbon. The organic compounds in living things are carbohydrates, lipids, proteins, and nucleic acids.

4. Organic and inorganic compounds are important to living things. *What organic compounds could be found in an elephant and a pumpkin?*

Section 2 Moving Cellular Materials

1. The selectively permeable cell membrane controls which molecules can pass into and out of the cell.

2. In diffusion, molecules move from areas where there are more of them into areas where there are fewer of them.  Osmosis is the diffusion of water through a cell membrane. *Why might these plants use osmosis?*

3. Cells use energy to move molecules by active transport but do not use energy for passive transport.

4. Cells move large particles through cell membranes by endocytosis and exocytosis.

Section 3 Energy for Life

1. Photosynthesis is the process by which some producers change light energy into chemical energy. *Why can't cells in these humans use sunlight to make food?*

2. Respiration that uses oxygen releases the energy in food molecules and produces waste carbon dioxide and water.

3. Some one-celled organisms and cells that lack oxygen use fermentation to release small amounts of energy from glucose. Wastes like alcohol, carbon dioxide, and lactic acid are produced.

FOLDABLES
Reading & Study Skills

After You Read

Under each tab of your Vocabulary Study Fold, write a sentence about one of the cell processes using the vocabulary word on the tab.

FOLDABLES
Reading & Study Skills

After You Read

After students have read the chapter and completed the Foldable described in Before You Read, have them do the activity on the student page.

Visualizing Main Ideas

Complete the following table on energy processes.

Energy Processes	Photosynthesis	Respiration	Fermentation
Energy Source	Sun	food (glucose)	food (glucose)
In plant and animal cells, occurs in	chloroplast	mitochondria	cytoplasm
Reactants are	water, carbon dioxide	glucose, oxygen	glucose, oxygen
Products are	glucose, oxygen	water, carbon dioxide	lactic acid, alcohol, carbon dioxide

Vocabulary Review

Vocabulary Words

a. active transport
b. diffusion
c. endocytosis
d. enzyme
e. equilibrium
f. exocytosis
g. fermentation
h. inorganic compound
i. metabolism
j. mixture
k. organic compound
l. osmosis
m. passive transport
n. photosynthesis
o. respiration

Using Vocabulary

Use what you know about the vocabulary words to answer the following questions.

1. What is the diffusion of water called?

2. What type of protein regulates nearly all chemical reactions in cells?

3. How do large food particles enter an amoeba?

4. What type of compound is water?

5. What process is used by producers to convert sunlight energy into chemical energy?

6. What type of compounds always contain carbon and hydrogen?

7. What process uses oxygen to break down glucose?

8. What is the total of all chemical reactions in an organism called?

Visualizing Main Ideas

See student page.

Vocabulary Review

Using Vocabulary

1. The diffusion of water is called osmosis.
2. The proteins that regulate nearly all chemical reactions in cells are enzymes.
3. Large food particles enter the amoeba by endocytosis.
4. Water is an inorganic compound.
5. Producers convert sunlight into chemical energy by photosynthesis.
6. An organic compound always contains carbon and hydrogen.
7. Respiration uses oxygen to break down glucose.
8. The total of all chemical reactions in an organism is metabolism.

◆ IDENTIFYING ▷ Misconceptions

Assess

Use the assessment as follow-up to page 66F after students have completed the chapter.

Discussion Do animals ever give off oxygen as a product of their metabolic activities? No **Explain.** Oxygen is given off as a product of photosynthesis, thus only organisms that can carry out photosynthesis produce this gas. Animals are not photosynthetic organisms. **What products do plants release during their metabolic processes?** both oxygen and carbon dioxide Specifically reinforce the idea that plants carry out both photosynthesis and respiration.

Expected Outcome At this point students should understand and be able to explain the complementary processes of photosynthesis and respiration in plants and animals.

Chapter 3 Assessment

Checking Concepts

1. C
2. B
3. A
4. B
5. D
6. C
7. A
8. C
9. D
10. D

Thinking Critically

11. The red blood cell would burst because water molecules would move into the cell. The water would move from an area of greater concentration (outside the cell) to an area of lesser concentration (inside the cell) in an effort to reach equilibrium.

12. Plants die as water molecules move out of the cells into the salty soil.

13. The molecules in hot water move faster than those in cold. These faster-moving molecules bump into the sugar molecules more often and more vigorously, dissolving the sugar faster.

14. Consumers would also die; they depend on producers for food.

15. The enzymes increase the rate at which protein bonds are broken; this makes the meat more tender.

Checking Concepts

Choose the word or phrase that best answers the question.

1. What is it called when cells use energy to move molecules?
   A) diffusion
   B) osmosis
   C) active transport
   D) passive transport

2. How might bacteria be taken into cells?
   A) osmosis
   B) endocytosis
   C) exocytosis
   D) diffusion

3. What occurs when molecules are distributed evenly through a solid, liquid, or gas?
   A) equilibrium
   B) metabolism
   C) fermentation
   D) cellular respiration

4. Which of the following substances is an example of a carbohydrate?
   A) enzymes
   B) sugars
   C) waxes
   D) proteins

5. What is RNA an example of?
   A) carbon dioxide
   B) water
   C) lipid
   D) nucleic acid

6. What organic molecule stores the greatest amount of energy?
   A) carbohydrate
   B) water
   C) lipid
   D) nucleic acid

7. Which of these formulas is an example of an organic compound?
   A) $C_6H_{12}O_6$
   B) NO_2
   C) H_2O
   D) O_2

8. What are organisms that cannot make their own food called?
   A) biodegradables
   B) producers
   C) consumers
   D) enzymes

9. Which one of these cellular processes requires the presence of chlorophyll?
   A) fermentation
   B) endocytosis
   C) respiration
   D) photosynthesis

10. What kind of molecule is water?
    A) organic
    B) lipid
    C) carbohydrate
    D) inorganic

Thinking Critically

11. If you could place one red blood cell in distilled water, what would you see happen to the cell? Explain.

12. In snowy places, salt is used to melt ice on the roads. Explain what could happen to many roadside plants as a result.

13. Why does sugar dissolve faster in hot tea than in iced tea?

14. What would happen to the consumers in a lake if all the producers died?

15. Meat tenderizers contain protein enzymes. How do these enzymes affect meat?

Developing Skills

16. **Concept Mapping** Complete the events-chain concept map to sequence the following parts of matter from smallest to largest: *atom, electron,* and *compound.*

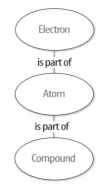

17. **Forming Hypotheses** Make a hypothesis about what will happen to wilted celery when placed in a glass of plain water.

Chapter ✔Assessment Planner

Portfolio Encourage students to place in their portfolios one or two items of what they consider to be their best work. Examples include:
• Science Journal, p. 72
• Visual Learning, p. 81
• Visual Learning, p. 87

Performance Additional performance assessments, Performance Task Assessment Lists, and rubrics for evaluating these activities can be found in Glencoe's **Performance Assessment in the Science Classroom.**

18. Interpreting Data Water plants were placed at different distances from a light source. Bubbles coming from the plants were counted to measure the rate of photosynthesis. What can you say about how the distance from the light affected the rate?

Photosynthesis in Water Plants		
Beaker Number	Distance from Light (cm)	Bubbles per Minute
1	10	45
2	30	30
3	50	19
4	70	6
5	100	1

19. Making and Using Graphs Using the data from question 18, make a line graph that shows the relationship between the rate of photosynthesis and the distance from light.

Performance Assessment

20. Puzzle Make a crossword puzzle with words describing ways substances are transported across cell membranes. Use the following words in your puzzle: *diffusion, osmosis, facilitated diffusion, active transport, endocytosis,* and *exocytosis.* Make sure your clues give good descriptions of each transport method.

TECHNOLOGY

Go to the Glencoe Science Web site at **science.glencoe.com** or use the **Glencoe Science CD-ROM** for additional chapter assessment.

THE PRINCETON REVIEW — Test Practice

Organic compounds called carbohydrates and proteins form many parts of a cell and also help connect cells to each other. Several organic compounds, along with their characteristics and where they are found, are listed below.

Cell Substances		
Organic Compound	Flexibility	Found In
Keratin	Not very flexible	Hair and skin of mammals
Collagen	Not very flexible	Skin, bones, and tendons of mammals
Chitin	Very rigid	Tough outer shell of insects, crabs
Cellulose	Very flexible	Trees and flowers

Study the chart and answer the following questions.

1. According to this information, which organic compound is the least flexible?
A) keratin
B) collagen
C) chitin
D) cellulose

2. According to the chart, cellulose might be found in _____.
F) mammals
G) bones
H) insects
J) trees

THE PRINCETON REVIEW — Test Practice

The Test-Taking Tip was written by The Princeton Review, the nation's leader in test preparation.
1. C
2. J

Developing Skills

16. See student page.
17. Wilted celery will become crisp as water molecules move by osmosis into its cells to reach equilibrium.
18. The closer a plant is to light, the faster its rate of photosynthesis.
19.

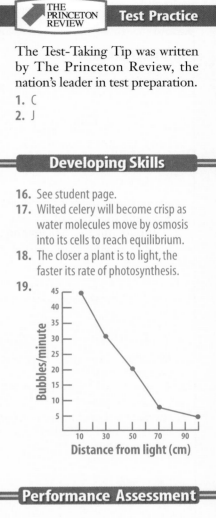

Performance Assessment

20. Definitions in the chapter for these terms can be used. Use **PASC**, p. 91.

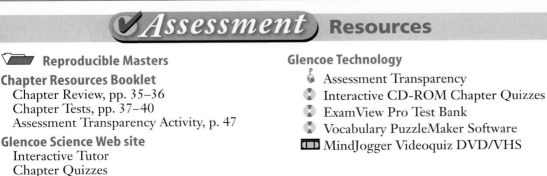

✓Assessment Resources

📁 **Reproducible Masters**

Chapter Resources Booklet
Chapter Review, pp. 35–36
Chapter Tests, pp. 37–40
Assessment Transparency Activity, p. 47

Glencoe Science Web site
Interactive Tutor
Chapter Quizzes

Glencoe Technology
🔊 Assessment Transparency
💿 Interactive CD-ROM Chapter Quizzes
💿 ExamView Pro Test Bank
💿 Vocabulary PuzzleMaker Software
📼 MindJogger Videoquiz DVD/VHS

Section/Objectives	Standards		Activities/Features
Chapter Opener	**National**	**State/Local**	**Explore Activity:** Infer about seed growth, p. 97 **Before You Read,** p. 97
	See p. 6T for a Key to Standards.		
Section 1 Cell Division and Mitosis ⏲ 2 sessions 🖻 1 block 1. **Explain** why mitosis is important. 2. **Examine** the steps of mitosis. 3. **Compare** mitosis in plant and animal cells. 4. **List** two examples of asexual reproduction.	National Content Standards: UCP3, A1, C1		**Health Integration,** p. 99 **Science Online,** p. 99 **MiniLAB:** Modeling Mitosis, p. 103 **Activity:** Mitosis in Plant Cells, p. 105
Section 2 Sexual Reproduction and Meiosis ⏲ 2 sessions 🖻 1 block 1. **Describe** the stages of meiosis and how sex cells are produced. 2. **Explain** why meiosis is needed for sexual reproduction. 3. **Name** the cells that are involved in fertilization. 4. **Explain** how fertilization occurs in sexual reproduction.	National Content Standards: UCP3, UCP4, C2		**Chemistry Integration,** p. 107 **Problem-Solving Activity:** How can chromosome numbers be predicted? p. 109 **Visualizing Polyploidy in Plants,** p. 110
Section 3 DNA ⏲ 3 sessions 🖻 1.5 blocks 1. **Identify** the parts of a DNA molecule and its structure. 2. **Explain** how DNA copies itself. 3. **Describe** the structure and function of each kind of RNA.	National Content Standards: UCP3, UCP4, A1, C1, C2, E2, F5, G1		**MiniLAB:** Modeling DNA Replication, p. 113 **Science Online,** p. 115 **Science Online,** p. 117 **Activity:** Mutations, pp. 118–119 **Oops! Accidents in Science:** A Tangled Tale, pp. 120–121

NATIONAL GEOGRAPHIC

Teacher's Corner

PRODUCTS AVAILABLE FROM GLENCOE
To order call 1-800-334-7344:
CD-ROM
NGS PictureShow: The Cell
NGS PictureShow: Plants: What It Means to Be Green
Curriculum Kit
GeoKit: Cells and Microorganisms

Transparency Sets
NGS PicturePack: The Cell
NGS PicturePack: What It Means to Be Green

PRODUCTS AVAILABLE FROM NATIONAL GEOGRAPHIC SOCIETY
To order call 1-800-368-2728:

Video
DNA: Laboratory of Life

INDEX TO NATIONAL GEOGRAPHIC SOCIETY
The following articles may be used for research relating to this chapter:
"The Rise of Life on Earth," by Richard Monastersky, March 1998.

Activity Materials	Reproducible Resources	Section Assessment	Technology
Explore Activity: soaked bean seeds, water, paper towels, self-sealing plastic bags, hand lens	**Chapter Resources Booklet** Foldables Worksheet, p. 15 Directed Reading Overview, p. 17 Note-taking Worksheets, pp. 31–33	GLENCOE'S **ASSESSMENT** ADVANTAGE	
MiniLAB: colored paper, poster board, markers, toothpicks, yarn, thread, glue, scissors **Activity:** prepared slide of onion root tip, microscope	**Chapter Resources Booklet** Transparency Activity, p. 42 MiniLAB, p. 3 Enrichment, p. 28 Reinforcement, p. 25 Transparency Activity, pp. 45–46 Activity Worksheet, pp. 5–6 Directed Reading, p. 18 Lab Activity, pp. 9–10	Portfolio Visual Learning, p. 99 Performance MiniLAB, p. 103 Skill Builder Activities, p. 104 Content Section Assessment, p. 104 Challenge, p. 104	Section Focus Transparency Teaching Transparency Interactive CD-ROM/DVD Guided Reading Audio Program
Need materials? Contact Science Kit at 1-800-828-7777 or www.sciencekit.com on the Internet.	**Chapter Resources Booklet** Transparency Activity, p. 43 Enrichment, p. 29 Reinforcement, p. 26 Directed Reading, p. 18 **Life Science Critical Thinking/ Problem Solving,** p. 19 **Mathematics Skill Activities,** p. 3 **Performance Assessment in the Science Classroom,** p. 57	Portfolio Make a Model, p. 109 Performance Skill Builder Activities, p. 111 Content Section Assessment, p. 111 Challenge, p. 111	Section Focus Transparency Interactive CD-ROM/DVD Guided Reading Audio Program
MiniLAB: pencil, paper **Activity:** Web sites and other resources on mutations	**Chapter Resources Booklet** Transparency Activity, p. 44 MiniLAB, p. 4 Enrichment, p. 30 Reinforcement, p. 27 Directed Reading, pp. 19, 20 Activity Worksheet, pp. 7–8 Lab Activity, pp. 11–13 **Home and Community Involvement,** p. 36 **Lab Management and Safety,** p. 58	Portfolio Extension, p. 115 Performance MiniLAB, p. 113 Skill Builder Activities, p. 117 Content Section Assessment, p. 117 Challenge, p. 117	Section Focus Transparency Interactive CD-ROM/DVD Guided Reading Audio Program

End of Chapter Assessment

GLENCOE'S **ASSESSMENT** ADVANTAGE

Blackline Masters	Technology	Professional Series
Chapter Resources Booklet Chapter Review, pp. 35–36 Chapter Tests, pp. 37–40 **Standardized Test Practice by The Princeton Review,** pp. 19–22	MindJogger Videoquiz CD-ROM Explorations and Quizzes Vocabulary Puzzle Makers ExamView Pro Test Bank Interactive Lesson Planner Interactive Teacher's Edition	Performance Assessment in the Science Classroom (PASC)

Transparencies

Section Focus

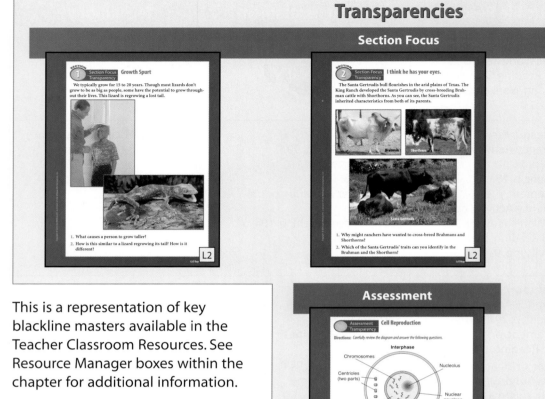

Section Focus Transparency 1 — Growth Spurt

We typically grow for 15 to 20 years. Though most lizards don't grow to be as big as people, some have the potential to grow throughout their lives. This lizard is regrowing a lost tail.

1. What causes a person to grow taller?
2. How is this similar to a lizard regrowing its tail? How is it different?

L2

Section Focus Transparency 2 — I think he has your eyes.

The Santa Gertrudis bull flourishes in the arid plains of Texas. The King Ranch developed the Santa Gertrudis by cross-breeding Brahman cattle with Shorthorns. As you can see, the Santa Gertrudis inherited characteristics from both of its parents.

1. Why might ranchers have wanted to cross-breed Brahmans and Shorthorns?
2. Which of the Santa Gertrudis' traits can you identify in the Brahman and the Shorthorn?

L2

Section Focus Transparency 3 — Curly Cat

This unusual cat is a Devon Rex. It appeared in Devonshire, England, in 1960 when a mutation occurred among British barn cats. The Devon Rex has a small head and a curly coat.

1. Based on the picture and the description above, what do you think a mutation is?
2. How can cat breeders attempt to continue the characteristics of the Devon Rex?

L2

This is a representation of key blackline masters available in the Teacher Classroom Resources. See Resource Manager boxes within the chapter for additional information.

Key to Teaching Strategies

The following designations will help you decide which activities are appropriate for your students.

- **L1** Level 1 activities should be appropriate for students with learning difficulties.

- **L2** Level 2 activities should be within the ability range of all students.

- **L3** Level 3 activities are designed for above-average students.

- **ELL** ELL activities should be within the ability range of English Language Learners.

- **COOP LEARN** Cooperative Learning activities are designed for small group work.

- **LS** Multiple Learning Styles logos are used throughout to indicate strategies that address different learning styles.

- **P** These strategies represent student products that can be placed into a best-work portfolio.

Assessment

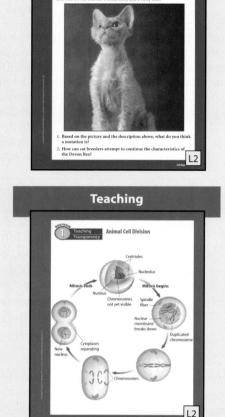

Assessment Transparency — Cell Reproduction

Directions: Carefully review the diagram and answer the following questions.

1. A cell produced by the fruit fly cell pictured above will most likely be ____.
   A identical to the fruit fly cell
   B a combination of its two parent fruit fly cells.
   C unable to reproduce
   D a genetic mutation
2. In which part of the cell are the chromosomes located?
   F Cell membrane
   G Cytoplasm
   H Nucleus
   J Mitochondrion
3. The fruit fly cell above contains eight chromosomes. How many chromosomes will cells produced by the above cell probably have?
   A sixteen   B eight   C four   D sixty-four

L2

Teaching

Teaching Transparency 1 — Animal Cell Division

L2

Hands-on Activities

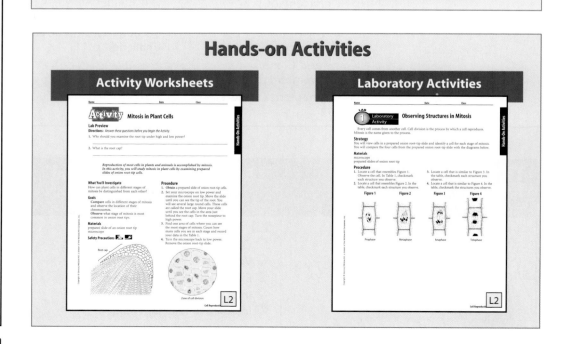

Activity Worksheets

Activity — Mitosis in Plant Cells

Lab Preview
Directions: Answer these questions before you begin the Activity

1. Why should you examine the root tip under high and low power?

2. What is the root cap?

Reproduction of most cells in plants and animals is accomplished by mitosis. In this activity, you will study mitosis in plant cells by examining prepared slides of onion root-tip cells.

What You'll Investigate
How can plant cells in different stages of mitosis be distinguished from each other?

Goals
Compare cells in different stages of mitosis and observe the location of their chromosomes.
Observe what stage of mitosis is most common in onion root tips.

Materials
prepared slide of an onion root tip
microscope

Safety Precautions

Procedure
1. Obtain a prepared slide of onion root-tip cells.
2. Set your microscope on low power and examine the onion root tip. Move the slide until you can see the tip of the root. You will see several large round cells. These cells are called the root cap. Move your slide until you see the cells in the area just behind the root cap. Turn the nosepiece to high power.
3. Find one area of cells where you can see the most stages of mitosis. Count how many cells you see in each stage and record your data in the Table 1.
4. Turn the microscope back to low power. Remove the onion root-tip slide.

L2

Laboratory Activities

Laboratory Activity 1 — Observing Structures in Mitosis

Every cell comes from another cell. Cell division is the process by which a cell reproduces. Mitosis is the name given to the process.

Strategy
You will view cells in a prepared onion root-tip slide and identify a cell for each stage of mitosis. You will compare the four cells from the prepared onion root-tip slide with the diagrams below.

Materials
microscope
prepared slides of onion root tip

Procedure
1. Locate a cell that resembles Figure 1. Observe the cell. In Table 1, checkmark each structure you observe.
2. Locate a cell that resembles Figure 2. In the table, checkmark each structure you observe.
3. Locate a cell that is similar to Figure 3. In the table, checkmark each structure you observe.
4. Locate a cell that is similar to Figure 4. In the table, checkmark the structures you observe.

Figure 1	Figure 2	Figure 3	Figure 4
Prophase	Metaphase	Anaphase	Telophase

L2

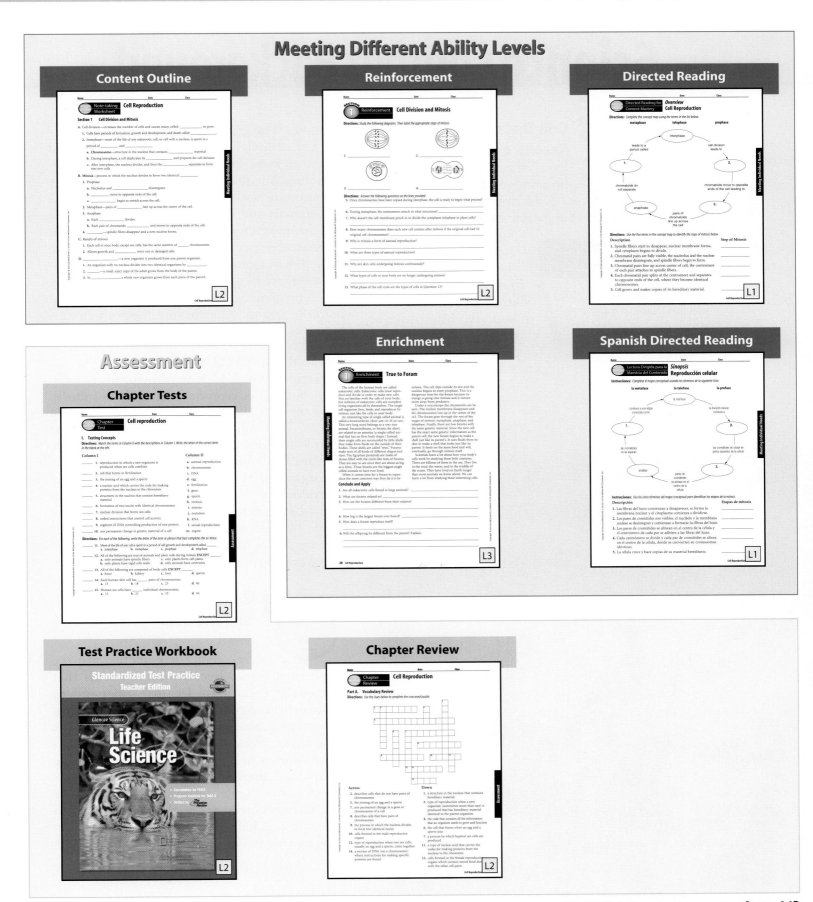

Meeting Different Ability Levels

Content Outline

Note-taking Worksheet — Cell Reproduction

Section 1 Cell Division and Mitosis

L2

Reinforcement

Reinforcement — Cell Division and Mitosis

L2

Directed Reading

Directed Reading for Content Mastery — Overview Cell Reproduction

L1

Assessment

Chapter Tests

Chapter Test — Cell reproduction

L2

Enrichment

Enrichment — True to Foram

L3

Spanish Directed Reading

Lectura Dirigida para la Maestría del Contenido — Sinopsis Reproducción celular

L1

Test Practice Workbook

Standardized Test Practice
Teacher Edition

Glencoe Science
Life Science

L2

Chapter Review

Chapter Review — Cell Reproduction

Part A. Vocabulary Review

L2

Science Content Background

Cell Division and Mitosis
Results of Mitosis

Every species has a characteristic number of chromosomes in each cell. A cat has 32 chromosomes, whereas a potato and a chimpanzee each have 48 chromosomes. In all sexually reproducing organisms, chromosomes occur in homologous pairs. Except for some sex chromosomes, homologous chromosomes are of equal length and have the same genes at the same relative

> **Fun Fact**
>
> The first pigs were cloned in 2000. Scientists think that organs from pigs could be transplanted into humans.

locations. The genes may or may not be identical. For example, the gene for hair color would be at the same location on homologous chromosomes but may code for brunette on one chromosome and blonde on the other.

Animals and some plants have one pair of sex chromosomes. In most animals, including humans, the sex chromosomes of the female are truly homologous, whereas the male sex chromosomes are of unequal lengths and have many different genes. This is reversed in birds and butterflies, with males having the truly homologous sex chromosomes.

Asexual Reproduction

Eukaryotes, which include many protists, some fungi, and plants, reproduce asexually by mitosis. Prokaryotes, like bacteria, reproduce by fission. Depending on the organism, one or several new organisms can be created that are genetically identical to, or clones of, the original organism. Most animals do not use asexual reproduction. Recently scientists have been able to stimulate cells from adult animals to divide by mitosis and reproduce new animals that are clones of the organism from which the cells were taken.

Sexual Reproduction and Meiosis
Sexual Reproduction

Sex cells, or gametes, are the result of meiosis. Because of a process that happens at metaphase I called independent assortment, the possible combination of chromosomes for each sex cell varies every time sex cells form. When duplicated homologous chromosomes line up at a cell's center during metaphase I, there are no rules about how a particular pair is aligned relative to any other pair. The only requirement is that the alignment results in one half of each duplicated chromosome moving in one direction and the other half

Reuters New Media, Inc./Corbis

moving in the opposite direction during anaphase I. The offspring formed by fertilization has its own unique combination of genetic material. This produces variation between parents and offspring and may give offspring a better chance of surviving in a changing environment.

Meiosis and Sex Cells

This process is often called reduction division since the number of chromosomes in the cells produced is half that of the original cell. Meiosis provides for great diversity within a species because of the many ways the chromosomes can align during metaphase I. There are more than 8 million possible gametes that can be produced from the 23 pairs of human chromosomes.

In animals, meiosis results in haploid egg and sperm cells. In plants, meiosis results in haploid spores that later produce egg and sperm cells.

SECTION 3

DNA

What is DNA?

The information in DNA that determines what an organism will be is contained in a code dictated by the order of subunits called nucleotides. A nucleotide consists of the sugar deoxyribose, a phosphate molecule, and one of the four possible nitrogen bases. A DNA molecule is two chains of nucleotides. These two chains are antiparallel and run in opposite directions. One chain ends with a phosphate, and the other chain ends with

SCIENCE Online

For additional content background on this topic, go to the Glencoe Science Web site at science.glencoe.com.

deoxyribose. Just as the order of letters on this page determines what words you are reading, the order of nucleotides determines the message on the DNA. Because DNA is copied from one generation to the next, any change, or mutation, in a gene is also preserved. If the change occurs in cells that become gametes, it is passed on to future generations in a process called heredity.

A DNA Model

The process of DNA replication is directed by the enzyme called DNA polymerase. It moves along the separated DNA molecule and inserts the correct, complementary nucleotides onto the exposed nitrogen bases. This happens at many locations along the length of the DNA molecule simultaneously. Otherwise the time it would take to match up the millions of nitrogen bases would be astronomical.

Mutations

A change in a cell's genetic message is called a mutation. Some mutations affect the message itself, altering the sequence of DNA nucleotides. Other classes of mutations involve sequences of DNA that can move from place to place and are often called jumping genes. When a particular gene is mutated, its function is often destroyed.

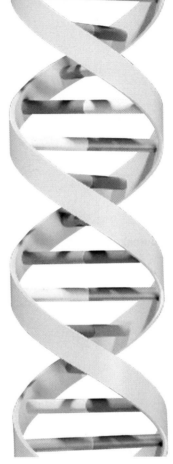

Michael Simpson/FPG International

Fun Fact

Barbara McClintock first published a paper on jumping genes in the 1940s. In 1983 she received the Nobel Prize for her work.

Cell Reproduction

Chapter Vocabulary

mitosis
chromosome
asexual reproduction
sexual reproduction
sperm
egg
fertilization
zygote
diploid
haploid
meiosis
DNA
gene
RNA
mutation

What do you think?

Science Journal The structures in the picture are duplicated chromosomes, which contain genetic information for the organism they belong to.

Cell Reproduction

How does a cut on your skin heal? Why doesn't a baby chicken grow up to look like a duck? Why do turtles, like the one in the photo to the right, and most other animals need to have two parents, when a sweet potato plant can be grown from just one potato? In this chapter, you will find answers to these questions as you learn about cell reproduction. You also will learn what genetic material is and how it functions.

What do you think?

Science Journal Look at the picture below with a classmate. Discuss what you think this might be. Here is a hint: *These structures contain important information for cells.* Write your answer or best guess in your Science Journal.

96 ◆ A

Theme Connection

Stability and Change DNA controls all cell activities by directing the production of proteins in living organisms. Changes in DNA can result in evolutionary changes that are inherited.

M ost flower and vegetable seeds sprout and grow into entire plants in just a few weeks. Although all of the cells in a seed have information and instructions to produce a new plant, only some of the cells in the seed use the information. Where are these cells in seeds? Do the following activity to find out.

Infer about seed growth

1. Carefully split open two bean seeds that have soaked in water overnight.
2. Observe both halves and record your observations.
3. Wrap all four halves in a moist paper towel. Then put them into a self-sealing, plastic bag and seal the bag.
4. Make observations for a few days.

Observe

In your Science Journal, describe what you observe. Hypothesize about which cells in seeds use information about how plants grow.

Before You Read

FOLDABLES
Reading & Study
Skills

Making an Organizational Study Fold When information is grouped into clear categories, it is easier to make sense of what you are learning. Make the following Foldable to help you organize information about cell reproduction.

1. Place a sheet of paper in front of you so the long side is at the top. Fold the paper in half from the left side to the right side and then unfold.
2. Fold in each side to the center line to divide the paper into fourths.
3. Use a pencil to draw a cell on the front of your Foldable as shown.
4. As you read the chapter, use a pen to illustrate how the cell divides into two cells. Under the flaps, list how cells divide. In the middle section, list why cells divide.

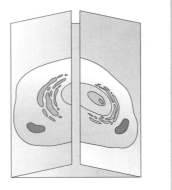

A ◆ 97

EXPLORE ACTIVITY

Purpose Use the Explore Activity to introduce students to growth; as they read the chapter, they will understand that growth is the result of mitosis. L2

Kinesthetic

Preparation Soak pinto beans or other large seeds for 24 hours.

Materials 2 soaked seeds, paper towels, self-sealing plastic bag, hand lens

Teaching Strategy After soaking, the seeds should split easily. If students have difficulty, forceps can be used to separate the seeds.

Observe

Students should observe and record the growth of a new plant from one half of each seed. They should predict that only some of the cells of the seed are able to use the information needed to grow into a plant.

✔ *Assessment*

Performance Have students repeat the experiment using corn seeds and observe the new plant that grows from each seed. Use **Performance Assessment in the Science Classroom,** p. 89.

Before You Read

FOLDABLES
Reading & Study
Skills

Dinah Zike Study Fold

Purpose Students should use this Foldable to diagram cells and organize information on cells and cell division as they read.

📁 For additional help, see Foldables Worksheet p. 15 in **Chapter Resources Booklet,** or go to the Glencoe Science Web site at **science.glencoe.com.** See After You Read in the Study Guide at the end of this chapter.

Cell Division and Mitosis

Cell Division and Mitosis

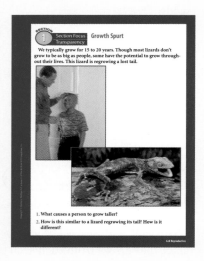
As You Read

What You'll Learn

- **Explain** why mitosis is important.
- **Examine** the steps of mitosis.
- **Compare** mitosis in plant and animal cells.
- **List** two examples of asexual reproduction.

Vocabulary
mitosis
chromosome
asexual reproduction

Why It's Important
Your growth, like that of many organisms, depends on cell division.

Figure 1
All organisms use cell division.

A Many-celled organisms, such as this octopus, grow by increasing the numbers of their cells.

Why is cell division important?

What do you, an octopus, and an oak tree have in common? You share many characteristics, but an important one is that you are all made of cells—trillions of cells. Where did all of those cells come from? As amazing as it might seem, many organisms, start as just one cell. That cell divides and becomes two, two become four, four become eight, and so on. Many-celled organisms, including you, grow because cell division increases the total number of cells in an organism. Even after growth stops, cell division is still important. Every day, billions of red blood cells in your body wear out and are replaced. During the few seconds it takes you to read this sentence, your bone marrow produced about six million red blood cells. Cell division is important to one-celled organisms, too—it's how they reproduce themselves, as shown in **Figure 1B.** Cell division isn't as simple as just cutting the cell in half, so how do cells divide?

The Cell Cycle

A living organism has a life cycle. A life cycle begins with the organism's formation, is followed by growth and development, and finally ends in death. Right now, you are in a stage of your life cycle called adolescence, which is a period of active growth and development. Individual cells also have life cycles.

B A one-celled organism, such as this amoeba, reaches a certain size and then reproduces.

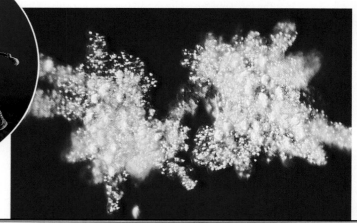

98 ◆ A

Figure 2
Interphase is the longest part of the cell cycle. *When do chromosomes duplicate?*

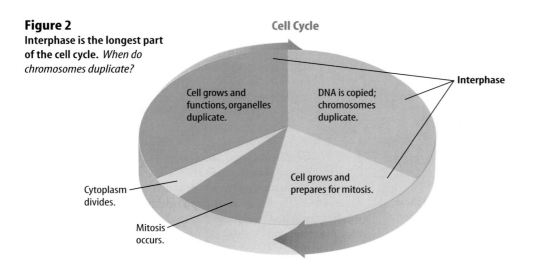

Cell Cycle

Cell grows and functions, organelles duplicate.

DNA is copied; chromosomes duplicate.

Interphase

Cell grows and prepares for mitosis.

Cytoplasm divides.

Mitosis occurs.

Length of Cycle The cell cycle, as shown in **Figure 2,** is a series of events that takes place from one cell division to the next. The time it takes to complete a cell cycle is not the same in all cells. For example, the cycle for cells in some bean plants takes about 19 h to complete. Cells in animal embryos divide rapidly and can complete their cycles is less than 20 min. In some human cells, the cell cycle takes about 16 h. Cells in humans that are needed for repair, growth, or replacement, like skin and bone cells, constantly repeat the cycle.

Interphase Most of the life of any eukaryotic cell—a cell with a nucleus—is spent in a period of growth and development called interphase. Cells in your body that no longer divide, such as nerve and muscle cells, are always in interphase. An actively dividing cell, such as a skin cell, copies its hereditary material and prepares for cell division during interphase.

Why is it important for a cell to copy its hereditary information before dividing? Imagine that you have a part in a play and the director has one complete copy of the script. If the director gave only one page to each person in the play, no one would have the entire script. Instead the director makes a complete, separate copy of the script for each member of the cast so that each one can learn his or her part. Before a cell divides, a copy of the hereditary material must be made so that each of the two new cells will get a complete copy. Just as the actors in the play need the entire script, each cell needs a complete set of hereditary material to carry out life functions.

After interphase, cell division begins. The nucleus divides, and then the cytoplasm separates to form two new cells.

Health
INTEGRATION

In most cells, the cell cycle is well controlled. However, cancerous cells have uncontrolled cell division. Some cancerous cells form a mass of cells called a tumor. Find out why some tumors are harmful to an organism. Write what you find out in your Science Journal.

SCIENCE *Online*

Research Nerve cells in adults usually do not undergo mitosis. Visit the Glencoe Science Web site at **science.glencoe.com** for more information about nerve cell regeneration. Communicate to your class what you learn.

SECTION 1 Cell Division and Mitosis **A** ◆ **99**

②Teach

The Cell Cycle

Caption Answer
Figure 2 during interphase

Figure 2 Have students make an events chain concept map that outlines the steps of the cell cycle as illustrated in **Figure 2**.
[L2] [IS] **Visual-Spatial** [P]

Health
INTEGRATION

Cancerous tumors grow rapidly and sometimes spread to infect healthy tissue.

SCIENCE *Online*
Internet Addresses

_____
_____
_____

Explore the Glencoe Science Web site at **science.glencoe.com** to find out more about topics in this section.

Resource Manager

Chapter Resources Booklet
  Transparency Activity, p. 42
  Directed Reading for Content Mastery, pp. 17, 18

Science Journal

Life of a Cell Have students write creative stories about the life cycle of a cell from its beginning to its end. Have them use section vocabulary as they describe what happens in the cell. [L2] [IS] **Linguistic**

Mitosis

Use an Analogy

Compare chromosome thickening to a coiled telephone cord. When stretched out, the cord is long and thin, like chromosomes during interphase. When the cord returns to its usual position, it shortens and thickens, like chromosomes preparing to divide. [L1]

IS **Visual-Spatial**

✔ Reading Check

Answer A duplicated chromosome is made up of two chromatids.

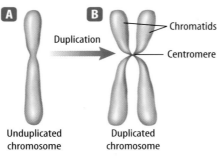

Figure 3
DNA is copied during interphase. **A** An unduplicated chromosome has one strand of DNA. **B** A duplicated chromosome has two identical DNA strands, called chromatids, that are held together at a region called the centromere.

Figure 4
The cell plate shown in this plant cell appears when the cytoplasm is being divided.

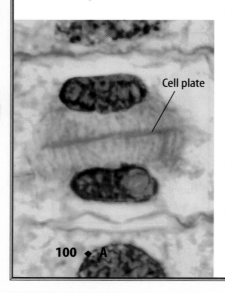

Cell plate

100 ◆ A

Mitosis

Mitosis (mi TOH sus) is the process in which the nucleus divides to form two identical nuclei. Each new nucleus also is identical to the original nucleus. Mitosis is described as a series of phases, or steps. The steps of mitosis in order are named prophase, metaphase, anaphase, and telophase.

Steps of Mitosis When any nucleus divides, the chromosomes (KROH muh sohmz) play the important part. A **chromosome** is a structure in the nucleus that contains hereditary material. During interphase, each chromosome duplicates. When the nucleus is ready to divide, each duplicated chromosome coils tightly into two thickened, identical strands called chromatids, as shown in **Figure 3.**

✔ Reading Check *How are chromosomes and chromatids related?*

During prophase, the pairs of chromatids are fully visible when viewed under a microscope. The nucleolus and the nuclear membrane disintegrate. Two small structures called centrioles (SEN tree olz) move to opposite ends of the cell. Between the centrioles, threadlike spindle fibers begin to stretch across the cell. Plant cells also form spindle fibers during mitosis but do not have centrioles.

In metaphase, the pairs of chromatids line up across the center of the cell. The centromere of each pair usually becomes attached to two spindle fibers—one from each side of the cell.

In anaphase, each centromere divides and the spindle fibers shorten. Each pair of chromatids separates, and chromatids begin to move to opposite ends of the cell. The separated chromatids are now called chromosomes. In the final step, telophase, spindle fibers start to disappear the chromosomes start to uncoil, and a new nucleus forms.

Division of the Cytoplasm For most cells, after the nucleus has divided, the cytoplasm separates and two new cells are formed. In animal cells, the cell membrane pinches in the middle, like a balloon with a string tightened around it, and the cytoplasm divides. In plant cells, the appearance of a cell plate, as shown in **Figure 4,** tells you that the cytoplasm is being divided. New cell walls form along the cell plate, and new cell membranes develop inside the cell walls. Following division of the cytoplasm, most new cells begin the period of growth, or interphase, again. Review cell division for an animal cell using the illustrations in **Figure 5.**

Inclusion Strategies

Visually Impaired Have selected students make three-dimensional models of mitosis on poster board. Display the posters in the classroom for visually impaired students to feel. [L2]

IS **Visual-Spatial**

Cultural Diversity

Historic Contributions In 1887, Edouard-Joseph-Marie van Beneden, a Belgian scientist, discovered that each species has a fixed number of chromosomes. He also observed the formation of a haploid cell. In 1956, J. Hin Tijo and Albert Levan showed that each human cell has 46 chromosomes.

Figure 5

Cell division for an animal cell is shown here. Each micrograph shown in this figure is magnified 600 times.

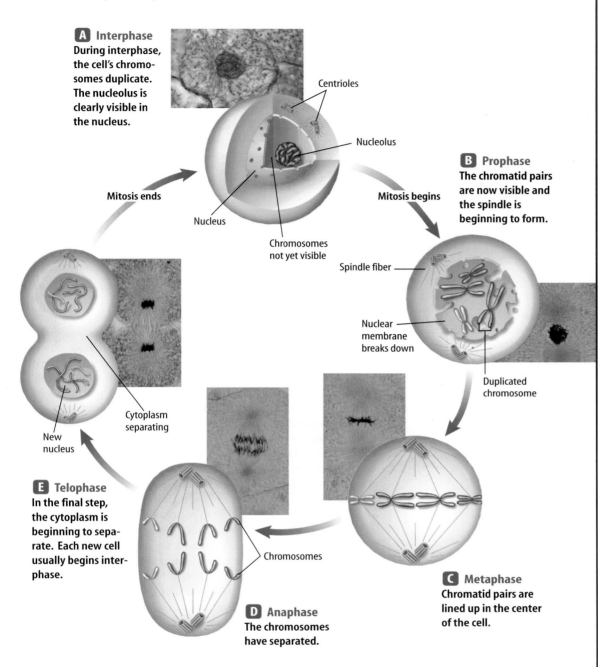

A Interphase
During interphase, the cell's chromosomes duplicate. The nucleolus is clearly visible in the nucleus.

Centrioles

Nucleolus

Mitosis ends

Nucleus

Chromosomes not yet visible

Mitosis begins

B Prophase
The chromatid pairs are now visible and the spindle is beginning to form.

Spindle fiber

Nuclear membrane breaks down

Duplicated chromosome

New nucleus

Cytoplasm separating

E Telophase
In the final step, the cytoplasm is beginning to separate. Each new cell usually begins interphase.

Chromosomes

D Anaphase
The chromosomes have separated.

C Metaphase
Chromatid pairs are lined up in the center of the cell.

SECTION 1 Cell Division and Mitosis **A ◆ 101**

Mitosis, continued

Discussion

Have students use their knowledge of the cell cycle to infer why even slight injuries to the brain and spinal cord can be serious and permanent. Because nerve cells do not undergo mitosis, damaged cells are not replaced, although some repair does occur.

Discussion

Many nonliving things such as icicles, stalagmites, crystals, and sand dunes appear to grow. Ask students to give examples of other nonliving things that appear to grow. Possible answers: highway systems, buildings, developments, shopping malls Have students distinguish between the processes involved in the growth of living things and the growth of nonliving things. In nonliving things, growth is caused by the surrounding environment. In living things, growth is caused by processes within the organism.

Caption Answer

Figure 6 the sex of the organism

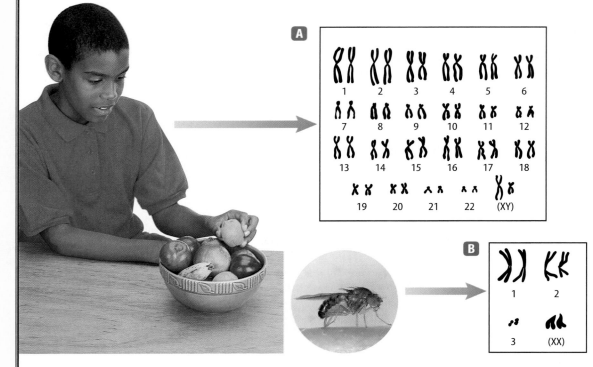

Figure 6
Pairs of chromosomes are found in the nucleus of most cells.
A Most human cells have 23 pairs of chromosomes including one pair of chromosomes that help determine sex such as the XY in pair 23 above. **B** Most fruit fly cells have four pairs of chromosomes. *What do you think the XX pair in fruit flies helps determine?*

Results of Mitosis You should remember two important things about mitosis. First, it is the division of a nucleus. Second, it produces two new nuclei that are identical to each other and the original nucleus. Each new nucleus has the same number and type of chromosomes. Every cell in your body, except sex cells, has a nucleus with 46 chromosomes—23 pairs. This is because you began as one cell with 46 chromosomes in its nucleus. Skin cells, produced to replace or repair your skin have the same 46 chromosomes as the original single cell you developed from. Each cell in a fruit fly has eight chromosomes, so each new cell produced by mitosis has a copy of those eight chromosomes. **Figure 6** shows the chromosomes found in most human cells and those found in most fruit fly cells.

Each of the trillions of cells in your body, except sex cells, has a copy of the same hereditary material. Even though all actors in a play have copies of the same script, they do not learn the same lines. Likewise, all of your cells use different parts of the same hereditary material to become different types of cells.

Cell division allows growth and replaces worn out or damaged cells. You are much larger and have more cells than a baby mainly because of cell division. If you cut yourself, the wound heals because cell division replaces damaged cells. Another way some organisms use cell division is to produce new organisms.

102 ◆ A CHAPTER 4 Cell Reproduction

LAB DEMONSTRATION

Purpose to observe asexual reproduction in a sweet potato
Materials sweet potato with leaf buds, water, widemouthed glass jar, 4 toothpicks
Preparation Obtain a sweet potato that has purple leaf buds growing at its scarred end.

Procedure Fill a jar almost full of water, and place sweet potato with buds or scarred end up so at least half of the potato is in water. Toothpicks can hold the potato in place. Keep water level constant and observe for three weeks.

Expected Outcome Students should observe the formation of roots and leaf growth.

✓Assessment

What part of the sweet potato produced leaves and roots? Leaves developed from the buds; roots grew from the bottom half of the sweet potato. **Is this an example of sexual or asexual reproduction? Explain.** Asexual; a new organism is produced from one parent.

Asexual Reproduction

Reproduction is the process by which an organism produces others of its same kind. Among living organisms, there are two types of reproduction—sexual and asexual. Sexual reproduction usually requires two organisms. In **asexual reproduction,** a new organism (sometimes more than one) is produced from one organism. The new organism will have hereditary material identical to the hereditary material of the parent organism.

✔ Reading Check *How many organisms are needed for asexual reproduction?*

Cellular Asexual Reproduction Organisms with eukaryotic cells asexually reproduce by cell division. A sweet potato growing in a jar of water is an example of asexual reproduction. All the stems, leaves, and roots that grow from the sweet potato have been produced by cell division and have the same hereditary material. New strawberry plants can be reproduced asexually from horizontal stems called runners. **Figure 7** shows asexual reproduction in a potato and a strawberry plant.

Recall that mitosis is the division of a nucleus. However, bacteria do not have a nucleus so they can't use mitosis. Instead, bacteria reproduce asexually by fission. During fission, an organism whose cells do not contain a nucleus copies its genetic material and then divides into two identical organisms.

Figure 7
Many plants can reproduce asexually.

 **A** A new potato plant can grow from each sprout on this potato.

B *How does the genetic material in the small strawberry plant compare to the genetic material in the large strawberry plant?*

Modeling Mitosis
Procedure
1. Make models of cell division using **materials supplied by your teacher.**
2. Use four chromosomes in your model.
3. When finished, arrange the models in the order in which mitosis occurs.

Analysis
1. In which steps is the nucleus visible?
2. How many cells does a dividing cell form?

Asexual Reproduction

✔ Reading Check

Answer one

Mini LAB

Purpose to construct a model of mitosis [L2] [ELL]
[IS] **Kinesthetic and Visual-Spatial**
Materials colored paper, poster board, markers, toothpicks, yarn, thread, glue, scissors
Teaching Strategy Student models should resemble mitosis as shown in **Figure 4.**
Analysis
1. prophase and telophase
2. two new cells

✔ Assessment

Performance Assess students' understanding of mitosis by making flash cards of the stages and having students arrange them in the proper order. Use **PASC,** p. 163.

Caption Answer
Figure 7 They are identical.

Resource Manager

Chapter Resources Booklet
MiniLAB, p. 3
Transparency Activity, pp. 45–46
Lab Activity, pp. 9–10

Science Journal

Cloning Have students use science reference books, newspapers, and the Internet to research cloning, a process that artificially reproduces an exact duplicate of a single parent. Have students write reports in their Science Journals on the medical uses as well as the negative ethical implications of cloning technology.
[L2] [IS] **Linguistic**

Asexual Reproduction, continued

Activity

Add one package of yeast and one teaspoon of sugar to a .5 L container of warm water. Let the container stand in a warm place for a few hours. Allow students to examine microscope slides of the mixture to observe budding in yeast cells. L2
 Visual-Spatial

Text Question Answers

No. Sea star numbers would increase because of regeneration.

③ Assess

Reteach

Have students draw the nucleus or chromosomes on cell cycle outlines and describe what is occurring at each stage. L1
ELL  Visual-Spatial

Challenge

At one time, interphase was called the resting stage. Why is this not a good description of interphase? A cell in interphase is carrying out all of the life processes.

✔ Assessment

Oral How is mitosis different from cell division? Mitosis is the division of the nucleus. Cell division includes mitosis and the division of the cytoplasm and its contents. Use **Performance Assessment in the Science Classroom**, p. 143.

Figure 8
Some organisms use mitosis for budding and regeneration.

B Some sea stars reproduce asexually by shedding arms. Each arm can grow into a new sea star.

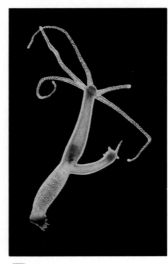

A Hydra, a freshwater animal, can reproduce asexually by budding. The bud is a small exact copy of the adult.

Budding and Regeneration Look at **Figure 8A.** A new organism is growing from the body of the parent organism. This organism, called a hydra, is reproducing by budding. Budding is a type of asexual reproduction made possible because of cell division. When the bud on the adult becomes large enough, it breaks away to live on its own.

Could you grow a new finger? Some organisms can regrow damaged or lost body parts, as shown in **Figure 8B.** Regeneration is the process that uses cell division to regrow body parts. Sponges, planaria, sea stars, and some other organisms can use regeneration for asexual reproduction. If these organisms break into pieces, a whole new organism will grow from each piece. Because sea stars eat oysters, oyster farmers dislike them. What would happen if an oyster farmer collected sea stars, cut them into pieces, and threw them back into the ocean?

Section ① Assessment

1. What is mitosis and how does it differ in plants and animals?
2. Give two examples of asexual reproduction in many-celled organisms.
3. What happens to chromosomes before mitosis begins?
4. After a cell undergoes mitosis, how are the two new cells alike?
5. **Think Critically** Why is it important for the nuclear membrane to disintegrate during mitosis?

Skill Builder Activities

6. **Testing a Hypothesis** A piece of leaf, stem, or root can grow into a new plant. Hypothesize how you would use one of these plant parts to grow a new plant. Test your idea. **For more help, refer to the** Science Skill Handbook.

7. **Solving One-Step Equations** If a cell undergoes cell division every 5 min, how many cells will there be after 1 h? Calculate and record the answer in your Science Journal. **For more help, refer to the** Math Skill Handbook.

104 ◆ A   CHAPTER 4 Cell Reproduction

Answers to Section Assessment

1. Mitosis is a process in which a cell nucleus divides into two nuclei, each of which has the same genetic information; in animal cells, the cytoplasm divides as the cell membrane pinches in the middle of the cell. In plant cells, the appearance of the cell plate indicates that the cytoplasm is being divided.

2. Possible answers: budding and fission
3. The chromosomes duplicate.
4. They both have the same genetic information.
5. Otherwise, the chromosomes would not be able to move to opposite ends of the cell.

6. Hypotheses will vary. Students may separate plant parts and place them in water or soil.
7. 60 minutes divided by 5 minutes = 12 cell divisions; $2^{12} = 4{,}096$ cells

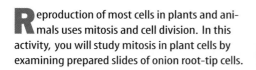

Mitosis in Plant Cells

Reproduction of most cells in plants and animals uses mitosis and cell division. In this activity, you will study mitosis in plant cells by examining prepared slides of onion root-tip cells.

What You'll Investigate
How can plant cells in different stages of mitosis be distinguished from each other?

Materials
prepared slide of an onion root tip
microscope

Goals
- **Compare** cells in different stages of mitosis and observe the location of their chromosomes.
- **Observe** what stage of mitosis is most common in onion root tips.

Safety Precautions 🔬 🧤

Procedure
1. Copy the data table in your Science Journal.
2. **Obtain** a prepared slide of cells from an onion root tip.
3. Set your microscope on low power and examine the onion root tip. Move the slide until you can see the tip of the root. You will see several large round cells. These cells are called the root cap. Move your slide until you see the cells in the area just behind the root cap. Turn the nosepiece to high power.
4. Find one area of cells where you can see the most stages of mitosis. Count how many cells you see in each stage and record your data in the table.
5. Turn the microscope back to low power. Remove the onion root-tip slide.

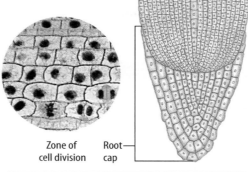

Zone of cell division   Root cap

Conclude and Apply
1. **Compare** the cells in the region behind the root cap to those in the root cap.
2. **Calculate** the percent of cells found in each stage of mitosis. Infer which stage of mitosis takes the longest period of time.

Number of Root-Tip Cells Observed

Stage of Mitosis	Number of Cells Observed	Percent of Cells Observed
Prophase	78	65
Metaphase	23	19
Anaphase	12	10
Telophase	7	6
Total	120	100

*C*ommunicating
Your Data

Write a story as if you were a cell in an onion root tip. Describe what changes occur as you go through mitosis. Use some of your drawings to illustrate the story. Share your story with your class. **For more help, refer to the** Science Skill Handbook.

ACTIVITY A ◆ 105

Purpose Students observe the stages of mitosis. L2 ELL IS **Visual-Spatial**

Process Skills observing, inferring, comparing and contrasting

Time Required 40 minutes

Teaching Strategy Review the stages of mitosis before beginning the activity.

Troubleshooting Students may have difficulty locating all the phases. You may want to place an onion root tip slide on the microprojector and point out the phases.

Answers to Questions
1. The cells behind the root cap are smaller than those in the root cap. Mitosis occurs at a faster rate in cells behind the root cap.
2. See student page; prophase takes the longest.

Assessment

Performance To further assess students' understanding of mitosis, give each one a sheet of paper listing a stage and have them describe what comes before and after that stage. Use **Performance Assessment in the Science Classroom,** p. 163.

Resource Manager

Chapter Resources Booklet
Reinforcement, p. 25
Activity Worksheet, pp. 5–6

*C*ommunicating
Your Data
The story and drawings should include the stages in mitosis.

Bellringer Transparency

Display the Section Focus Transparency for Section 2. Use the accompanying Transparency Activity Master. L2 ELL

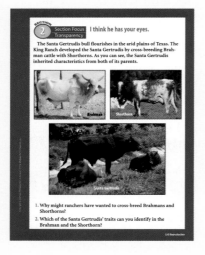

Tie to Prior Knowledge

As a review, ask students to describe the stages in mitosis. Then tell the students that for certain cells, the nucleus divides twice. They will learn why in this section.

SECTION

2

Sexual Reproduction and Meiosis

As You Read

What You'll Learn

- **Describe** the stages of meiosis and how sex cells are produced.
- **Explain** why meiosis is needed for sexual reproduction.
- **Name** the cells that are involved in fertilization.
- **Explain** how fertilization occurs in sexual reproduction.

Vocabulary

sexual reproduction	zygote
sperm	diploid
egg	haploid
fertilization	meiosis

Why It's Important

Because of meiosis and sexual reproduction, no one is exactly like you.

Figure 9
A human sperm or egg cell contains only 23 chromosomes.

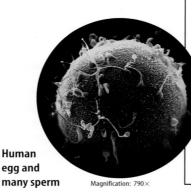

Human egg and many sperm

Magnification: 790×

Sexual Reproduction

Sexual reproduction is another way that a new organism can be produced. During **sexual reproduction,** two sex cells, sometimes called an egg and a sperm, come together. Sex cells, like those in **Figure 9,** are formed from cells in reproductive organs. **Sperm** are formed in the male reproductive organs. **Eggs** are formed in the female reproductive organs. The joining of an egg and a sperm is called **fertilization,** and the cell that forms is called a **zygote** (ZI goht). Generally, the egg and the sperm come from two different organisms of the same species. Following fertilization, mitosis begins. A new organism with a unique identity develops.

Diploid Cells Your body forms two types of cells—body cells and sex cells. Body cells far outnumber sex cells. Your brain, skin, bones, and other tissues and organs are formed from body cells. A typical human body cell has 46 chromosomes. Each chromosome has a mate that is similar to it in size and shape and has similar DNA. Human body cells have 23 pairs of chromosomes. When cells have pairs of similar chromosomes, they are said to be **diploid** (DIH ployd).

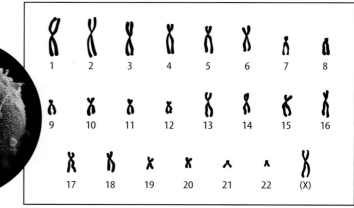

106 ◆ A CHAPTER 4 Cell Reproduction

Section ✔Assessment Planner

PORTFOLIO
Make a Model, p. 109
PERFORMANCE ASSESSMENT
Skill Builder Activities, p. 111
See page 124 for more options.

CONTENT ASSESSMENT
Section, p. 111
Challenge, p. 111
Chapter, pp. 124–125

Haploid Cells Because sex cells do not have pairs of chromosomes, they are said to be **haploid** (HA ployd). They have only half the number of chromosomes as body cells. *Haploid* means "single form." Human sex cells have only 23 chromosomes—one from each of the 23 pairs of similar chromosomes. Compare the chromosomes found in a sex cell, as shown in **Figure 9,** to the full set of human chromosomes seen in **Figure 6A.**

 **Reading Check** *How many chromosomes are usually in each human sperm?*

Meiosis and Sex Cells

A process called **meiosis** (mi OH sus) produces haploid sex cells. What would happen in sexual reproduction if two diploid cells combined? The offspring would have twice as many chromosomes as its parent. Although plants with twice the number of chromosomes are often produced, most animals would not survive with a double number of chromosomes. Meiosis ensures that the offspring will have the same diploid number as its parent, as shown in **Figure 10.** After two haploid sex cells combine, a diploid zygote is produced that develops into a new diploid organism.

During meiosis, two divisions of the nucleus occur. These divisions are called meiosis I and meiosis II. The steps of each division have names like those in mitosis and are numbered for the division in which they occur.

Chemistry INTEGRATION

The human egg releases a chemical into the surrounding fluid that attracts sperm. Usually, only one sperm fertilizes the egg. After the sperm nucleus enters the egg, the cell membrane of the egg changes in a way that prevents other sperm from entering. What adaptation in this process guarantees that the zygote will be diploid? Write a paragraph describing your ideas in your Science Journal.

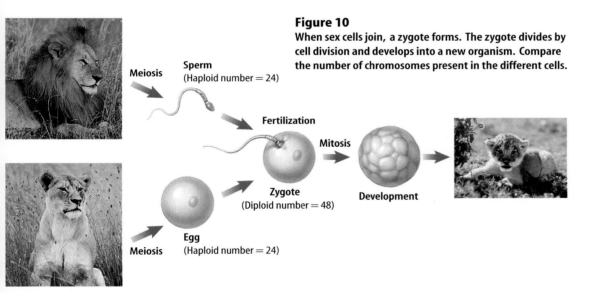

Figure 10
When sex cells join, a zygote forms. The zygote divides by cell division and develops into a new organism. Compare the number of chromosomes present in the different cells.

Meiosis

Sperm
(Haploid number = 24)

Fertilization

Mitosis

Zygote
(Diploid number = 48)

Development

Egg
(Haploid number = 24)

Meiosis

---

2 Teach

Sexual Reproduction

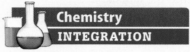 **Reading Check**

Answer 23 chromosomes

Meiosis and Sex Cells

Chemistry INTEGRATION

The changes in the egg prevent fertilization by more than one sperm.

Use Science Words
Word Origin The term *meiosis* comes from a Greek word for "diminution" or becoming less. Ask students what diminishes or becomes less in meiosis. The chromosome number in each cell is diminished.

Fun Fact

With 23 pairs of chromosomes in the human body, there are more than 8 million different combinations of chromosomes possible for every human cell formed by meiosis.

Caption Answer
Figure 10 Fertilized cells have twice the number of chromosomes found in sex cells.

Curriculum Connection

Math Have students use library references to find the number of chromosomes in the body cells of various plants and animals. Then have them determine the number of chromosomes in the sex cells of each one. The number of chromosomes in sex cells should be half the number of chromosomes in body cells. L3 **Logical-Mathematical**

Teacher FYI

In-vitro fertilization is a procedure that joins sperm and eggs outside the body. Fertilized eggs (actually two-day-old embryos) are then implanted into the female.

Extension

Have students research and report on the contribution of African American cell biologist Everett Anderson to the modern understanding of meiosis. Anderson is one of the leading researchers in developing electron microscopic techniques to study meiosis. [L2]

INS Linguistic

✔ Reading Check

Answer The duplicated chromosomes of each similar pair are pulled to opposite ends of the cell.

Use Science Words

Word Meaning Have students use a dictionary to find out what *triploid* and *tetraploid* mean. Have them write an explanation of how this condition occurs. *triploid*—each cell in the organism contains three sets of chromosomes; plant endosperm is triploid and normal. *tetraploid* organisms have four sets of chromosomes in each cell; these conditions arise from total nondisjunction during mitosis or meiosis [L2] **INS Linguistic**

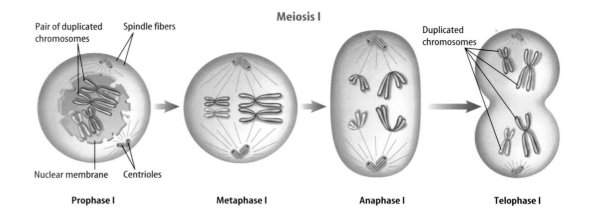

Meiosis I

Pair of duplicated chromosomes   Spindle fibers

Duplicated chromosomes

Nuclear membrane   Centrioles

Prophase I   Metaphase I   Anaphase I   Telophase I

Figure 11
Meiosis has two divisions of the nucleus—meiosis I and meiosis II. *How many sex cells are finally formed after both divisions are completed?*

Meiosis I Before meiosis begins, each chromosome is duplicated, just as in mitosis. When the cell is ready for meiosis, each duplicated chromosome is visible under the microscope as two chromatids. As shown in **Figure 11,** the events of prophase I are similar to those of prophase in mitosis. In meiosis, each duplicated chromosome comes near its similar duplicated mate. In mitosis they do not come near each other.

In metaphase I, the pairs of duplicated chromosomes line up in the center of the cell. The centromere of each chromatid pair becomes attached to one spindle fiber so, the chromatids do not separate in anaphase I. The two pairs of chromatids of each similar pair move away from each other to opposite ends of the cell. Each duplicated chromosome still has two chromatids. Then, in telophase I, the cytoplasm divides, and two new cells form. Each new cell has one duplicated chromosome from each similar pair.

✔ Reading Check   *What happens to duplicated chromosomes during anaphase I?*

Meiosis II The two cells formed during meiosis I now begin meiosis II. The chromatids of each duplicated chromosome will be separated during this division. In prophase II, the duplicated chromosomes and spindle fibers reappear in each new cell. Then in metaphase II, the duplicated chromosomes move to the center of the cell. Unlike what occurs in metaphase I, each centromere now attaches to two spindle fibers instead of one. The centromere divides during anaphase II, and the chromatids separate and move to opposite ends of the cell. Each chromatid now is an individual chromosome. As telophase II begins, the spindle fibers disappear, and a nuclear membrane forms around the chromosomes at each end of the cell. When meiosis II is finished, the cytoplasm divides.

Resource Manager

Chapter Resources Booklet
   Enrichment, p. 29
Mathematics Skill Activities, p. 3

Inclusion Strategies

Learning Disabled Students who are dyslexic may have trouble distinguishing between the first and second parts of meiosis. Instead of Roman numbers, as in prophase I and prophase II, use Arabic numbers for easier identification (prophase 1 and prophase 2).

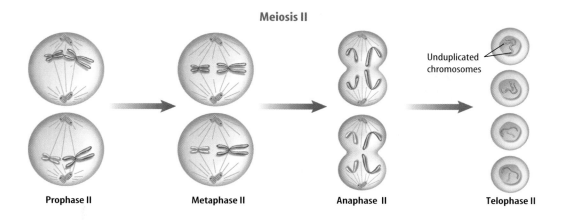

Meiosis II

Prophase II Metaphase II Anaphase II Telophase II

Unduplicated chromosomes

Summary of Meiosis Two cells form during meiosis I. In meiosis II, both of these cells form two cells. The two divisions of the nucleus result in four sex cells, each has one-half the number of chromosomes in its nucleus that was in the original nucleus. From a human cell with 46 paired chromosomes, meiosis produces four sex cells each with 23 unpaired chromosomes.

Problem-Solving Activity

How can chromosome numbers be predicted?

Offspring get half of their chromosomes from one parent and half from the other. What happens if each parent has a different diploid number of chromosomes?

Identifying the Problem

A zebra and a donkey can mate to produce a zonkey. Zebras have a diploid number of 46. Donkeys have a diploid number of 60.

Solving the Problem

1. How many chromosomes would the zonkey receive from each parent?
2. What is the chromosome number of the zonkey?
3. What would happen when meiosis occurs in the zonkey's reproductive organs?
4. Predict why zonkeys are usually sterile.

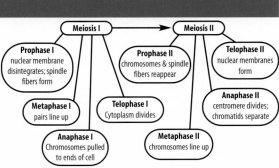

Donkey
60 Chromosomes

Zonkey

Zebra
46 Chromosomes

SECTION 2 Sexual Reproduction and Meiosis **A ◆ 109**

Make a Model

Have students make a model of the stages of meiosis in an organism with three pairs of chromosomes. Have them use shapes to distinguish the chromosomes. L1 IS **Kinesthetic**

Activity

Using one of their favorite songs, have students write substitute lyrics about what happens in meiosis. L2 IS **Auditory-Musical**

Problem-Solving Activity

National Math Standards
Correlation to Mathematics Objectives
1, 6, 8, 9

Answers
1. 23 from the zebra and 30 from the donkey
2. 53
3. Normal sex cells would not form because there are unpaired chromosomes.
4. Each sex cell could not have one-half the chromosomes of the original cell.

Extension

In areas throughout the world, people have similar genetically controlled traits including skin color, height, and face shape. Have students determine why. Cultures of people were unable to travel great distances for thousands of years and therefore reproduced mainly among themselves, so genetic instructions for such traits remained within given cultures. L3 IS **Logical-Mathematical**

✔ Active Reading

Flow Chart A flow chart helps students logically sequence events. Students will write major stages of the sequence in large ovals and write substages in smaller ovals under the larger ovals. Have students design a flow chart for a concept in this section. Sample flow chart:

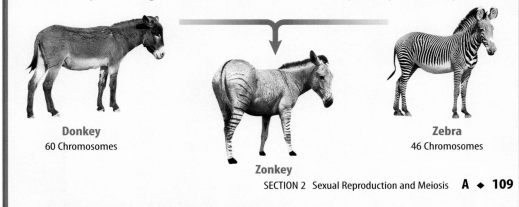

Meiosis I → Meiosis II

Prophase I nuclear membrane disintegrates; spindle fibers form

Metaphase I pairs line up

Anaphase I Chromosomes pulled to ends of cell

Telophase I Cytoplasm divides

Prophase II chromosomes & spindle fibers reappear

Metaphase II chromosomes line up

Anaphase II centromere divides; chromatids separate

Telophase II nuclear membranes form

Visualizing Polyploidy in Plants

Have students examine the pictures and read the captions. Then ask the following questions.

What kinds of mistakes in meiosis or mitosis could result in a polyploid plant? A mistake that caused chromosome sets not to separate, allowing more than one full set to be present in a cell after division to form sex cells.

What is the main advantage of bananas being triploid? Triploid plants have very small seeds, so people can eat bananas without removing seeds.

Why wouldn't you find triploid peanuts in the grocery store? The part of a peanut plant you eat is a seed, but triploid plants have little or no seeds.

Activity

Have students use pipe cleaners to model the chromosomes of one of the plants featured here. For example, a banana with 3 sets of 11 chromosomes, a strawberry with 8 sets of 7 chromosomes or a peanut with 4 sets of 10 chromosomes.

Extension

Have students research the meaning of the terms *allopolyploidy* and *autopolyploidy*. Have the students find and list some examples of plants that each term applies to.

Figure 12

Y ou received a haploid (n) set of chromosomes from each of your parents, making you a diploid (2n) organism. In nature, however, many plants are polyploid—they have three (3n), four (4n), or more sets of chromosomes. We depend on some of these plants for food.

▲ **TRIPLOID** Bright yellow bananas typically come from triploid (3n) banana plants. Plants with an odd number of chromosome sets usually cannot reproduce sexually and have very small seeds or none at all.

▲ **TETRAPLOID** Polyploidy occurs naturally in many plants—including peanuts and daylilies—due to mistakes in mitosis or meiosis.

▼ **HEXAPLOID** Modern cultivated strains of oats have six sets of chromosomes, making them hexaploid (6n) plants.

▲ **OCTAPLOID** Polyploid plants often are bigger than nonpolyploid plants and may have especially large leaves, flowers, or fruits. Strawberries are an example of octaploid (8n) plants.

110 ◆ A

Resource Manager

Chapter Resources Booklet
  Reinforcement, p. 26

Performance Assessment in the Science Classroom, p. 57

Visual Learning

Figure 13 Have students follow the unseparated chromosome pair through each stage of meiosis. **How did this error affect the sex cells?** Some had too many chromosomes; others not enough.

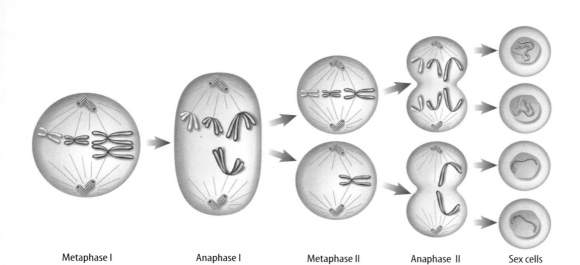

Metaphase I   Anaphase I   Metaphase II   Anaphase II   Sex cells

Mistakes in Meiosis Meiosis occurs many times in reproductive organs. Although mistakes in plants, as shown in **Figure 12,** are common, mistakes are less common in animals. These mistakes can produce sex cells with too many or too few chromosomes, as shown in **Figure 13.** Sometimes, zygotes produced from these sex cells die. If the zygote lives, every cell in the organism that grows from that zygote usually will have the wrong number of chromosomes. Organisms with the wrong number of chromosomes may not grow normally.

Figure 13
This diploid cell has four chromosomes. During anaphase I, one pair of duplicated chromosomes did not separate. *How many chromosomes does each sex cell usually have?*

Section 2 Assessment

1. Compare and contrast sexual and asexual reproduction.
2. What is a zygote, and how is it formed?
3. Give two examples of sex cells. Where are sex cells formed?
4. Compare what happens to chromosomes during anaphase I and anaphase II.
5. **Think Critically** Plants grown from runners and leaf cuttings have the same traits as the parent plant. Plants grown from seeds can vary from the parent plants in many ways. Suggest an explanation for why this can happen.

Skill Builder Activities

6. **Making and Using Tables** Make a table to compare mitosis and meiosis in humans. Vertical headings should include: *What Type of Cell (Body or Sex), Beginning Cell (Haploid or Diploid), Number of Cells Produced, End-Product Cell (Haploid or Diploid),* and *Number of Chromosomes in Cells Produced.* **For more help, refer to the** Science Skill Handbook.

7. **Communicating** Write a poem, song, or another memory device to help you remember the steps and outcome of meiosis. **For more help, refer to the** Science Skill Handbook.

Answers to Section Assessment

1. Sexual reproduction: offspring is produced when sex cells combine; asexual reproduction: genetically identical offspring produced from one parent.
2. A zygote is the cell that forms when sperm fertilizes an egg.
3. sperm cells—form in male reproductive organs; egg cells—

form in female reproductive organs
4. Anaphase I—duplicated chromosome pairs separate and move to opposite ends of the cell; anaphase II—chromatids separate and move to opposite ends of the cell.
5. Plants produced by asexual reproduction are the result of mitosis, which

duplicates the genetic material of the parent. Plants grown from seeds have a combination of traits from their parents, because seeds are produced by sexual reproduction.
6. See table.
7. Allow students to share their memory devices with the class.

Feature	Mitosis	Meiosis
Type of cell	Body cell	Sex cell
Beginning cell	Diploid	Diploid
Number of cells produced	Two	Four
End-product	Diploid	Haploid
Number of chromosomes	Same as original cell	Half the original cell

SECTION

DNA

1 Motivate

Bellringer Transparency

Display the Section Focus Transparency for Section 3. Use the accompanying Transparency Activity Master. L2 ELL

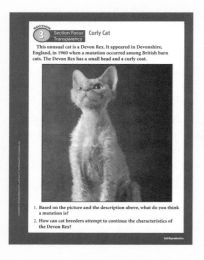

Tie to Prior Knowledge

Students should be familiar with template systems, such as keys and locks and peg-and-hole games. Ask for other examples. Use this knowledge to explain that DNA in the nucleus serves as a template for RNA.

As You Read

What You'll Learn
- **Identify** the parts of a DNA molecule and its structure.
- **Explain** how DNA copies itself.
- **Describe** the structure and function of each kind of RNA.

Vocabulary

DNA	RNA
gene	mutation

Why It's Important
DNA helps determine nearly everything your body is and does.

Figure 14
DNA is part of the chromosomes found in a cell's nucleus.

What is DNA?

Why was the alphabet one of the first things you learned when you started school? Letters are a code that you need to know before you learn to read. A cell also uses a code that is stored in its hereditary material. The code is a chemical called deoxyribonucleic (dee AHK sih ri boh noo klay ihk) acid, or **DNA.** It contains information for an organism's growth and function. **Figure 14** shows how DNA is stored in cells that have a nucleus. When a cell divides, the DNA code is copied and passed to the new cells. In this way, new cells receive the same coded information that was in the original cell. Every cell that has ever been formed in your body or in any other organism contains DNA.

Discovering DNA Since the mid-1800s, scientists have known that the nuclei of cells contain large molecules called nucleic acids. By 1950, chemists had learned what the nucleic acid DNA was made of, but they didn't understand how the parts of DNA were arranged.

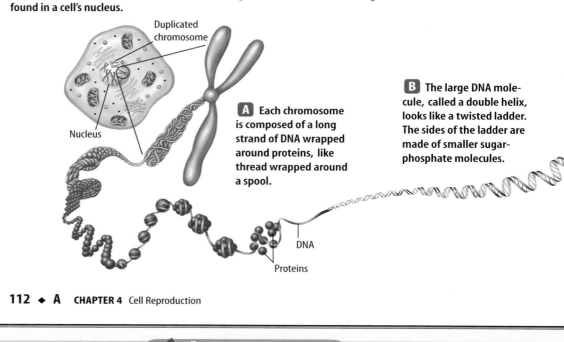

Duplicated chromosome

Nucleus

A Each chromosome is composed of a long strand of DNA wrapped around proteins, like thread wrapped around a spool.

B The large DNA molecule, called a double helix, looks like a twisted ladder. The sides of the ladder are made of smaller sugar-phosphate molecules.

DNA

Proteins

112 ◆ A CHAPTER 4 Cell Reproduction

Section ✓ Assessment Planner

PORTFOLIO
Extension, p. 115
PERFORMANCE ASSESSMENT
Try at Home MiniLAB, p. 113
Skill Builder Activities, p. 117
See page 124 for more options.

CONTENT ASSESSMENT
Section, p. 117
Challenge, p. 117
Chapter, pp. 124–125

C The rungs of the ladder are paired nitrogen bases. Notice that the pairs fit together much like puzzle pieces.

Guanine — Cytosine — Adenine — Thymine — Phosphate — Sugar (deoxyribose)

DNA's Structure In 1952, scientist Rosalind Franklin discovered that DNA is two chains of molecules in a spiral form. By using an X-ray technique, Dr. Franklin showed that the large spiral was probably made up of two spirals. As it turned out, the structure of DNA is similar to a twisted ladder. In 1953, using the work of Franklin and others, scientists James Watson and Francis Crick made a model of a DNA molecule.

A DNA Model What does DNA look like? According to the Watson and Crick DNA model, each side of the ladder is made up of sugar-phosphate molecules. Each molecule consists of the sugar called deoxyribose (dee AHK sih ri bohs) and a phosphate group. The rungs of the ladder are made up of other molecules called nitrogen bases. Four kinds of nitrogen bases are found in DNA—adenine (AD un een), guanine (GWAHN een), cytosine (SITE uh seen), and thymine (THI meen). The bases are represented by the letters A, G, C, and T. The amount of cytosine in cells always equals the amount of guanine, and the amount of adenine always equals the amount of thymine. This led to the hypothesis that these bases occur as pairs in DNA. **Figure 14** shows that adenine always pairs with thymine, and guanine always pairs with cytosine. Like interlocking pieces of a puzzle, each base bonds only with its correct partner.

✔ **Reading Check** *What are the nitrogen base pairs in a DNA molecule?*

TRY AT HOME Mini LAB

Modeling DNA Replication

Procedure
1. Suppose you have a segment of DNA that is six nitrogen base pairs in length. On **paper,** using the letters A, T, C, and G, write a combination of six pairs remembering that A and T are always a pair and C and G are always a pair.
2. Duplicate your segment of DNA. On paper, diagram how this happens and show the new DNA segments.

Analysis
Compare the order of bases of the original DNA to the new DNA molecules.

What is DNA?

TRY AT HOME Mini LAB

Purpose to model DNA replication L2 IS **Visual-Spatial**
Materials pencil and paper
Teaching Strategy Make sure students understand that they are to make up a sample strand of DNA, then make the complementary strand, then split the two strands and make those complementary strands, so they can see that the new strands are identical to the original.

Analysis
Answers will vary with the bases chosen, but bases should be in the same order as the original DNA.

✔ Assessment

Performance Draw and label one strand of DNA. Have students draw the complementary strand. Use **PASC,** p. 127.

✔ Reading Check

Answer Adenine pairs with thymine, and guanine with cytosine.

Resource Manager

Chapter Resources Booklet
   Transparency Activity, p. 44
   MiniLAB, p. 4
Home and Community Involvement, p. 36

Inclusion Strategies

Learning Disabled Use unifix cubes to demonstrate the various bases. Have students make their own models of base pairs, using a different color for each base. L2 ELL IS **Kinesthetic**

What is DNA?
continued

Use an Analogy

Students are probably familiar with Morse code. Morse code uses only two symbols—the dot and the dash—in combinations to represent numbers and letters of the alphabet. DNA has four symbols. The order of nitrogen bases, rather than the sequence of dots and dashes, expresses the information needed for life processes.

Discussion

How can you predict the base sequence of a second strand of DNA? by knowing the base pairing rules and the sequence of the original DNA strand

Genes

Text Question Answer

It could cause serious health problems.

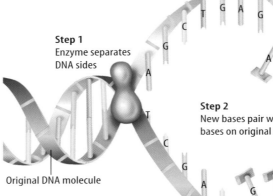

Step 1
Enzyme separates DNA sides

Step 2
New bases pair with bases on original DNA.

Step 3
Two new identical DNA molecules are produced.

Original DNA molecule

Figure 15
DNA unzips when it is about to be copied. A protein called an enzyme helps unzip the DNA.

Figure 16
This diagram shows just a few of the genes that have been identified on human chromosome 7. The bold print is the name that has been given to each gene.

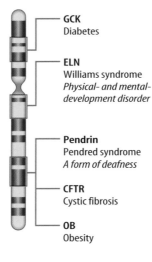

Chromosome 7

GCK
Diabetes

ELN
Williams syndrome
Physical- and mental-development disorder

Pendrin
Pendred syndrome
A form of deafness

CFTR
Cystic fibrosis

OB
Obesity

114 ◆ A   CHAPTER 4 Cell Reproduction

Copying DNA When chromosomes are duplicated before mitosis or meiosis, the amount of DNA in the nucleus is doubled. The Watson and Crick model shows how this takes place. The two sides of DNA unwind and separate. Each side then becomes a pattern on which a new side forms, as shown in **Figure 15.** The new DNA has bases that are identical to those of the original DNA and are in the same order.

Genes

Most of your characteristics, such as the color of your hair, your height, and even how things taste to you, depend on the kinds of proteins your cells make. DNA in your cells stores the instructions for making these proteins.

Proteins build cells and tissues or work as enzymes. The instructions for making a specific protein are found in a **gene** which is a section of DNA on a chromosome. Each chromosome may contain hundreds of genes, as shown in **Figure 16.** Proteins are made of chains of hundreds or thousands of amino acids. The gene determines the order of amino acids in a protein. Changing the order of the amino acids makes a different protein. What might occur if an important protein couldn't be made or if the wrong protein was made in your cells?

Making Proteins Genes are found in the nucleus, but proteins are made on ribosomes in cytoplasm. The codes for making proteins are carried from the nucleus to the ribosomes by another type of nucleic acid called ribonucleic acid, or **RNA.**

DNA as Evidence Have students research the use of DNA technology in law enforcement and write a report in their Science Journals. Have them use the Internet, news magazines, reference books, and interview forensic scientists. L2 **Linguistic**

Curriculum Connection

Math The DNA code is written in four "letters" and the cell "reads" the code in groups of three. Have students determine how many different ways the four "letters" (A, T, G, and C) can be arranged in groups of three. There are 64 possible combinations. L2 **Logical-Mathematical**

Ribonucleic Acid RNA is made in the nucleus on a DNA pattern. However, RNA is different from DNA. If DNA is like a ladder, RNA is like a ladder that has all its rungs sawed in half. Compare the DNA molecule in **Figure 14** to the RNA molecule in **Figure 17.** RNA has the bases A, G, and C like DNA but has the base uracil (U) instead of thymine (T). The sugar-phosphate molecules in RNA contain the sugar ribose, not deoxyribose.

The three main kinds of RNA made from DNA in a cell's nucleus are messenger RNA (mRNA), ribosomal RNA (rRNA), and transfer RNA (tRNA). Protein production begins when mRNA moves into the cytoplasm. There, ribosomes attach to it. Ribosomes are made of rRNA. Transfer RNA molecules in the cytoplasm bring amino acids to these ribosomes. Inside the ribosomes, three nitrogen bases on the mRNA temporarily match with three nitrogen bases on the tRNA. The same thing happens for the mRNA and another tRNA molecule, as shown in **Figure 17.** The amino acids that are attached to the two tRNA molecules bond. This is the beginning of a protein. The code carried on the mRNA directs the order in which the amino acids bond. After a tRNA molecule has lost its amino acid, it can move about the cytoplasm and pick up another amino acid just like the first one. The ribosome moves along the mRNA. New tRNA molecules with amino acids match up and add amino acids to the protein molecule.

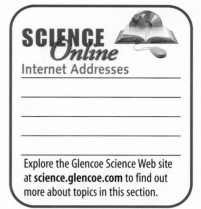

Data Update The Human Genome Project was begun in 1990. One of its goals is to identify all of the genes on human chromosomes. To find out how the project is progressing, visit the Glencoe Science Web site at **science.glencoe.com.** Communicate to your class what you learn.

SCIENCE Online
Internet Addresses

Explore the Glencoe Science Web site at **science.glencoe.com** to find out more about topics in this section.

Figure 17
Cells need DNA, RNA, and amino acids to make proteins.

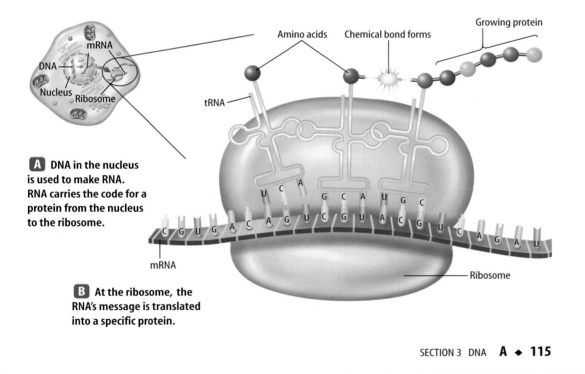

A DNA in the nucleus is used to make RNA. RNA carries the code for a protein from the nucleus to the ribosome.

B At the ribosome, the RNA's message is translated into a specific protein.

SECTION 3 DNA **A** ◆ **115**

Make a Model

Have students draw a cell on poster board and make a model demonstrating protein synthesis using materials such as craft sticks, beads, yarn, and so on. L2 LS **Visual-Spatial**

Activity

On the board or an overhead transparency, write the sequence for one strand of DNA. Have students copy the sequence and write the corresponding sequence for mRNA and tRNA. L2
LS **Visual-Spatial**

Extension

Have students choose one of the following DNA pioneers for a written report: Francis Crick, James Watson, Barbara McClintock, Maurice Wilkins, Martha Chase, A.D. Hershey, Rosalind Franklin. L2 LS **Linguistic** P

Visual Learning

Figure 17 Have students make an events chain concept map to outline the stages of protein synthesis. L2 LS **Visual-Spatial**

Resource Manager

Chapter Resources Booklet
  Enrichment, p. 30
  Directed Reading for Content Mastery, pp. 19, 20
Cultural Diversity, p. 19

Curriculum Connection

History Have students study the history of DNA research. Then using poster board, students should draw and label a timeline showing the events of DNA research since DNA was first removed from a cell nucleus in 1869. L2
LS **Visual-Spatial and Kinesthetic**

Mutations

Cells in the iris of the eye produce proteins needed for eye color.

Muscle cells produce proteins that result in making muscles move.

Cells in the stomach produce proteins necessary for that cell to digest food.

Figure 18
Each cell in the body produces only the proteins that are necessary to do its job.

Controlling Genes You might think that because most cells in an organism have exactly the same chromosomes and the same genes, they would make the same proteins, but they don't. In many-celled organisms like you, each cell uses only some of the thousands of genes that it has to make proteins. Just as each actor uses only the lines from the script for his or her role, each cell uses only the genes that direct the making of proteins that it needs. For example, muscle proteins are made in muscle cells but not in nerve cells, as shown in **Figure 18.**

Cells must be able to control genes by turning some genes off and turning other genes on. They do this in many different ways. Sometimes the DNA is twisted so tightly that no RNA can be made. Other times, chemicals bind to the DNA so that it cannot be used. If the incorrect proteins are produced, the organism cannot function properly.

Mutations

Sometimes mistakes happen when DNA is being copied. Imagine that the copy of the script the director gave you was missing three pages. You use your copy to learn your lines. When you begin rehearsing for the play, everyone is ready for one of the scenes except for you. What happened? You check your copy of the script against the original and find that three of the pages are missing. Because your script is different from the others, you cannot perform your part correctly.

If DNA is not copied exactly, the proteins made from the instructions may not be made correctly. These mistakes, called **mutations,** are any permanent change in the DNA sequence of a gene or chromosome of a cell. Some mutations include cells that receive an entire extra chromosome or are missing a chromosome. Outside factors such as X rays, sunlight, and some chemicals have been known to cause mutations.

✔ **Reading Check** *When are mutations likely to occur?*

Effects of Mutation Have students research and write a report on mutations. Have them give examples of mutations, indicate whether the mutation is harmful, benign, or beneficial, and include the cause of the mutation. L2 LS **Linguistic**

Figure 19
Because of a defect on chromosome 2, the mutant fruit fly has short wings and cannot fly. *Could this defect be transferred to the mutant's offspring? Explain.*

Results of a Mutation Genes control the traits you inherit. Without correctly coded proteins, an organism can't grow, repair, or maintain itself. A change in a gene or chromosome can change the traits of an organism, as illustrated in **Figure 19.**

If the mutation occurs in a body cell, it might or might not be life threatening to the organism. However, if a mutation occurs in a sex cell, then all the cells that are formed from that sex cell will have that mutation. Mutations add variety to a species when the organism reproduces. Many mutations are harmful to organisms, often causing their death. Some mutations do not appear to have any effect on the organism, and some can even be beneficial. For example, a mutation to a plant might cause it to produce a chemical that certain insects avoid. If these insects normally eat the plant, the mutation will help the plant survive.

SCIENCE Online

Research Visit the Glencoe Science Web site at **science.glencoe.com** for more information about what genes are present on the chromosomes of a fruit fly. Make a poster that shows one of the chromosomes and some of the genes found on that chromosome.

Section 3 Assessment

1. How does DNA make a copy of itself?
2. How are the codes for proteins carried from the nucleus to the ribosomes?
3. A single strand of DNA has the bases AGTAAC. Using letters, show a matching DNA strand from this pattern.
4. How is tRNA used when cells build proteins?
5. **Think Critically** You begin as one cell. Compare the DNA in one of your brain cells to the DNA in one of your heart cells.

Skill Builder Activities

6. **Concept Mapping** Using a network tree concept map, show how DNA and RNA are alike and how they are different. **For more help, refer to the** Science Skill Handbook.
7. **Using a Word Processor** Use a word processor to make an outline of the events that led up to the discovery of DNA. Use library resources to find this information. **For more help, refer to the** Technology Skill Handbook.

SECTION 3 DNA **A ◆ 117**

Section 3 DNA **A ◆ 117**

Caption Answer
Figure 19 yes, if it affects reproductive cells

SCIENCE Online
Internet Addresses
_____
_____
_____
_____

Explore the Glencoe Science Web site at **science.glencoe.com** to find out more about topics in this section.

3 Assess

Reteach
Have students make a drawing of DNA replication and protein synthesis. L2 LS **Visual-Spatial**

Challenge
Why does the mutation of a sperm or egg cell have a potential for different results from that of a body cell? A mutation in a reproductive cell will affect offspring. A mutation in a body cell will affect only the individual.

✓ Assessment

Oral What are the three kinds of RNA and their functions? Messenger RNA, transfer RNA, and ribosomal RNA; mRNA is copied from DNA and moves from the nucleus to a ribosome; tRNA carries amino acids to ribosomes; rRNA makes up ribosomes. Use **Performance in the Science Classroom,** p. 143.

Answers to Section Assessment

1. The two sides unwind and separate; a complementary strand is formed for each, and the resulting double-stranded DNA has one original strand and one new strand.
2. The codes are carried by mRNA from the nucleus to the ribosome.
3. TCATTG

4. The tRNA in the cytoplasm brings amino acids to the ribosomes. There, three nitrogen bases on the mRNA template match with three bases on the tRNA. The amino acids bond, and protein synthesis begins.
5. The DNA is identical.

6. Answers should be similar to the table for question 16 in the Chapter Assessment.
7. Students should be sure to include the contributions of Miescher, Griffith, Avery, Hershey, Chase, Chargraff, Wilkins, Franklin, Crick, and Watson.

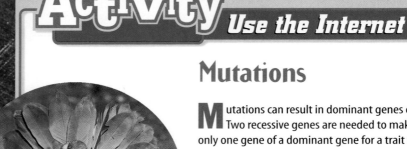

Mutations

BENCH TESTED

Recognize the Problem

Internet Students will use Internet sites that can be accessed through the Glencoe Science Web site. They will observe genetic traits and mutations in animals.

Non-Internet Sources Collect books describing animals and their genetic traits.

Time Required
about three days

Preparation

Internet Access the Glencoe Science Web site to run through the steps that students will follow.

Non-Internet Have students use books to select an animal and one of its traits to investigate.

Form a Hypothesis

Possible Hypotheses

Most students will select a phenotype to hypothesize about. For example, a tiger's white fur is a mutation that can become a common trait.

Fantail Pigeon

Mutations can result in dominant genes or recessive genes. Two recessive genes are needed to make a trait appear. You need only one gene of a dominant gene for a trait to appear. Why do some mutations become common traits while others don't?

Recognize the Problem

How can a mutation become a common trait?

Form a Hypothesis

Form a hypothesis about how a mutation can become a common trait.

Goals
- **Observe** traits of various animals.
- **Research** how mutations become traits.
- Gather data about mutations.
- Make a frequency table of your findings and communicate them to other students.

Data Source

SCIENCE *Online* Go to the Glencoe Science Web site at **science.glencoe.com** for more information on common genetic traits in different animals, recessive and dominant genes, and data from other students.

White tiger

Resource Manager

Chapter Resources Booklet
 Activity Worksheet, pp. 7–8
Lab Management and Safety, p. 58

SCIENCE *Online*

Internet Addresses

_____
_____
_____

Explore the Glencoe Science Web site at **science.glencoe.com** to find out more about topics in this activity.

Test Your Hypothesis

Plan

1. **Observe** common traits in various animals, such as household pets or animals you might see in a zoo.

2. **Learn** what genes carry these traits in each animal.

3. **Research** the traits to discover which ones are results of mutations. Are all mutations dominant? Are any of these mutations beneficial?

Do

1. Make sure your teacher approves your plan before you start.

2. Visit the Glencoe Science Web site for links to different sites about mutations and genetics.

3. **Research** various traits to discover whether or not they are mutations.

4. **Decide** if a mutation is beneficial, harmful, or neither. Record your data in your Science Journal.

Siberian Husky's eyes

Analyze Your Data

1. **Record** in your Science Journal a list of traits that are results of mutations.

2. **Describe** an animal, such as a pet or an animal you've seen in the zoo. Point out which traits are known to be the result of a mutation.

3. Make a chart that compares recessive mutations to dominant mutations. Which are more common?

4. Share your data with other students by posting it on the Glencoe Science Web site.

Draw Conclusions

1. **Compare** your findings to those of your classmates and other data on the Glencoe Science Web site. What were some of the traits your classmates found that you did not? Which were the most common?

2. Look at your chart of mutations. Are all mutations beneficial? When might a mutation be harmful to an organism?

3. How would your data be affected if you had performed this activity when one of these common mutations first appeared? Do you think you would see more or less animals with this trait?

4. Mutations occur every day but we only see a few of them. Infer how many mutations over millions of years can lead to a new species.

Communicating Your Data

SCIENCE Online Find this *Use the Internet* activity on the Glencoe Science Web site at **science.glencoe.com. Post** your data in the table provided. Combine your data with that of other students and make a chart that shows all of the data.

Teaching Strategy

Have students use animal population data to see how often that mutation is found.

Analyze Your Data

1. Answers will vary. Color can result from a mutation.

2. Answers will depend upon animals chosen.

3. Answers will vary, but dominant genes are not necessarily more common.

4. Students may need help posting data.

Draw Conclusions

1. Answers will vary. Remind students that the most common traits may be the result of mutations.

2. Answers will vary. Have students think about the mutation they are investigating and how helpful or harmful it is to the animal.

3. If you had investigated the mutation when it first appeared, you may have seen fewer animals with the trait. With the passage of time, you can determine if the mutation is beneficial.

4. Organisms with mutations may be better suited to a particular environment. These traits would be passed on to their offspring. Many mutations may lead to a new species.

Communicating Your Data

Have students use the Internet to collect pictures of the animal they are investigating. Have them find pictures that show the mutation.

✓Assessment

Oral Students describe mutations they researched and discuss how helpful they are to animals. Show pictures of animals with the mutation. Use **Performance Assessment in the Science Classroom,** p. 143.

Content Background

Cytogenetics is the branch of science that studies heredity both through genetics and studies of the cell. 1956 is when modern human cytogenetics began, thanks to the discovery of the number of human chromosomes present in each cell of the body. As early as 1905 scientists had determined that chromosomes are found in pairs and in 1915 Thomas Hunt Morgan discovered that genes were found on chromosomes. It wasn't until 1952 that Dr. Hsu's work occurred, and 1953 when Watson and Crick used Rosalind Franklin's work to determine the structure of DNA. Studies of human chromosomes and genes have progressed at an astounding rate since that time. Scientists have determined the particular chromosome that carries the gene for many human diseases and other traits.

Discussion

Explain what type of mistake the lab technician in Dr. Hsu's lab might have made while mixing the solution that caused mysterious behavior of the chromosomes. Possible answer: The technician either added too little of the solute to a set amount of water, or too much water to a set amount of solvent, causing the solution to have a higher water content than the cells.

A Tangled

How did a scientist get chromosomes to separate?

Thanks to chromosomes, each of us is unique!

120 ◆ A

Resources for Teachers and Students

"Genetics and Genetic Engineering," by Lisa Yount, Facts on File, Inc., 1997.

"The Big Idea," by Paul Strathern, Doubleday, 1999.

"The History of Genetics," by Robert Snedden, Thomas Learning, 1995.

Viewed under a microscope, chromosomes in cells sometimes look a lot like tangled spaghetti. That's why during the early 1900s, scientists had such a hard time figuring out how many chromosomes are in each human cell.

Tale

Imagine then, how Dr. Tao-Chiuh Hsu (dow shew•SEW) must have felt when he looked into a microscope and saw "beautifully scattered chromosomes." The problem was, Hsu didn't know what he had done to separate the chromosomes into countable strands.

"I tried to study those slides and set up some more cultures to repeat the miracle," Hsu explained. "But nothing happened."

For three months, Hsu toiled in the lab, changing every variable he could think of to make the chromosomes separate again.

In April 1952, he reduced the amount of salt and increased the amount of water in the solution used to prepare the cells for study, and his efforts were finally rewarded. Hsu quickly realized that the chromosomes separated because of osmosis.

Osmosis is the movement of water molecules through cell membranes. This movement occurs in predictable ways. The water molecules move from areas with higher concentrations of water to areas with lower concentrations of water. In Hsu's case, the solution had a higher concentration of water than the cell did. So water moved from the solution into the cell and the cell swelled until it finally exploded. The chromosomes suddenly were visible as separate strands.

What made the cells swell the first time? Apparently, a lab technician had mixed the solution incorrectly. "Since nearly four months had elapsed, there was no way to trace who actually had prepared that particular [solution]," Hsu noted. "Therefore, this heroine must remain anonymous."

The Real Count

Although Hsu's view of the chromosomes was fairly clear, he mistakenly estimated the number of chromosomes in a human cell. He put the count at 48, which was the number that most scientists of the day accepted. By 1956, however, other scientists improved upon Hsu's techniques and concluded that there are 46 chromosomes in a human cell. Because chromosomes contain the genes that determine each person's characteristics, this discovery helped scientists better understand genetic diseases and disorders. Scientists also have a better idea of why every person, including you, is unique.

These chromosomes are magnified 500 times.

CONNECTIONS Research Until the 1950s, scientists believed that there were 48 chromosomes in a human cell. Research the developments that led scientists to the conclusion that the human cell has 46 chromosomes. Use the Glencoe Science Web site to get started.

SCIENCE *Online*
For more information, visit science.glencoe.com

Activity

Have students work in teams to research the major discoveries in the field of genetics. Have each team display their results on a timeline made on a long piece of paper. Students should be encouraged to include discoveries from early research until present times, and to include the names of the scientists who made the discoveries.

Analyze the Event

Ask the student to brainstorm what other positive or negative effects a mistake in making a lab solution could have. Possible answers: In some cases a mistake could result in better than expected results or a discovery that would not have otherwise been made. Negative results could include work that can't be repeated, the need to re-do the entire experiment, skewed results, or potential fire or poisoning hazards. Point out to students that because Dr. Hsu's results were due to a mistake it took him months to find the cause of the good results. In general, mistakes of this type in the lab bring only negative outcomes.

CONNECTIONS As students research research the history of research on human chromosomes, have them consider the rate at which discoveries occurred then and now. Point out that the Human Genome Project has increased the knowledge of genetics at an amazing rate.

SCIENCE *Online*

Internet Addresses

_____

_____

_____

Explore the Glencoe Science Web site at **science.glencoe.com** to find out more about topics in this feature.

Chapter 4 Study Guide

Reviewing Main Ideas

Preview

Students can answer the questions in their Science Journals. Discuss the answers as you go through the chapter. [LS] **Linguistic**

Review

Students can write their answers, then compare them with those of other students. [LS] **Interpersonal**

Reteach

Students can look at the illustrations and describe details that support the main ideas of the chapter. [LS] **Visual-Spatial**

Answers to Chapter Review

SECTION 1

4. Mitosis produces new bone cells to replace damaged ones.

SECTION 2

4. 26

SECTION 3

4. It has a mutation that affects its number of wings.

Reviewing Main Ideas

Section 1 Cell Division and Mitosis

1. The life cycle of a cell has two parts— growth and development and cell division. Cell division includes mitosis and the division of the cytoplasm.

2. In mitosis, the nucleus divides to form two identical nuclei. Mitosis occurs in four continuous steps, or phases—prophase, metaphase, anaphase, and telophase.

3. Cell division in animal cells and plant cells is similar, but plant cells do not have centrioles and animal cells do not form cell walls.

4. Organisms use cell division to grow, to replace cells, and for asexual reproduction. Asexual reproduction produces organisms with DNA identical to the parent's DNA. Fission, budding, and regeneration can be used for asexual reproduction. *How would cell division help heal this broken bone?*

Section 2 Sexual Reproduction and Meiosis

1. Sexual reproduction results when a male sex cell enters the female sex cell. This event is called fertilization, and the cell that forms is called the zygote.

2. Before fertilization, meiosis occurs in the reproductive organs, producing four haploid sex cells from one diploid cell.

3. During meiosis, two divisions of the nucleus occur.

4. Meiosis ensures that offspring produced by fertilization have the same number of chromosomes as their parents. *If the diploid number of a frog is 26, how many chromosomes does this tadpole have?*

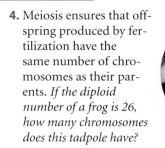

Section 3 DNA

1. DNA—the genetic material of all organisms—is a large molecule made up of two twisted strands of sugar-phosphate molecules and nitrogen bases.

2. All cells contain DNA. The section of DNA on a chromosome that directs the making of a specific protein is a gene.

3. DNA can copy itself and is the pattern from which RNA is made. Messenger RNA, ribosomal RNA, and transfer RNA are used to make proteins.

4. Sometimes changes in DNA occur. Permanent changes in DNA are called mutations. *Why does this fruit fly have four wings instead of the normal two?*

FOLDABLES
Reading & Study Skills

After You Read

To help you review cell reproduction, use the Organizational Study Fold about the cell you made at the beginning of the chapter.

FOLDABLES
Reading & Study Skills

After You Read

After students have read the chapter and completed the Foldable described in Before You Read, have them do the activity on the student page.

Dinah Zike

Visualizing Main Ideas

Think of four ways that organisms can use mitosis and fill out the spider diagram below.

Growth

Asexual reproduction

used for   used for

Mitosis

used for   used for

Cell replacement

Regeneration

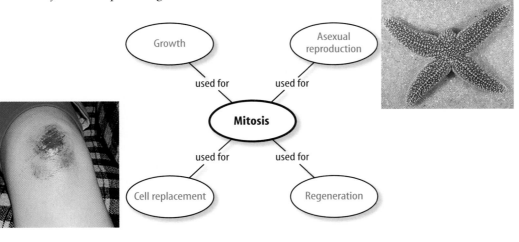

Vocabulary Review

Vocabulary Words

a. asexual reproduction
b. chromosome
c. diploid
d. DNA
e. egg
f. fertilization
g. gene
h. haploid

i. meiosis
j. mitosis
k. mutation
l. RNA
m. sexual reproduction
n. sperm
o. zygote

THE PRINCETON REVIEW

Study Tip

Be a teacher—organize a group of friends and instruct each person to review a section of the chapter for the group. Teaching helps you remember and understand information thoroughly.

Using Vocabulary

Replace each underlined word in the following statements with the correct vocabulary word.

1. <u>Muscle</u> and <u>skin</u> cells are sex cells.

2. <u>Digestion</u> produces two identical cells.

3. An example of a nucleic acid is <u>sugar</u>.

4. A <u>cell</u> is the code for a protein.

5. A <u>diploid</u> sperm is formed during meiosis.

6. Budding is a type of <u>meiosis</u>.

7. A <u>ribosome</u> is a structure in the nucleus that contains hereditary material.

8. <u>Respiration</u> produces four sex cells.

9. As a result of <u>fission</u>, a new organism develops that has its own unique identity.

10. An error made during the copying of DNA is called a <u>protein</u>.

CHAPTER STUDY GUIDE   A ◆ 123

Chapter 4 Study Guide

Visualizing Main Ideas

See student page.

Vocabulary Review

Using Vocabulary

1. Egg, sperm
2. Mitosis
3. DNA or RNA
4. gene
5. haploid
6. asexual reproduction
7. chromosome
8. Meiosis
9. Fertilization, meiosis, or sexual reproduction
10. mutation

CHAPTER STUDY GUIDE   A ◆ 123

Checking Concepts

1. D
2. D
3. B
4. C
5. A
6. A
7. D
8. D
9. C
10. B

Thinking Critically

11. TAGGCAG
12. UAGGCAG
13. No; in order for a mutation to be passed to offspring, the mutation must take place in a sex cell.
14. the copying of chromosomes in interphase; the separation of the copies at anaphase; the separation of two new cells at telophase
15. This could happen if nondisjunction (failure of like chromosomes or chromatids to separate) occurs during anaphase I or II.

Checking Concepts

Choose the word or phrase that best answers the question.

1. Which of the following is a double spiral molecule with pairs of nitrogen bases?
   A) RNA
   C) protein
   B) amino acid
   D) DNA

2. What is in RNA but NOT in DNA?
   A) thymine
   C) adenine
   B) thyroid
   D) uracil

3. If a diploid tomato cell has 24 chromosomes, how many chromosomes will the tomato's sex cells have?
   A) 6
   C) 24
   B) 12
   D) 48

4. During a cell's life cycle, when do chromosomes duplicate?
   A) anaphase
   C) interphase
   B) metaphase
   D) telophase

5. When do chromatids separate during mitosis?
   A) anaphase
   C) metaphase
   B) prophase
   D) telophase

6. How many chromosomes are in the original cell compared to those in the new cells formed by cell division?
   A) the same amount
   C) twice as many
   B) half as many
   D) four times as many

7. What can budding, fission, and regeneration be used for?
   A) mutations
   B) sexual reproduction
   C) cell cycles
   D) asexual reproduction

8. What is any permanent change in a gene or a chromosome called?
   A) fission
   C) replication
   B) reproduction
   D) mutation

9. What does meiosis produce?
   A) cells with the diploid chromosome number
   B) cells with identical chromosomes
   C) sex cells
   D) a zygote

10. What type of nucleic acid carries the codes for making proteins from the nucleus to the ribosome?
   A) DNA
   C) protein
   B) RNA
   D) genes

Thinking Critically

11. If the sequence of bases on one side of DNA is ATCCGTC, what is the sequence on its other side?

12. A strand of RNA made using the DNA pattern ATCCGTC would have what base sequence? Look at **Figure 14** for a hint.

13. Will a mutation in a human skin cell be passed on to the person's offspring? Explain.

14. What occurs in mitosis that gives the new cells identical DNA?

15. How could a zygote end up with an extra chromosome?

Developing Skills

16. **Classifying** Copy and complete this table about DNA and RNA.

DNA and RNA		
	DNA	**RNA**
Number of Strands	2	1
Type of Sugar	deoxyribose	ribose
Letter Names of Bases	G, A, C, T	G, A, C, U
Where Found	nucleus	nucleus & cytoplasm

Chapter ✓Assessment Planner

Portfolio Encourage students to place in their portfolios one or two items of what they consider to be their best work. Examples include:
• Visual Learning, p. 99
• Make a Model, p. 109
• Extension, p. 115

Performance Additional performance assessments, Performance Task Assessment Lists, and rubrics for evaluating these activities can be found in Glencoe's **Performance Assessment in the Science Classroom.**

17. Concept Mapping Complete the events chain concept map of DNA synthesis.

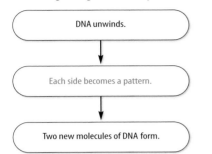

DNA unwinds.

↓

Each side becomes a pattern.

↓

Two new molecules of DNA form.

18. Comparing and Contrasting Make a table about mitosis and meiosis. Include the number of divisions, number of cells produced, and chromosomes in parent cells and in sex cells.

19. Forming Hypotheses Make a hypothesis about the effect of an incorrect mitotic division on the new cells produced.

20. Concept Mapping Make an events chain concept map of what occurs from interphase in the parent cell to the formation of the zygote. Tell whether the chromosome's number at each stage is haploid or diploid.

Performance Assessment

21. Flash Cards Make a set of 11 flash cards with drawings of a cell that show the different stages of meiosis. Shuffle your cards and then put them in the correct order. Give them to another student in the class to try.

TECHNOLOGY

Go to the Glencoe Science Web site at **science.glencoe.com** or use the **Glencoe Science CD-ROM** for additional chapter assessment.

THE PRINCETON REVIEW — Test Practice

A scientist studied the reproduction of human skin cells. The scientist examined several skin cells using a microscope. The table below summarizes what she learned.

Skin Cells		
Cell	**Phase of Division**	**Characteristic**
1	Anaphase	Chromosome separation
2	Telophase	Cytoplasm division
3	Prophase	Visible chromosomes
4	Metaphase	Chromosomes line up

Use the information in the table to answer the following questions.

1. What process is taking place in all of the cells?
   A) cell division
   B) fertilization
   C) cytoplasm division
   D) chromosome separation

2. Which is the correct order of the stages, from first to last, in the cell division of a skin cell?
   F) 3, 4, 1, 2   **H)** 1, 2, 4, 3
   G) 1, 3, 2, 4   **J)** 2, 1, 3, 4

3. Since the process described in the table produces two new identical cells, before it begins the chromosomes in the cell must _____ .
   A) divide in half   **C)** duplicate
   B) find a mate   **D)** disintegrate

THE PRINCETON REVIEW — Test Practice

The Test-Taking Tip was written by The Princeton Review, the nation's leader in test preparation.
1. A
2. F
3. C

Developing Skills

16. See student page.
17. See student page.
18. mitosis: 1 division, 2 cells produced, diploid parent cells, diploid sex cells; meiosis: 2 divisions, 4 cells produced, diploid parent cells, haploid sex cells
19. Incorrect division can result in an incorrect number of chromosomes, often leading to abnormal offspring.
20. The order of events given for meiosis should reflect **Figure 11** and formation of the zygote, **Figure 10.** The cell at the beginning of meiosis is diploid. The four cells at the end of meiosis are all haploid.

Performance Assessment

21. Cards should be sequenced as shown in **Figure 11.** If interphase is included, it should come before prophase I. Use **Performance Assessment in the Science Classroom,** p. 163.

✓Assessment Resources

📁 **Reproducible Masters**

Chapter Resources Booklet
   Chapter Review, pp. 35–36
   Chapter Tests, pp. 37–40
   Assessment Transparency Activity, p. 47

Glencoe Science Web site
   Interactive Tutor
   Chapter Quizzes

Glencoe Technology
   🖐 Assessment Transparency
   💿 Interactive CD-ROM Chapter Quizzes
   💿 ExamView Pro Test Bank
   💿 Vocabulary PuzzleMaker Software
   📼 MindJogger Videoquiz DVD/VHS

Section/Objectives	Standards		Activities/Features
Chapter Opener	**National**	**State/Local**	**Explore Activity:** Observe dimples on faces, p. 127 **Before You Read,** p. 127
	See p. 6T for a Key to Standards.		
Section 1 Genetics ⏱ 2 sessions 📦 1 block 1. **Explain** how traits are inherited. 2. **Identify** Mendel's role in the history of genetics. 3. **Use** a Punnett square to predict the results of crosses. 4. **Compare and contrast** the difference between an individual's genotype and phenotype.	National Content Standards: UCP2, A1, C2, G3		**Science Online,** p. 129 **MiniLAB:** Comparing Common Traits, p. 130 **Visualizing Mendel's Experiments,** p. 131 **Math Skills Activity:** Calculating Probability Using a Punnett Square, p. 133 **Activity:** Predicting Results, p. 135
Section 2 Genetics Since Mendel ⏱ 2 sessions 📦 1 block 1. **Explain** how traits are inherited by incomplete dominance. 2. **Compare** multiple alleles and polygenic inheritance, and give examples of each. 3. **Describe** two human genetic disorders and how they are inherited. 4. **Explain** how sex-linked traits are passed to offspring.	National Content Standards: UCP2, A1, C2, F1		**Science Online,** p. 137 **MiniLAB:** Interpreting Polygenic Inheritance, p. 138 **Chemistry Integration,** p. 140
Section 3 Advances in Genetics ⏱ 3 sessions 📦 1.5 blocks 1. **Evaluate** the importance of advances in genetics. 2. **Sequence** the steps in making genetically engineered organisms.	National Content Standards: UCP2, A1, C2, E1, E2, F5, G1		**Environmental Science Integration,** p. 144 **Activity:** Tests for Color Blindness, pp. 146–147 **Science Stats:** The Human Genome, pp. 148–149

Activity Materials	Reproducible Resources	Section Assessment	Technology
Explore Activity: Science Journal	**Chapter Resources Booklet** Foldables Worksheets, p. 13 Directed Reading Overview, p. 15 Note-taking Worksheets, pp. 29–31	GLENCOE'S ASSESSMENT ADVANTAGE	
MiniLAB: paper and pencil **Activity:** 2 paper bags, 100 red beans, 100 white beans	**Chapter Resources Booklet** Transparency Activity, p. 40 MiniLAB, p. 3 Directed Reading, p. 16 Enrichment, p. 26 Reinforcement, p. 23 Activity Worksheet, pp. 5–6 Lab Activity, pp. 9–10, 11–12 **Mathematics Skill Activities,** p. 23 **Home and Community Involvement,** p. 36 **Performance Assessment in the Science Classroom,** p. 57	Portfolio Extension, p. 132 Performance MiniLAB, p. 130 Math Skills Activity, p. 133 Skill Builder Activities, p. 134 Content Section Assessment, p. 134	Section Focus Transparency Interactive CD-ROM/DVD Guided Reading Audio Program
MiniLAB: paper, pencil, ruler *Need materials?* Contact Science Kit at 1-800-828-7777 or www.sciencekit.com on the Internet.	**Chapter Resources Booklet** Transparency Activity, p. 41 MiniLAB, p. 4 Enrichment, p. 27 Reinforcement, p. 24 Directed Reading, p. 16 Transparency Activity, pp. 43–44 **Life Science Critical Thinking/ Problem Solving,** p. 19	Portfolio Science Journal, p. 137 Performance MiniLAB, p. 138 Skill Builder Activities, p. 142 Content Section Assessment, p. 142	Section Focus Transparency Teaching Transparency Interactive CD-ROM/DVD Guided Reading Audio Program
Activity: white paper or poster board, colored markers	**Chapter Resources Booklet** Transparency Activity, p. 42 Enrichment, p. 28 Reinforcement, p. 25 Directed Reading, pp. 17, 18 Activity Worksheet, pp. 7–8 **Lab Management and Safety,** p. 74	Portfolio Assessment, p. 145 Performance Skill Builder Activities, p. 145 Content Section Assessment, p. 145	Section Focus Transparency Interactive CD-ROM/DVD Guided Reading Audio Program

End of Chapter Assessment

GLENCOE'S ASSESSMENT ADVANTAGE

Blackline Masters	Technology	Professional Series
Chapter Resources Booklet Chapter Review, pp. 33–34 Chapter Tests, pp. 35–38 **Standardized Test Practice by The Princeton Review,** pp. 23–26	MindJogger Videoquiz CD-ROM Explorations and Quizzes Vocabulary Puzzle Makers ExamView Pro Test Bank Interactive Lesson Planner Interactive Teacher's Edition	Performance Assessment in the Science Classroom (PASC)

Transparencies

Section Focus

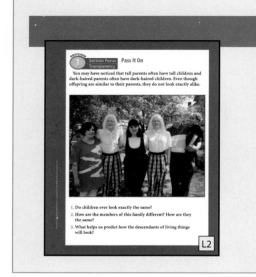

This is a representation of key blackline masters available in the Teacher Classroom Resources. See Resource Manager boxes within the chapter for additional information.

Key to Teaching Strategies

The following designations will help you decide which activities are appropriate for your students.

L1 Level 1 activities should be appropriate for students with learning difficulties.

L2 Level 2 activities should be within the ability range of all students.

L3 Level 3 activities are designed for above-average students.

ELL ELL activities should be within the ability range of English Language Learners.

COOP LEARN Cooperative Learning activities are designed for small group work.

LS Multiple Learning Styles logos are used throughout to indicate strategies that address different learning styles.

P These strategies represent student products that can be placed into a best-work portfolio.

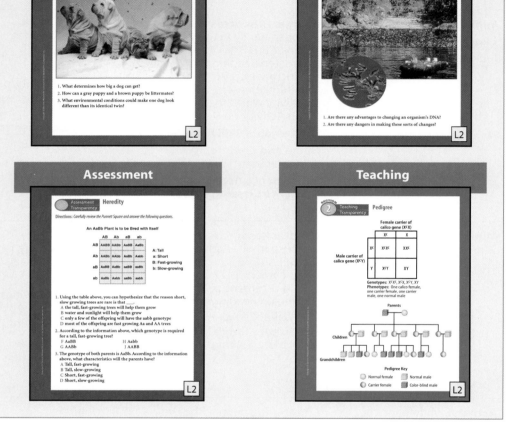

Hands-on Activities

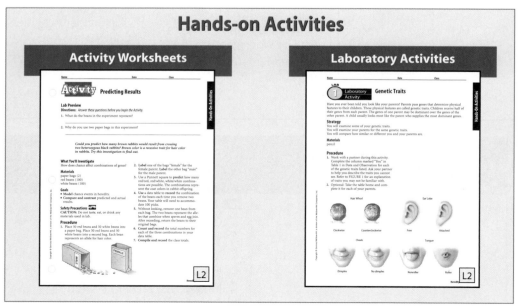

Meeting Different Ability Levels

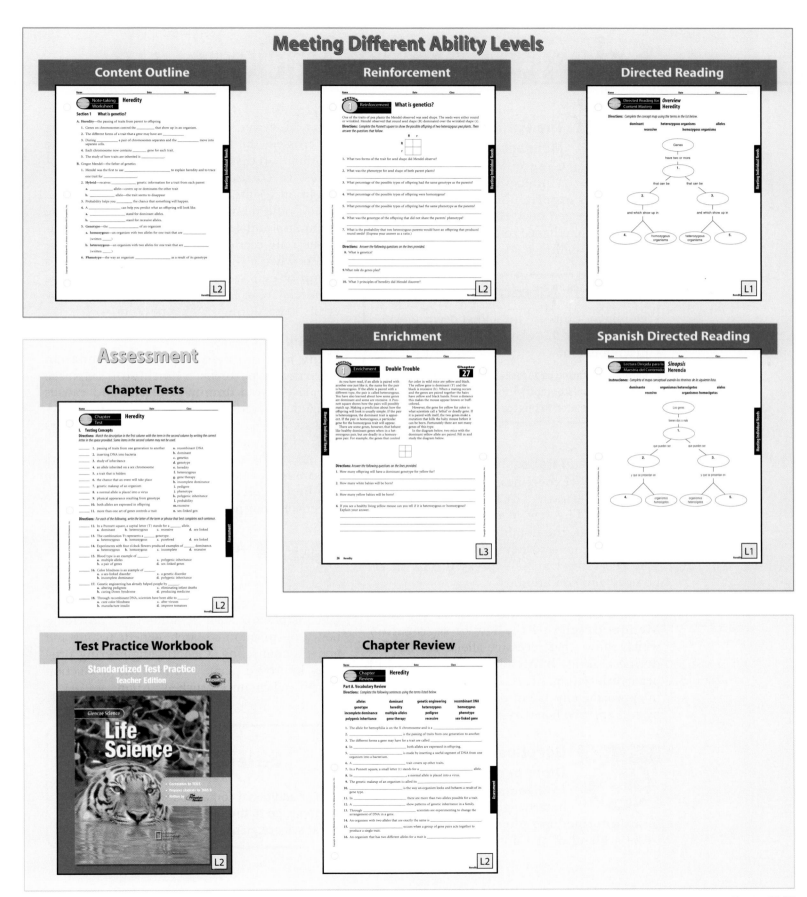

Content Outline

Reinforcement

Directed Reading

Assessment

Chapter Tests

Enrichment

Spanish Directed Reading

Test Practice Workbook

Chapter Review

Science Content Background

SECTION 1

The Father of Genetics
Mendelian inheritance

Gregor Mendel, an Austrian Monk, was the first scientist to bring an experimental and quantitative approach to genetics, the study of heredity. Mendelian inheritance reflects the mathematical rules of probability.

Student Misconception

Dominant traits are those that occur most frequently, or those that will "take over" in a population.

Refer to the facing page for teaching strategies to address this misconception. Refer to pages 130–132 for content related to this topic.

Dominant and Recessive Factors

In Mendel's experiments, the inheritance patterns of characters each possessed two traits or alleles. The law of dominance explains that one trait, the dominant trait, is expressed in homozygous and heterozygous conditions. The recessive trait is expressed only in the homozygous condition.

Using a Punnett Square

Mendel developed the law of segregation, which shows that recessive alleles are not lost during meiosis. In Mendel's experiments with pea hybridization, the recessive trait reappeared in approximately 1/4 of the offspring produced by crossing two heterozygous pea plants.

SECTION 2

Genetics Since Mendel
Other modes of inheritance

In incomplete dominance, the heterozygous condition results in an intermediate phenotype that appears to be a blend of the dominant and recessive traits. However, when heterozygous offspring are crossed, the next generation expresses the dominant, recessive and intermediate phenotypes. In co-dominance, the heterozygous condition results in a phenotype that is a mixture of both dominant alleles. Sometimes there are multiple alleles for a trait, though each individual only carries two. Polygenic inheritance occurs when a trait is produced as a result of a group of genes. Mutations and chromosome disorders are caused by changes in genes or by errors made during DNA replication.

Genetic Disorders

Many human disorders follow Mendelian inheritance patterns. Huntington's disease is carried on a dominant allele, and causes lethal degeneration of the nervous system. Tay-Sachs is caused by a recessive allele and occurs most often in people of Jewish descent. Sickle-cell anemia is a recessive disorder that occurs most often in people of African descent. The red blood cells are malformed, and cannot effectively transport oxygen.

SECTION 3

Advances in Genetics
Benefits of genetic research

Advances made in the search for the molecular basis of inheritance is phenomenal. Technology is providing new tools to aid in research, genetic testing and genetic counseling. Genetic engineering provides improved plants and efficient production of artificial chemicals such as insulin.

SCIENCE *Online*

For additional content background on this topic, go to the Glencoe Science Web site at science.glencoe.com.

IDENTIFYING Misconceptions

Find Out What Students Think

Students may think that . . .

• **Dominant traits are the strongest, most superior, or most common traits in a population.**

Genes coding for eye color in humans come in two alleles. The dominant allele causes brown pigment to be produced in the iris, and the recessive allele does not produce a functional protein or pigment. Each person receives two copies of each gene, one from each parent. If a person inherits at least one "brown" allele, the person's eyes will produce pigment. If a person has only recessive alleles, no pigment is made and the eyes appear blue. Human eye color is actually somewhat more complex than this, as it is controlled by several genes (not a single pair) as opposed to simple Mendelian inheritance. The more dominant alleles a person has, the darker the eyes appear.

Discussion

Ask the class, "If brown eyes are dominant over blue eyes, does this mean that someday all people will be brown eyed?" Let students form small discussion groups. After a set time limit, let students present their answers and supporting evidence. Their answers will reveal their preconceived notions and their reasoning.

Promote Understanding

Activity

Group students in pairs, and give each pair an envelope containing five brown and five blue squares.

• Have each student draw one brown and one blue square. These squares represent the eye color alleles of an imaginary person. Ask what color of eyes the person has (brown).

• Tell students that their two imaginary people will have a child, so each must contribute one allele. Students should randomly draw a square from the envelope. Have students lay their contributed squares side by side and determine the eye color of the child.

• Count the number of blue-eyed and brown-eyed offspring produced in the class. Ask students why some of the brown-eyed parents had a child with blue eyes.

• Poll the class to see how many students have a widow's peak hairline (dominant) vs. a straight hairline (recessive), and how many have a dimple in the chin (dominant) vs. no dimple in the chin (recessive). These two traits have dominant forms that are usually infrequent in a population.

Assess

After completing the chapter, see *Identifying Misconceptions* in the Study Guide.

CHAPTER 5

Heredity

Chapter Vocabulary

heredity
alleles
genetics
hybrid
dominant
recessive
Punnett square
genotype
phenotype
homozygous
heterozygous
incomplete dominance
polygenic inheritance
sex-linked gene
genetic engineering

What do you think?

Science Journal The cells in the picture are a human sperm and egg at the time of fertilization. The union of these cells determines a child's genetic make-up.

CHAPTER 5 Heredity

Wherever you go, look around you. You don't have the same skin color, the same kind of hair, or the same height as everyone else. Why do you resemble some people but do not look like others at all? In this chapter, you'll find out how differences are determined, and you will learn how to predict when certain traits might appear. You also will learn what causes some hereditary disorders.

What do you think?

Science Journal Look at the picture below with a classmate. Discuss what you think this might be or what is happening. Here's a hint: *The secret to why you look the way you do is found in this picture.* Write your answer or best guess in your Science Journal.

Theme Connection

Stability and Change Genes control stability through homeostasis at the organism level. Genetics provides background for understanding the changes involved in evolution.

You and your best friend enjoy the same sports, like the same food, and even have similar haircuts. But, there are noticeable differences between your appearances. Most of these differences are controlled by the genes you inherited from your parents. In the following activity, you will observe one of these differences.

Observe dimples on faces

1. Notice the two students in the photographs. One student has dimples when she smiles, and the other student doesn't have dimples.

2. Ask your classmates to smile naturally. In your Science Journal, record the name of each classmate and whether each one has dimples.

Observe

In your Science Journal, calculate the percentage of students who have dimples. Are facial dimples a common feature among your classmates?

FOLDABLES
Reading & Study Skills

Before You Read

Making a Classify Study Fold As you read this chapter about heredity, you can use the following Foldable to help you classify characteristics. When you classify, you organize objects or events into groups based on their common features.

1. Place a sheet of paper in front of you so the short side is at the top. Fold both sides in to divide the paper into thirds. Unfold the paper so three columns show.

2. Fold the paper in half from top to bottom. Then fold it in half again two more times. Unfold all the folds.

3. Trace over all the fold lines and label the columns you created: *Personal Characteristics*, *Inherited*, and *Not Inherited*, as shown. List personal characteristics down the left-hand column, as shown.

4. Before you read the chapter, predict which characteristics are inherited or not inherited. As you read the chapter, check and change the table.

Personal Characteristics	Inherited	Not Inherited
eyes		
hair		
dimples		

A ◆ 127

EXPLORE ACTIVITY

Purpose Use the Explore Activity to introduce students to inheritance. Inform students that they will be learning about inheritance and genetics as they read the chapter. ⌊L2⌋ ⌊ELL⌋ ⌊COOP LEARN⌋ ⌊IS⌋ **Logical-Mathematical**

Preparation Discuss the photograph as a class to ensure that students recognize what dimples are.

Teaching Strategy Record data for each class and have students compare their results with those of other classes.

Observe

Percentages will vary depending upon how many students in the class have and do not have dimples. Generally, the percentage of students having dimples falls between 10 and 40 percent.

Assessment

Oral Have students suggest other features that are inherited. Possible answers: hair color and texture, skin and eye color, height, shape of facial features. Use **Performance Assessment in the Science Classroom,** p. 89.

FOLDABLES
Reading & Study Skills

Before You Read

Dinah Zike Study Fold
Purpose Students will define genetics by using a Foldable classification chart to record inherited and non-inherited characteristics, or traits.

 For additional help, see Foldables Worksheet, p. 13 in **Chapter Resources Booklet,** or go to the Glencoe Science Web site at **science.glencoe.com.** See After You Read in the Study Guide at the end of this chapter.

SECTION
1 Genetics

1 Motivate

Bellringer Transparency

Display the Section Focus Transparency for Section 1. Use the accompanying Transparency Activity Master. L2
ELL

Tie to Prior Knowledge

Show a picture of a mother dog and her puppies (or a cat and her kittens). Have students list characteristics of the offspring they think are inherited from the parents. Lead students to understand that all of the general physical traits, such as number of legs, length and shape of ears, eye color and shape, and so on, are inherited.

As You Read

What You'll Learn
- **Explain** how traits are inherited.
- **Identify** Mendel's role in the history of genetics.
- **Use** a Punnett square to predict the results of crosses.
- **Compare and contrast** the difference between an individual's genotype and phenotype.

Vocabulary
heredity　　Punnett square
allele　　genotype
genetics　　phenotype
hybrid　　homozygous
dominant　　heterozygous
recessive

Why It's Important
Heredity and genetics help explain why people are different.

Inheriting Traits

Do you look more like one parent or grandparent? Do you have your father's eyes? What about Aunt Isabella's cheekbones? Eye color, nose shape, and many other physical features are some of the traits that are inherited from parents, as **Figure 1** shows. An organism is a collection of traits, all inherited from its parents. **Heredity** (huh REH duh tee) is the passing of traits from parent to offspring. What controls these traits?

What is genetics? Generally, genes on chromosomes control an organism's form and function. The different forms of a trait that a gene may have are called **alleles** (uh LEELZ). When a pair of chromosomes separates during meiosis (mi OH sus), alleles for each trait also separate into different sex cells. As a result, every sex cell has one allele for each trait, as shown in **Figure 2.** The allele in one sex cell may control one form of the trait, such as having facial dimples. The allele in the other sex cell may control a different form of the trait—not having dimples. The study of how traits are inherited through the interactions of alleles is the science of **genetics** (juh NET ihks).

Figure 1
Note the strong family resemblance among these four generations.

Section ✓*Assessment* Planner

PORTFOLIO
Extension, p. 132
PERFORMANCE ASSESSMENT
Try at Home MiniLab, p. 130
Math Skills Activity, p. 133
Skill Builder Activities, p. 134
See page 152 for more options.

CONTENT ASSESSMENT
Section, p. 134
Challenge, p. 134
Chapter, pp. 152–153

Figure 2
An allele is one form of a gene. Alleles separate into separate sex cells during meiosis. In this example, the alleles that control the trait for dimples include *D,* the presence of dimples, and *d,* the absence of dimples.

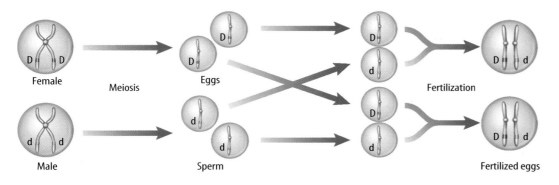

A The alleles that control a trait are located on each duplicated chromosome.

B During meiosis, duplicated chromosomes separate.

C During fertilization, each parent donates one chromosome. This results in two alleles for the trait of dimples in the new individual formed.

Mendel—The Father of Genetics

Did you know that an experiment with pea plants helped scientists understand why your eyes are the color that they are? Gregor Mendel was an Austrian monk who studied mathematics and science but became a gardener in a monastery. His interest in plants began as a boy in his father's orchard where he could predict the possible types of flowers and fruits that would result from crossbreeding two plants. Curiosity about the connection between the color of a pea flower and the type of seed that same plant produced inspired him to begin experimenting with garden peas in 1856. Mendel made careful use of scientific methods, which resulted in the first recorded study of how traits pass from one generation to the next. After eight years, Mendel presented his results with pea plants to scientists.

Before Mendel, scientists mostly relied on observation and description, and often studied many traits at one time. Mendel was the first to trace one trait through several generations. He was also the first to use the mathematics of probability to explain heredity. The use of math in plant science was a new concept and not widely accepted then. Mendel's work was forgotten for a long time. In 1900, three plant scientists, working separately, reached the same conclusions as Mendel. Each plant scientist had discovered Mendel's writings while doing his own research. Since then, Mendel has been known as the father of genetics.

Research Visit the Glencoe Science Web site at **science.glencoe.com** for more information about early genetics experiments. Write a paragraph in your Science Journal about a scientist, other than Gregor Mendel, who studied genetics.

Genetics in a Garden

TRY AT HOME

Mini LAB

Purpose to observe and calculate the occurrence of various traits in dogs |L2| ELL

[IS] **Logical-Mathematical**

Teaching Strategies Make sure students understand that variations make each dog unique.

Safety Precautions Caution students not to touch or approach dogs they do not know.

Analysis
1. Answers will vary depending on dogs observed.
2. There are many variations. Each dog looks different.

✔ Assessment

Performance To further assess students' understanding of inherited traits, have volunteers observe and tabulate several traits among children, parents, and grandparents. Use **PASC,** p. 109.

✔ Reading Check

Answer They can be relied upon to produce the same traits generation after generation.

IDENTIFYING Misconceptions

Some students think that dominant traits are those that will "take over" in a population. Refer to page 126F for teaching strategies that address this misconception.

Table 1 Traits Compared by Mendel							
Traits	Shape of Seeds	Color of Seeds	Color of Pods	Shape of Pods	Plant Height	Position of Flowers	Flower Color
Dominant Trait	Round	Yellow	Green	Full	Tall	At leaf junctions	Purple
Recessive Trait	Wrinkled	Green	Yellow	Flat, constricted	Short	At tips of branches	White

TRY AT HOME

Mini LAB

Comparing Common Traits

Procedure
1. Safely survey as many **dogs** in your neighborhood as you can for the presence of a solid color or spotted coat, short or long hair, and floppy ears or ears that stand up straight.
2. Make a data table that lists each of the traits. Record your data in the data table.

Analysis
1. Compare the number of dogs that have one form of a trait with those that have the other form. How do those two groups compare?
2. What can you conclude about the variations you noticed in the dogs?

Genetics in a Garden

Each time Mendel crossed two plants with different expressions of a trait to study that trait, he found that the new plants all looked like one of the two parents. He called these new plants **hybrids** (HI brudz) because they receive different genetic information, or different alleles, for a trait from each parent. These results made Mendel even more curious about how traits are inherited.

Garden peas are easy to breed for pure traits. An organism that always produces the same traits generation after generation is called a purebred. For example, tall plants that always produce seeds that produce tall plants are purebred for the trait of tall height. **Table 1** shows other pea plant traits Mendel studied.

✔ Reading Check *Why might farmers plant purebred crop seeds?*

Dominant and Recessive Factors In nature, insects randomly pollinate plants as they move from flower to flower. In his experiments, Mendel used pollen from the flowers of purebred tall plants to pollinate by hand the flowers of purebred short plants. This process is called cross-pollination. He found that tall plants crossed with short plants produced seeds that produced all tall plants. Whatever caused the plants to be short had disappeared. Mendel called the tall form the **dominant** (DAHM uh nunt) factor because it dominated, or covered up, the short form. He called the form that seemed to disappear the **recessive** (rih SES ihv) factor. Today, these are called dominant alleles and recessive alleles. What happened to the recessive form? **Figure 3** answers this question.

Resource Manager

Chapter Resources Booklet
  MiniLAB, p. 3

Home and Community Involvement, p. 36

Performance Assessment in the Science Classroom, p. 57

Figure 3

Gregor Mendel discovered that the experiments he carried out on garden plants provided an understanding of heredity. For eight years he crossed plants that had different characteristics and recorded how those characteristics were passed from generation to generation. One such characteristic, or trait, was the color of pea pods. The results of Mendel's experiment on pea pod color are shown below.

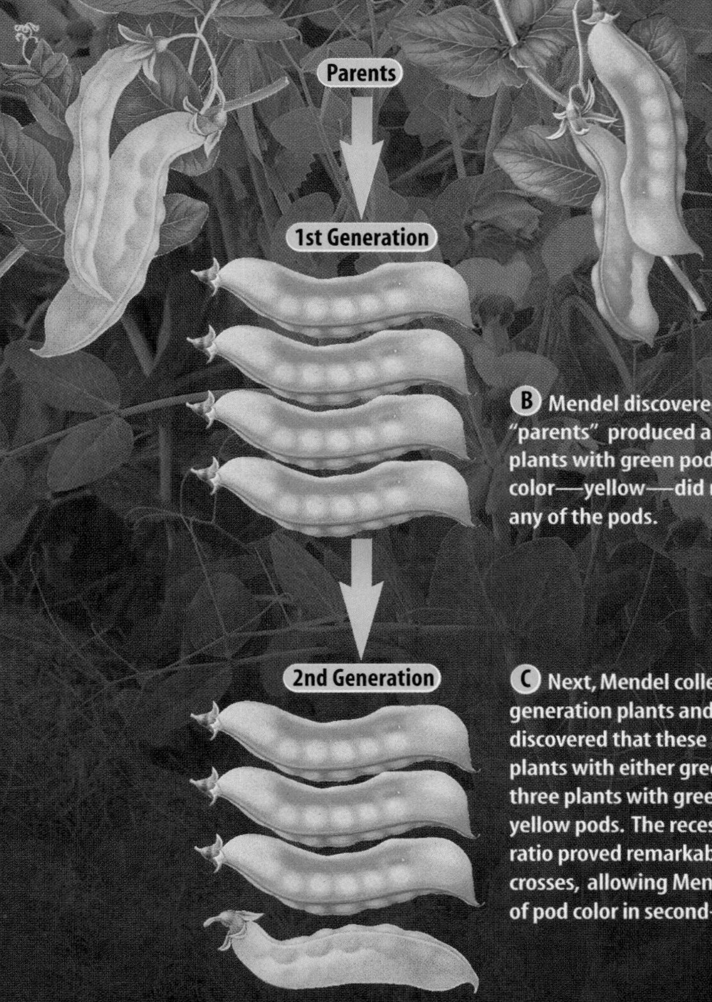

Parents

A One of the so-called "parent plants" in Mendel's experiment had pods that were green, a dominant trait. The other parent plant had pods that were yellow, a recessive trait.

1st Generation

B Mendel discovered that the two "parents" produced a generation of plants with green pods. The recessive color—yellow—did not appear in any of the pods.

2nd Generation

C Next, Mendel collected seeds from the first-generation plants and raised a second generation. He discovered that these second-generation plants produced plants with either green or yellow pods in a ratio of about three plants with green pods for every one plant with yellow pods. The recessive trait had reappeared. This 3:1 ratio proved remarkably consistent in hundreds of similar crosses, allowing Mendel to accurately predict the ratio of pod color in second-generation plants.

A ◆ 131

Visualizing Mendel's Experiments

Have students examine the pictures and read the captions. Then ask the following questions:

Why is it important that Mendel based his conclusions on the results of hundreds of pea plant crosses? It's important to have as much data as possible before drawing conclusions about any experiment, and in general, the larger your sample size, the more accurate your results will be.

Would the allele for the recessive trait of yellow pea pod color be present in the first generation of pea plants? Yes, the allele would be present, but it would not be expressed because none of the plants is homozygous recessive.

Activity

Have students work in small groups. Using the example shown in the Visualizing, have the students use Mendel's ratios to determine the number of yellow pea plants in the 2nd generation if the 2nd generation of plants contained the following: 100 total plants (25) 300 total plants (75).

Extension

Have students learn about one of the researchers who, in 1900, rediscovered Mendel's work while analyzing their own experiments, and report their finding to the class.

Genetics in a Garden, continued

Use an Analogy

The probability of genetic events is analogous to rolling a die and other games of chance.

Make a Model

Provide students with blocks of two different colors. Have them use the blocks to model the cross involving pea plant flowers described in the text. Help them use these tools to distinguish between genotype and phenotype, and homozygous and heterozygous.

Extension

Challenge students to form Punnett squares that show the results of first- and second-generation crosses between organisms purebred for two traits. If purebred organisms are crossed, the first generation will result in all heterozygous organisms. When these are crossed, students should obtain a 9:3:3:1 ratio, as shown below. L3 ELL COOP LEARN P

Caption Answer

Figure 4 No; if red is recessive, then the genotype is homozygous recessive (rr), but if red is dominant, then the flower could be either homozygous (RR) or heterozygous (Rr).

✔ Reading Check

Answer Homozygous organisms carry the same two alleles for a trait. Heterozygous organisms carry two different alleles for a trait.

Figure 4
This snapdragon's phenotype is red. *Can you tell what the flower's genotype for color is? Explain your answer.*

Using Probability to Make Predictions If you and your sister can't agree on what movie to see, you could solve the problem by tossing a coin. When you toss a coin, you're dealing with probabilities. Probability is a branch of mathematics that helps you predict the chance that something will happen. If your sister chooses tails while the coin is in the air, what is the probability that the coin will land tail-side up? Because a coin has two sides, there are two possible outcomes, heads or tails. One outcome is tails. Therefore, the probability of one side of a coin showing is one out of two, or 50 percent.

Mendel also dealt with probabilities. One of the things that made his predictions accurate was that he worked with large numbers of plants. He studied almost 30,000 pea plants over a period of eight years. By doing so, Mendel increased his chances of seeing a repeatable pattern. Valid scientific conclusions need to be based on results that can be duplicated.

Punnett Squares Suppose you wanted to know what colors of pea plant flowers you would get if you pollinated white flowers on one pea plant with pollen from purple flowers on a different plant. How could you predict what the offspring would look like without making the cross? A handy tool used to predict results in Mendelian genetics is the **Punnett** (PUN ut) **square.** In a Punnett square, letters represent dominant and recessive alleles. An uppercase letter stands for a dominant allele. A lowercase letter stands for a recessive allele. The letters are a form of code. They show the **genotype** (JEE nuh tipe), or genetic makeup, of an organism. Once you understand what the letters mean, you can tell a lot about the inheritance of a trait in an organism.

The way an organism looks and behaves as a result of its genotype is its **phenotype** (FEE nuh tipe), as shown in **Figure 4.** If you have brown hair, then the phenotype for your hair color is brown.

Alleles Determine Traits Most cells in your body have two alleles for every trait. These alleles are located on chromosomes within the nucleus of cells. An organism with two alleles that are the same is called **homozygous** (hoh muh ZI gus). For Mendel's peas, this would be written as *TT* (homozygous for the tall-dominant trait) or *tt* (homozygous for the short-recessive trait). An organism that has two different alleles for a trait is called **heterozygous** (het uh roh ZI gus). The hybrid plants Mendel produced were all heterozygous for height, *Tt*.

✔ Reading Check

What is the difference between homozygous and heterozygous organisms?

Sample Punnet Square for Extension:

Parent 1 (RrYy)

Parent 2 (RrYy)	RY	Ry	rY	ry
RY	RRYY	RRYy	RrYY	RrYy
Ry	RRYy	RRyy	RrYy	Rryy
rY	RrYY	RrYy	rrYY	rrYy
ry	RrYy	Rryy	rrYy	rryy

Making a Punnett Square In a Punnett square for predicting one trait, the letters representing the two alleles from one parent are written along the top of the grid, one letter per section. Those of the second parent are placed down the side of the grid, one letter per section. Each square of the grid is filled in with one allele donated by each parent. The letters that you use to fill in each of the squares represent the genotypes of possible offspring that the parents could produce.

Math Skills Activity

Calculating Probability Using a Punnett Square

You can determine the probability of certain traits by using a Punnett square. Letters are used to represent the two alleles from each parent and are combined to determine the possible genotypes of the offspring.

Example Problem

One dog carries heterozygous, black-fur traits (Bb), and its mate carries homogeneous, blond-fur traits (bb). Calculate the probability of the puppy having black fur.

Solution

1 *This is what you know:*
dominant allele is represented by *B*
recessive allele is represented by *b*

2 *This is what you need to find:*
the probability of a puppy's fur color being black using a Punnett square

3 *This is the diagram you need to use:*

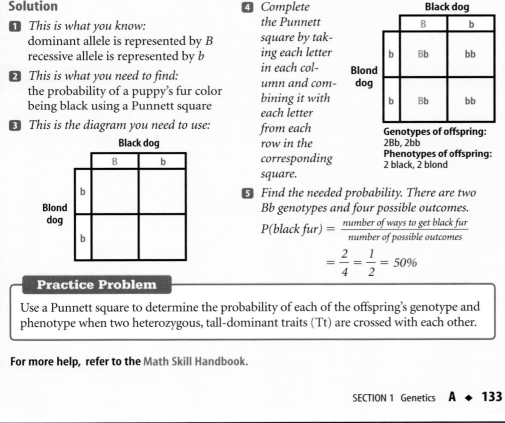

4 *Complete the Punnett square by taking each letter in each column and combining it with each letter from each row in the corresponding square.*

Genotypes of offspring:
2Bb, 2bb
Phenotypes of offspring:
2 black, 2 blond

5 *Find the needed probability. There are two Bb genotypes and four possible outcomes.*

$$P(black\ fur) = \frac{number\ of\ ways\ to\ get\ black\ fur}{number\ of\ possible\ outcomes}$$

$$= \frac{2}{4} = \frac{1}{2} = 50\%$$

Practice Problem

Use a Punnett square to determine the probability of each of the offspring's genotype and phenotype when two heterozygous, tall-dominant traits (Tt) are crossed with each other.

For more help, refer to the Math Skill Handbook.

SECTION 1 Genetics **A ◆ 133**

Genetics in a Garden, continued

Visual Learning

Table 2 Have students relate the principles of heredity to genetic examples they have studied in this section.

3 Assess

Reteach

Have students role play the alleles in a cross. Take the class to a paved portion of the school yard. Use masking tape to mark out a large Punnett square on the pavement. Assign students to be certain alleles and allow them to arrange themselves and announce the phenotypes and genotypes produced. L2 ELL  Visual-Spatial

Challenge

Have students determine the number of combinations possible in a trihybrid cross. There are 64 possibilities. L3 IS Logical-Mathematical

✓ Assessment

Performance Have students use a Punnett square to demonstrate their answer to Question 6. Use **PASC,** p. 97.

Principles of Heredity Even though Gregor Mendel didn't know anything about DNA, genes, or chromosomes, he succeeded in beginning to describe and mathematically represent how inherited traits are passed from parents to offspring. He realized that some factor in the pea plant produced certain traits. Mendel also concluded that these factors separated when the pea plant reproduced. Mendel arrived at his conclusions after years of detailed observation, careful analysis, and repeated experimentation. **Table 2** summarizes Mendel's principles of heredity.

Table 2 Principles of Heredity	
1	Traits are controlled by alleles on chromosomes.
2	An allele's effect is dominant or recessive.
3	When a pair of chromosomes separates during meiosis, the different alleles for a trait move into separate sex cells.

Section 1 Assessment

1. Alleles are described as being dominant or recessive. What is the difference between a dominant and a recessive allele?
2. How are dominant and recessive alleles represented in a Punnett square?
3. Explain the difference between genotype and phenotype. Give examples.
4. Gregor Mendel, an Austrian monk who lived in the 1800s, is known as the father of genetics. Explain why Mendel has been given this title.
5. **Think Critically** If an organism expresses a recessive phenotype, can you tell the genotype? Explain your answer by giving an example.

Skill Builder Activities

6. **Predicting** Hairline shape is an inherited trait in humans. The widow's peak allele is dominant, and the straight hairline allele is recessive. Predict how both parents with widow's peaks could have a child without a widow's peak hairline. **For more help, refer to the** Science Skill Handbook.

7. **Using Percentages** One fruit fly is heterozygous for long wings, and another fruit fly is homozygous for short wings. Long wings are dominant to short wings. Using a Punnett square, find out what percent of the offspring are expected to have short wings. **For more help, refer to the** Math Skill Handbook.

Answers to Section Assessment

1. A dominant allele covers up the trait of a recessive allele.
2. Dominant alleles are represented with a capital letter, recessive alleles with a lowercase letter.
3. Genotype is the combination of alleles an organism contains; phenotype is the expression of the alleles in an organism. For example, a genotype might be Tt (heterozygous dominant), and the phenotype might be tall.
4. He was the first person to explain the mechanisms of heredity.
5. Yes, because two copies of the recessive allele must be present for the recessive phenotype to show up.
6. Both parents would have to be heterozygous to produce children without the widow's peak trait.
7. 50%

Activity

Predicting Results

Could you predict how many brown rabbits would result from crossing two heterozygous black rabbits? Brown color is a recessive trait for hair color in rabbits. Try this investigation to find out.

What You'll Investigate
How does chance affect combinations of genes?

Materials
paper bags (2)   white beans (100)
red beans (100)

Goals
■ **Model** chance events in heredity.
■ **Compare and contrast** predicted and actual results.

Safety Precautions
WARNING: *Do not taste, eat, or drink any materials used in the lab.*

Procedure

1. Use a Punnett square to predict how many red/red, red/white, and white/white bean combinations are possible. The combinations represent the coat colors in rabbit offspring.

2. Place 50 red beans and 50 white beans in a paper bag. Place 50 red beans and 50 white beans in a second bag. Red beans represent black alleles and white beans represent brown alleles.

3. Label one of the bags *female* for the female parent. Label the other bag *male* for the male parent.

4. Use a data table to record the combination each time you remove two beans. Your table will need to accommodate 100 picks.

5. Without looking, remove one bean from each bag. The two beans represent the alleles that combine when sperm and egg join. After recording, return the beans to their bags.

6. **Count** and record the total numbers for each of the three combinations in your data table.

7. **Compile** and record the class totals.

Conclude and Apply

1. Which combination occurred most often?

2. **Calculate** the ratio of red/red to red/white to white/white. What hair color in rabbits do these combinations represent?

3. **Compare** your predicted (expected) results with your observed (actual) results.

4. **Hypothesize** how you could get predicted results to be closer to actual results.

Sample data

Gene Combinations			
Rabbits	**Red/ Red**	**Red/ White**	**White/ White**
Your Total			
Class Total			

Communicating
Your Data

Write a paragraph that clearly describes your results. Have another student read your paragraph. Ask if he or she could understand what happened. If not, rewrite your paragraph and have the other student read it again. **For more help, refer to the** Science Skill Handbook.

Activity

BENCH TESTED

Purpose Students use a model to investigate how the principles of heredity are related to chance.
L2 ELL IS **Logical-Mathematical Process Skills** predicting, observing, recording data, interpreting data, using numbers, making and using tables

Time Required one class period

Safety Precautions Remind students not to eat or throw the beans.

Teaching Strategies

• All the beans should be approximately the same size.

• Emphasize the importance of completing all 100 trials.

• **Troubleshooting** Explain to students that beans must be returned to the bag after each draw so that the probability of choosing the different color combinations remains the same throughout the activity.

Answers to Questions

1. red/white

2. Results should be close to 1:2:1; red/red represents a black rabbit, red/white represents a black rabbit, and white/white represents a brown rabbit.

3. Answers will vary, but should follow expected results closely.

4. A larger sample could be used or more trials done.

Assessment

Performance To further assess students' knowledge of probability, have them repeat the activity using three different kinds of beans. Use the **PASC,** p. 97.

Resource Manager

Chapter Resources Booklet
Activity Worksheet, pp. 5–6
Reinforcement, p. 23
Lab Activity, pp. 11–12

Communicating
Your Data

Students' paragraphs should indicate methods and results, as well as how the model relates to actual heredity principles.

1 Motivate

Bellringer Transparency

Display the Section Focus
Transparency for Section 2.
Use the accompanying Trans-
parency Activity Master. L2
ELL

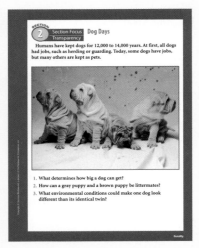

Tie to Prior Knowledge

Ask students if any of them
have eye color different from
either parent. Have students
brainstorm how this could happen, based on what they have
learned about dominant and
recessive genes. Then explain
that some inherited traits
involve more complex patterns
of inheritance, and students will
learn about them in this section.

Caption Answer

Figure 5E 1 chestnut horse: 2 appaloosa
horses:1 white horse

As You Read

What You'll Learn

- **Explain** how traits are inherited by incomplete dominance.
- **Compare** multiple alleles and polygenic inheritance, and give examples of each.
- **Describe** two human genetic dis-orders and how they are inherited.
- **Explain** how sex-linked traits are passed to offspring.

Vocabulary
incomplete dominance
polygenic inheritance
sex-linked gene

Why It's Important
Most of your inherited traits involve more complex patterns of inheri-tance than Mendel discovered.

Figure 5
These Punnett squares show how the color of horses may be inher-ited by incomplete dominance.
A **When a chestnut horse is bred with** B **a white horse, all the offspring will be Appaloosa, as shown in** C **, the first Punnett square.** D **When two Appaloosa horses from the offspring are bred, many phenotypes are pro-duced as illustrated in** E **, the second Punnett square.** *What is the ratio of the different phenotypes produced in this second generation?*

Incomplete Dominance

Not even in science do things remain the same. After Mendel's work was rediscovered in 1900, scientists repeated his experiments, and for some plants, such as peas, Mendel's results proved true. However, when different plants were crossed, the results were sometimes different. One scientist crossed purebred red four-o'clock plants with purebred white four-o'clock plants. He expected to get all red flowers, but they were pink. Neither allele for flower color seemed dominant. Had the colors become blended like paint colors? He crossed the pink-flowered plants with each other, and red, pink, and white flowers were produced. The red and white alleles had not become blended. Instead, when the allele for white flowers and the allele for red flowers com-bined, the result was an intermediate phenotype—a pink flower. Similar results for horses are shown in **Figure 5. Incomplete dominance** produces a phenotype that is intermediate between the two homozygous parents. Feather color in some types of chickens also is inherited by incomplete dominance.

A

B

C

	Chestnut horse (CC)	
	C	C
White horse (C'C') C'	CC'	CC'
C'	CC'	CC'

Genotypes: All CC'
Phenotypes: All Appaloosa horses

Section ✓Assessment Planner

Multiple Alleles Mendel studied traits in peas that were controlled by just two alleles. However, many traits are controlled by more than two alleles. A trait that is controlled by more than two alleles is said to be controlled by multiple alleles. Traits controlled by multiple alleles produce more than three phenotypes of that trait.

Imagine that only three types of coins are made—nickels, dimes, and quarters. If every person can have only two coins, six different combinations are possible. In this problem, the coins represent alleles of a trait. The sum of each two-coin combination represents the phenotype. Can you name the six different phenotypes possible with two coins?

Blood type in humans is an example of multiple alleles that produce only four phenotypes. The alleles for blood types are called A, B, and O. The O allele is recessive to both the A and B alleles. When a person inherits one A allele and one B allele for blood type, both are expressed—phenotype AB. A person with phenotype A blood has the genetic makeup, or genotype—AA or AO. Someone with phenotype B blood has the genotype BB or BO. Finally, a person with phenotype O blood has the genotype OO.

Research Visit the Glencoe Science Web site at **science.glencoe.com** for information on the importance of blood types in blood transfusions. In your Science Journal, draw a chart showing which blood types can be used safely during transfusions.

 **Reading Check** *What are the six different blood type genotypes?*

D

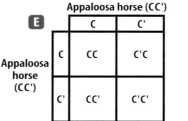
E

Appaloosa horse (CC')

Appaloosa horse (CC')	C	C'
C	CC	C'C
C'	CC'	C'C'

Genotypes: CC, CC', C'C'
Phenotypes: One chestnut, two Appaloosas, and one white horse

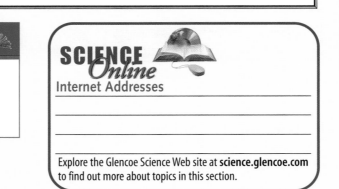

SECTION 2 Genetics Since Mendel **A ◆ 137**

---

② Teach

Incomplete Dominance

Discussion

Discuss why traits governed by incomplete dominance or multiple alleles might be more difficult to study. Help students see that these patterns do not conform to Mendel's prediction of a simple 3:1 ratio.

Text Question Answer

Possible combinations: nickel, dime; nickel, quarter; dime, quarter; nickel, nickel; dime, dime; quarter, quarter

Fun Fact

Blood types are important to the health profession. Matching blood types—both ABO and Rh—is important in transfusions. The recessive blood type, O, occurs in more than 30 percent of Americans.

Reading Check

Answer AA, AO, AB, BB, BO, OO

Science Journal

Genetics of Flower Color

Explain that in hibiscus flowers, red is dominant to white. Have students explain why they can tell the genotype of a red four-o'clock, but not of a red hibiscus. Four-o'clocks inherit color by incomplete dominance. A red four-o'clock must be homozygous. If it were heterozygous, it would be pink. A red hibiscus might be heterozygous or homozygous. L2 P

SCIENCE Online
Internet Addresses

_____
_____
_____
_____

Explore the Glencoe Science Web site at **science.glencoe.com** to find out more about topics in this section.

Polygenic Inheritance

Use Science Words

Word Origin Polygenic inheritance involves many genes. The prefix *poly-* means "many." Have students use a dictionary to find other words with this prefix and explain their meanings. Possible answers: polygon—many sided figure; polychromatic—made of many colors

Purpose to determine the inheritance pattern that controls hand span L2 ELL

Logical-Mathematical

Materials paper, pencil, ruler

Teaching Strategy It may be easier for students to have each subject place his or her hand on a piece of paper and mark the width of the hand span before measuring it.

Analysis

1. Answers will vary. Spans may range from 12.5 cm to 24 cm or more.
2. Hand spans are determined by polygenic inheritance, not by a simple Mendelian pattern.

Oral Ask students to determine if identical twins have identical hand spans. The spans are usually very close, but not identical because of environmental factors that affect growth. Use **Performance Assessment in the Science Classroom,** p. 89.

Interpreting Polygenic Inheritance

Procedure

1. Measure the hand spans of your classmates.
2. Using a **ruler,** measure from the tip of the thumb to the tip of the little finger when the hand is stretched out. Read the measurement to the nearest centimeter.
3. Record the name and hand-span measurement of each person in a data table.

Analysis

1. What range of hand spans did you find?
2. Are hand spans inherited as a simple Mendelian pattern or as a polygenic or incomplete dominance pattern? Explain.

Figure 6
Himalayan rabbits have alleles for dark-colored fur. However, this allele is able to express itself only at lower temperatures. Only the areas located farthest from the rabbit's main body heat (ears, nose, feet, tail) have dark-colored fur.

Polygenic Inheritance

Eye color is an example of a trait that is produced by a combination of many genes. **Polygenic** (pahl ih JEHN ihk) **inheritance** occurs when a group of gene pairs acts together to produce a trait. The effects of many alleles produces a wide variety of phenotypes. For this reason, it may be hard to classify all the different shades of eye color.

Your height and the color of your eyes and skin are just some of the many human traits controlled by polygenic inheritance. It is estimated that three to six gene pairs control your skin color. Even more gene pairs might control the color of your hair and eyes. The environment also plays an important role in the expression of traits controlled by polygenic inheritance. Polygenic inheritance is common and includes such traits as grain color in wheat and milk production in cows. Egg production in chickens is also a polygenic trait.

Impact of the Environment Your environment plays a role in how some of your genes are expressed or whether they are expressed at all, as shown in **Figure 6.** Environmental influences may be internal or external. For example, most male birds are more brightly colored than females. Chemicals in their bodies determine whether the gene for brightly colored feathers is expressed.

Although genes determine many of your traits, you might be able to influence their expression by the decisions you make. Some people have genes that make them at risk for developing certain cancers. Whether they get cancer might depend on external environmental factors. For instance, if some people at risk for skin cancer limit their exposure to the Sun and take care of their skin, they might never develop cancer.

✔ **Reading Check** *What environmental factors might affect the size of leaves on a tree?*

Resource Manager

Chapter Resources Booklet
  MiniLAB, p. 4
Life Science Critical Thinking/Problem Solving, p. 19

✔ Active Reading

Reflective Journal In this strategy, students identify activities and what they learned and record responses to the activities. Have students divide pieces of paper into several columns. Have them record their thoughts under headings such as "What I did," "What I learned," "What questions do I have," "What surprises did I experience," and "Overall response." Have students write a Reflective Journal entry for the MiniLAB.

Human Genes and Mutations

Sometimes a gene undergoes a change that results in a trait that is expressed differently. Occasionally errors occur in the DNA when it is copied inside of a cell. Such changes and errors are called mutations. Not all mutations are harmful. They might be helpful or have no effect on an organism.

Certain chemicals are known to produce mutations in plants or animals, including humans. X rays and radioactive substances are other causes of some mutations. Mutations are changes in genes.

Chromosome Disorders In addition to individual mutations, problems can occur if the incorrect number of chromosomes is inherited. Every organism has a specific number of chromosomes. However, mistakes in the process of meiosis can result in a new organism with more or fewer chromosomes than normal. A change in the total number of human chromosomes is usually fatal to the unborn embryo or fetus, or the baby may die soon after birth.

Look at the human chromosomes in **Figure 7.** If three copies of chromosome 21 are produced in the fertilized human egg, Down's syndrome results. Individuals with Down's syndrome can be short, exhibit learning disabilities, and have heart problems. Such individuals can lead normal lives if they have no severe health complications.

Figure 7
Humans usually have 23 pairs of chromosomes. Notice that three copies of chromosome 21 are present in this photo, rather than the usual two chromosomes. This change in chromosome number results in Down's syndrome. Chris Burke, a well-known actor, has this syndrome.

Human Genes and Mutations

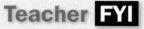

Teacher FYI

Somatic mutations occur in body cells and can produce a localized change—e.g., the streak of white sometimes found in the hair of an otherwise normal individual. All the cells descended from the mutant body cell will carry the mutation, but it cannot be passed on to offspring. Germinal mutations affect the sex cells (eggs or sperm) and can be transmitted to the individual's offspring.

LAB DEMONSTRATION

Purpose to show how mutations are passed to daughter cells

Materials blue and red overhead acetate, yarn, scissors, overhead projector

Preparation Cut out several 2-, 4-, and 6-cm long pairs of blue chromosomes. Cut one 4-cm long red chromosome.

Procedure Make a circle of yarn on the projector to represent a cell. Place the blue chromosome pairs in the cell. "Mutate" one chromosome from blue to red. Divide the chromosomes to make two new cells surrounded by yarn as if the cell had undergone mitosis.

Expected Outcome One daughter cell carries a mutation.

✔ Assessment

What will happen when the cell carrying the mutation reproduces? The mutation will be reproduced. **How might this explain how a person could have a white stripe in his hair, while the rest of his hair remains black?** The mutation is in the hair cells. It is passed along when the hair cells undergo mitosis.

Recessive Genetic Disorders

Discussion

Point out that about 1,000 simple recessive human disorders are presently known. Genetic disorders caused by dominant alleles are less common. An example is Huntington's disease, which usually does not express itself until the person is an adult. **Why are most human genetic disorders recessive?** If a disorder caused by a dominant allele becomes apparent when the person is young, the person might elect not to have children and pass on the allele. People who are heterozygous for a recessive disorder may not know they are carriers and pass the allele on to offspring.

Answer Cystic fibrosis is a recessive disorder.

Caption Answer

Figure 8 The X chromosome is larger than the Y, and looks like an X. The Y chromosome looks like the V part of a Y.

Chemistry INTEGRATION

If both parents are heterozygous for the trait, they have a 25 percent chance of producing an offspring with PKU with each pregnancy.

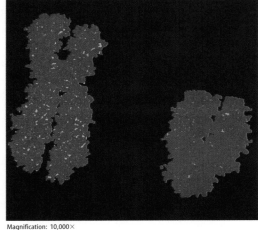

Magnification: 10,000×

Figure 8
Sex in many organisms is determined by X and Y chromosomes. *How do the X (left) and Y (right) chromosomes differ from one another in shape and size?*

Chemistry INTEGRATION

People with PKU, a recessive disorder, are missing the enzyme needed to break down a substance found in some artificially sweetened drinks. Soft-drink cans must be labeled to ensure that individuals with this disorder do not unknowingly consume the substance. Explain in your Science Journal how a person can be born with PKU if neither parent has this recessive disorder.

Recessive Genetic Disorders

Most human genetic disorders, such as cystic fibrosis, are caused by recessive genes. Some recessive genes are the result of a mutation within the gene. Many of these alleles are rare. Such genetic disorders occur when both parents have a recessive allele responsible for this disorder. Because the parents are heterozygous, they don't show any symptoms. However, if each parent passes the recessive allele to the child, the child inherits both recessive alleles and will have a recessive genetic disorder.

Reading Check *How is cystic fibrosis inherited?*

Cystic fibrosis is a homozygous recessive disorder. It is the most common genetic disorder that may lead to death among Caucasian Americans. In most people, a thin fluid is produced that lubricates the lungs and intestinal tract. People with cystic fibrosis produce thick mucus instead of this thin fluid. The thick mucus builds up in the lungs and makes it hard to breathe. This buildup often results in repeated bacterial respiratory infections. The thick mucus also reduces or prevents the flow of substances necessary for digesting food. Physical therapy, special diets, and new drug therapies have increased the life spans of patients with cystic fibrosis.

Sex Determination

What determines the sex of an individual? Much information on sex inheritance came from studies of fruit flies. Fruit flies have only four pairs of chromosomes. Because the chromosomes are large and few in number, they are easy to study. Scientists identified one pair that contains genes that determine the sex of the organism. They labeled the pair XX in females and XY in males. Geneticists use these labels when studying organisms, including humans. You can see human X and Y chromosomes in **Figure 8.**

Each egg produced by a female normally contains one X chromosome. Males produce sperm that normally have either an X or a Y chromosome. When a sperm with an X chromosome fertilizes an egg, the offspring is a female, XX. A male offspring, XY, is the result of a Y-containing sperm fertilizing an egg. What pair of sex chromosomes is in each of your cells? Sometimes chromosomes do not separate during meiosis. When this occurs, an individual may inherit an abnormal number of sex chromosomes.

Inclusion Strategies

Learning Disabled Some students may appreciate seeing photos or videos that depict much of the information presented here. The March of Dimes and other foundations supply free or low-cost classroom materials that summarize many of these concepts. L1 IS **Visual-Spatial**

Teacher FYI

Most students will be aware of someone with a genetic disorder. Be sensitive to the possibility that students may have someone in their own family with a disorder.

Sex-Linked Disorders

Some inherited conditions are linked with the X and Y chromosomes. An allele inherited on a sex chromosome is called a **sex-linked gene.** Color blindness is a sex-linked disorder in which people cannot distinguish between certain colors, particularly red and green. This trait is a recessive allele on the X chromosome. Because males have only one X chromosome, a male with this allele on his X chromosome is color-blind. However, a color-blind female occurs only when both of her X chromosomes have the allele for this trait.

The allele for the distinct patches of three different colors found in calico cats is recessive and carried on the X chromosome. As shown in **Figure 9,** calico cats have inherited two X chromosomes with this recessive allele—one from both parents.

Pedigrees Trace Traits

How can you trace a trait through a family? A pedigree is a visual tool for following a trait through generations of a family. Males are represented by squares and females by circles. A completely filled circle or square shows that the trait is seen in that person. Half-colored circles or squares indicate carriers. A carrier is heterozygous for the trait and it is not seen. People represented by empty circles or squares do not have the trait and are not carriers. The pedigree in **Figure 10** shows how the trait for color blindness is carried through a family.

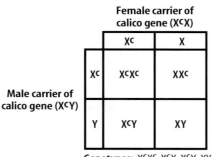

Female carrier of calico gene (XᶜX)

	Xᶜ	X
Xᶜ	XᶜXᶜ	XXᶜ
Y	XᶜY	XY

Male carrier of calico gene (XᶜY)

Genotypes: XᶜXᶜ, XᶜX, XᶜY, XY
Phenotypes: One calico female, one carrier female, one carrier male, one normal male

Figure 9
Calico cat fur is a homozygous recessive sex-linked trait. Female cats that are heterozygous are not calico but are only carriers. Two recessive alleles must be present for this allele to be expressed. *Why aren't all the females calico?*

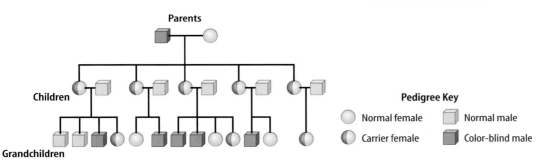

Parents

Children

Grandchildren

Pedigree Key
○ Normal female   ▢ Normal male
◐ Carrier female   ▨ Color-blind male

Figure 10
The symbols in this pedigree's key mean the same thing on all pedigree charts. The grandfather in this family was color-blind and married to a woman who was not a carrier of the color-blind allele. *Why are no women in this family color-blind?*

SECTION 2   Genetics Since Mendel   **A ◆ 141**

Sex-Linked Disorders

Quick Demo
Use Punnett squares to demonstrate inheritance patterns discussed in this section, such as the combination of X and Y chromosomes that determines the sex of an individual.

Make a Model
Have students use a set of cutouts of X and Y chromosomes to model how a sex-linked disorder can be inherited.

Caption Answer
Figure 9 All the females aren't calico because some are heterozygous.

Pedigrees Trace Traits

Visual Learning

Figure 10 Have students use this figure to answer the following questions. **How many children are carriers for color blindness?** 5 **How many grandchildren?** 3 **What percent is this of each generation?** 100% of children, 23% of grandchildren are carriers.

Extension
Have students find out the pros and cons of purebred breeding. For example, some purebred dog breeds have fragile bone structure or poor kidney functioning. Breeding with other breeds might lessen these weaknesses. L2

Caption Answer
Figure 10 Because color-blind women must inherit the allele from both mother and father, more women are carriers of color blindness than have the disorder.

Pedigrees Trace Traits, continued

✔ **Reading Check**

Answer It helps him or her predict the probability of offspring showing certain traits.

3 Assess

Reteach

Have students compare the three inheritance patterns in this section by making a chart. [L1]
[IS] **Visual-Spatial**

Challenge

Which would be more difficult to predict, the results of incomplete dominance, multiple alleles, or polygenic inheritance? The number of variations is usually much greater with polygenic inheritance than with the other two patterns.

✔ Assessment

Process Have students prepare a table that lists types of inheritance, their descriptions, and examples of each. Use **PASC,** p. 109.

Resource Manager

Chapter Resources Booklet
Reinforcement, p. 24

Figure 11
A variety of traits are considered when breeding dogs. **A** Black Labrador retrievers often are bred to be sporting dogs.
B Shih tzus are usually companion or show dogs.

Field GUIDE

What traits are cats bred for? to find out more about cat breeds, see the **Feline Traits Field Guide** at the back of the book.

Using Pedigrees A pedigree is a useful tool for a geneticist. Sometimes a geneticist needs to understand who has had a trait in a family over several generations to determine its pattern of inheritance. A geneticist determines if a trait is recessive, dominant, sex-linked, or has some other pattern of inheritance. When geneticists understand how a trait is inherited, they can predict the probability that a baby will be born with a specific trait.

✔ **Reading Check** *Why is a pedigree a useful tool for a geneticist?*

Pedigrees also are important in breeding animals or plants. Because livestock and plant crops are used as sources of food, these organisms are bred to increase their yield and nutritional content. Breeders of pets, like the dogs pictured in **Figure 11,** and show animals also examine pedigrees carefully for possible desirable physical and ability traits. Issues concerning health also are considered when researching pedigrees.

Section 2 Assessment

1. Compare inheritance by multiple alleles and polygenic inheritance.
2. Explain why a trait inherited by incomplete dominance, such as the color of Appaloosa horses, is not a blend of two alleles.
3. Describe two genetic disorders and discuss how they are inherited.
4. Using a Punnett square, explain why males are affected more often than females by sex-linked genetic disorders.
5. **Think Critically** Calico male cats are rare. Explain how such a cat can exist.

Skill Builder Activities

6. **Predicting** A man with blood type B marries a woman with blood type A. Their first child has blood type O. Predict what other blood types are possible for their future children. Explain your answer using a Punnett square. **For more help, refer to the** Science Skill Handbook.
7. **Communicating** In your Science Journal, write an essay that explains why the offspring of two parents may or may not show much resemblance to either parent. **For more help, refer to the** Science Skill Handbook.

Answers to Section Assessment

1. Multiple alleles involves a single pair of genes that have more than two alleles; polygenic inheritance involves multiple pairs of genes, each with two or more alleles, all affecting the same trait.
2. The two alleles are present in the offspring, and are available to be passed on. But when combined, they produce a phenotype that is intermediate between those shown by homozygous individuals.
3. Answers will vary. Sample response: cystic fibrosis, a disease affecting the lungs and other organs, is inherited as a simple recessive trait.
4. Males only need to inherit one gene encoding for the disorder to be affected. Females must inherit two genes for the disorder to appear.
5. Possible answer: A mutation may allow a male cat to inherit an extra X chromosome in addition to a Y chromosome. Both X chromosomes may carry the recessive calico trait.
6. Children may have blood types A, B, O, or AB. The Punnett square should show heterozygous parents with the alleles AO and BO.
7. There are many genes and combinations, so an individual may look very different from either parent.

Advances in Genetics

Why is genetics important?

If Mendel were to pick up a daily newspaper in any country today, he'd probably be surprised. News articles about developments in genetic research appear almost daily. The term *gene* has become a common word. The laws of heredity are being used to change the world.

Genetic Engineering

You may know that chromosomes are made of DNA and are in the nucleus of a cell. Sections of DNA in chromosomes that direct cell activities are called genes. Through **genetic engineering,** scientists are experimenting with biological and chemical methods to change the arrangement of DNA that makes up a gene. Genetic engineering already is used to help produce large volumes of medicine. Genes also can be inserted into cells to change how those cells perform their normal functions, as shown in **Figure 12.** Other research is being done to find new ways to improve crop production and quality, including the development of plants that are resistant to disease.

As You Read

What You'll Learn
- **Evaluate** the importance of advances in genetics.
- **Sequence** the steps in making genetically engineered organisms.

Vocabulary
genetic engineering

Why It's Important
Advances in genetics can affect your health, the foods that you eat, and your environment.

Figure 12
DNA from one organism is placed into another species. This method is used to produce human insulin, human growth hormone, and other chemicals by bacteria.

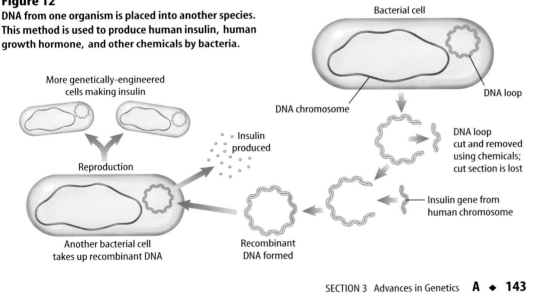

More genetically-engineered cells making insulin

Reproduction

Insulin produced

Bacterial cell

DNA chromosome

DNA loop

DNA loop cut and removed using chemicals; cut section is lost

Insulin gene from human chromosome

Another bacterial cell takes up recombinant DNA

Recombinant DNA formed

SECTION 3 Advances in Genetics **A ◆ 143**

Advances in Genetics

Motivate

Bellringer Transparency

Display the Section Focus Transparency for Section 3. Use the accompanying Transparency Activity Master. L2
ELL

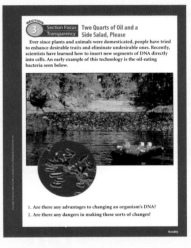

Tie to Prior Knowledge

Explain that in selective breeding, specific crosses are made to accentuate a desired trait in offspring. Discuss with students how this might be advantageous to a plant breeder trying to produce a corn plant that has higher yields. Then explain that scientists are trying to find new ways to change traits without the time involved in selective breeding. They will learn about these techniques in this section.

Section ✓ Assessment Planner

PORTFOLIO
Assessment, p. 145
PERFORMANCE ASSESSMENT
Skill Builder Activities, p. 145
See page 152 for more options.

CONTENT ASSESSMENT
Section, p. 145
Challenge, p. 145
Chapter, pp. 152–153

Genetic Engineering

Visual Learning

Figure 13 Explain that gene therapy is still in its infancy. As more is learned, the applications are likely to extend to many more genetic disorders. Remind students of the demonstration of a mutation in a cell being propagated by mitosis. **How is gene therapy similar to the way a mutation is propagated through body cells?** The mechanisms are similar, but in gene therapy, a mutation is corrected by the propagation, instead of spread.

Environmental Science

INTEGRATION

Crop plants are now being genetically engineered to produce chemicals that kill specific pests that feed on them. Some of the pollen from pesticide-resistant canola crops is capable of spreading up to 8 km from the plant, while corn and potato pollen can spread up to 1 km. What might be the effects of pollen landing on other plants?

Recombinant DNA Making recombinant DNA is one method of genetic engineering. Recombinant DNA is made by inserting a useful segment of DNA from one organism into a bacterium, as illustrated in **Figure 12.** Large quantities of human insulin, a substance needed by people with diabetes to control the level of sugar in their blood, are made by organisms that have been genetically engineered. Other uses include the production of growth hormone to treat dwarfism and chemicals to treat cancer.

Gene Therapy Gene therapy is a kind of genetic engineering. In gene therapy, a normal allele is placed in a virus, as shown in **Figure 13.** The virus then delivers the normal allele when it infects its target cell. The normal allele replaces the defective one. Scientists are conducting experiments that use this method to test ways of controlling cystic fibrosis and some kinds of cancer. More than 2,000 people already have taken part in gene therapy experiments. Gene therapy might be a method of curing several other genetic disorders in the future.

Figure 13
Gene therapy involves placing a normal allele in a cell that has a mutation. When the normal allele begins to function, a genetic disorder such as cystic fibrosis (CF) may be corrected.

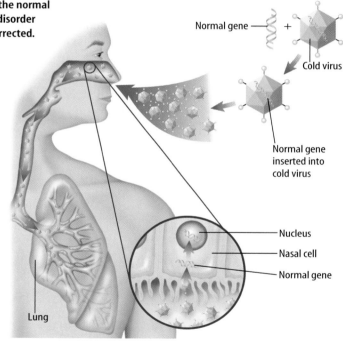

Normal gene

Cold virus

Normal gene inserted into cold virus

Nucleus

Nasal cell

Normal gene

Lung

Genetically Engineered Plants For thousands of years people have improved the plants they use for food and clothing even without the knowledge of genotypes. Until recently, these improvements were the results of selecting plants with the most desired traits to bred for the next generation. This process is called selective breeding. Recent advances in genetics have not replaced selective breeding. Although a plant may be bred for a particular phenotype, the genotype and pedigree of the plants also are considered.

Genetic engineering can produce improvements in crop plants, such as corn, wheat, and rice. One type of genetic engineering involves finding the genes that produce desired traits in one plant and then inserting those genes into a different plant. Scientists recently have made genetically engineered tomatoes with a gene that allows tomatoes to be picked green and transported great distances before they ripen completely. Ripe, firm tomatoes are then available in the local market. In the future, additional food crops may be genetically engineered so that they are not desirable food for insects.

Figure 14
Genetically engineered produce is sometimes labeled. This allows consumers to make informed choices about their foods.

✔ **Reading Check** *What other types of traits would be considered desirable in plants?*

Because some people might prefer foods that are not changed genetically, some stores label such produce, as shown in **Figure 14.** The long-term effects of consuming genetically engineered plants are unknown.

Answer Possible answers: increased growth rate, increased fruit size and production, reduced need for water, improved flavor, desirable flower color

③ Assess

Reteach
Have students make flash cards that illustrate steps in the process of genetic engineering. Have students practice identifying and ordering the steps using these cards.

Challenge
Should gene therapy be made available for all genetic disorders, or only those that are most harmful? Support your answer. Individual responses will vary. Accept all responses for which students provide support.

✔ *Assessment*

Performance Have students make a model that demonstrates the process of genetic engineering. Use **Performance Assessment in the Science Classroom,** p. 123. P

Resource Manager

Chapter Resources Booklet
Transparency Activity, p. 42
Reinforcement, p. 25
Directed Reading for
Content Mastery, pp. 17, 18

Section ③ Assessment

1. Give examples of areas in which advances in genetics are important.
2. Compare and contrast the technologies of using recombinant DNA and gene therapy.
3. What are some benefits of genetically engineered crops?
4. How does selective breeding differ from genetic engineering?
5. **Think Critically** Why might some people be opposed to genetically engineered plants?

Skill Builder Activities

6. **Concept Mapping** Make an events chain concept map of the steps used in making recombinant DNA. **For more help, refer to the** Science Skill Handbook.
7. **Using a Word Processor** Use a computer word processing program to write predictions about how advances in genetics might affect your life in the next ten years. **For more help, refer to the** Technology Skill Handbook.

SECTION 3 Advances in Genetics **A ◆ 145**

Answers to Section Assessment

1. Answers may include agriculture, health, and medicine.
2. Recombinant DNA inserts a segment of DNA from an organism into a bacterium to produce needed substances. Gene therapy places a normal allele into a virus, which delivers the allele to its target cell. There, it replaces the defective allele.
3. They may lead to increased crop production or be pest-resistant.
4. Selective breeding is usually slower and relies on phenotypes that are found in an existing population. Genetic engineering may take traits from one organism and place them into another.
5. Some people are concerned about pesticide resistance in weeds or other unforeseen consequences.
6. Answers should reflect steps shown in **Figure 12.**
7. Answers may include increased food production, curing genetic disorders, or providing new medicines.

Activity

Recognize the Problem

Purpose

Students will devise a method to test for color blindness, and administer the test to determine the percentage of affected individuals.

Process Skills

interpreting data, designing an experiment, forming a hypothesis, communicating, using numbers

Time Required

one class period

Materials

colored markers, blank white paper

Form a Hypothesis

Possible Hypothesis

Students may hypothesize that color blindness will affect more males than females.

Test Your Hypothesis

Possible Procedures

Students may choose to create a picture or number out of green circles. They can then use circles of red, orange, or yellow to surround the picture or number. Using this test, students would determine whether individuals could see the "hidden" picture or number.

Activity · Design Your Own Experiment

Tests for Color Blindness

What do color-blind people see? People who have inherited color blindness can see most colors, but they have difficulty telling the difference between two specific colors. You have three genes that help you see color. One gene lets you see red, another blue, and the third gene allows you to see green. In the most common type of color blindness, red-green blindness, the green gene does not work properly. What is the percentage of people who are color-blind?

Recognize the Problem

What percentages of males and females in your school are color-blind?

Form a Hypothesis

Based on your reading and your own experiences, form a hypothesis about how common color blindness is among males and females.

Goals
- **Design** an experiment that tests for a specific type of color blindness in males and females.
- **Calculate** the percentage of males and females with the disorder.

Possible Materials
white paper or poster board
colored markers: red, orange, yellow, bright green, dark green, blue
*computer and color printer
*Alternate materials

To a person with red-green blindness, bright green appears tan in color, and dark green looks like brown. The color red also looks brown, making it difficult to tell the different between green and red. A person without red-green color blindness could see a "6" in this test, while a red-green color blind person cannot see this number.

Resource Manager

Chapter Resources Booklet
  Activity Worksheet, pp. 7–8
  Enrichment, p. 28
Lab Management and Safety, p. 74

Test Your Hypothesis

Plan

1. Decide what type of color blindness you will test for—the common green-red blindness or the more rare green-blue blindness.
2. **List** the materials you will need and describe how you will create test pictures. Tests for color blindness use many circles of red, orange, and yellow as a background, with circles of dark and light green to make a picture or number. List the steps you will take to test your hypothesis.
3. Prepare a data table in your Science Journal to record your test results.

4. **Examine** your experiment to make sure all steps are in logical order.
5. **Identify** which pictures you will use as a control and which pictures you will use as variables.

Do

1. Make sure your teacher approves your plan before you start.
2. **Draw** the pictures that you will use to test for color blindness.
3. Carry out your experiment as planned and record your results in your data table.

Analyze Your Data

1. **Calculate** the percentage of males and females that tested positive for color blindness.
2. **Compare** the frequency of color blindness in males with the frequency of the color blindness in females.

Draw Conclusions

1. Did the results support your hypothesis? Explain.
2. Use your results to explain why color blindness is called a sex-linked disorder.
3. **Infer** how common the color-blind disorder is in the general population.
4. **Predict** your results if you were to test a larger number of people.

Communicating Your Data

Using a word processor, **write** a short article for the advice column of a fashion magazine about how a color-blind person can avoid wearing outfits with clashing colors. **For more help, refer to the** Technology Skill Handbook.

ACTIVITY   A ◆ 147

Teaching Strategy

Allow students to test individuals outside of class. Encourage them to test family, friends, and other teachers. Have them turn in their results after one week.

Expected Outcome

More males than females will test positive for color blindness.

Analyze Your Data

1. More males should test positive than females.
2. Males are much more likely to be color blind than females.

Error Analysis

Have students compare results to identify errors in data collection. Some possible sources of error are colors on the test pictures not being right or students overhearing the results of others so as not to give a true result.

Draw Conclusions

1. Answers will vary.
2. The allele for this trait is only located on the X chromosome. Because males only have one X chromosome, males with this allele will be color blind. A female will be color blind only when both of her X chromosomes have the color blind allele.
3. Color blindness afflicts 8 percent of males and 0.04 percent of females.
4. A larger sample will give more accurate results.

Process Have students create a similar test for another type of color blindness. After getting results, have students make a bar graph showing the percentages of individuals affected with each type of color blindness. Use **Performance Assessment in the Science Classroom,** p. 107.

Communicating Your Data

Students might suggest that matching colors be grouped in different areas of the closet, or that a tagging system be developed so that one group of matching clothing is labeled *A*, a second group is labeled *B*, and so on.

Science Stats

Content Background

The human genome project, an international, cooperative effort to sequence the human genome, is making continual contributions to our knowledge of human genetics. Scientists involved in the project are quick to point out the many things they don't know, even though the genome is complete. For example, the exact mechanism that turns genes on and off as needed, the exact function of many genes, and how some genes work together to cause disease are known. Students may be curious to know whose genome is being sequenced. The government and private companies working on genomes are using several anonymous donors of various racial and ethnic backgrounds.

Discussion

Mice and humans have many similar genes. What is one characteristic or function shared by mice and humans that might be coded for by similar genes? Possible answer: Both mice and humans have digestive enzymes that could be coded for by similar genes.

Activity

Have students write a story from the point of view of a human gene. Students should include details such as which chromosome the gene is located on, the function of the gene, and whether the gene functions all the time or is switched on and off. Students can either use an imaginary gene, or an actual human gene. **Linguistic**

Science Stats

The Human Genome

Did you know...

. . . The human genome is not very different from the genome of mice. As shown to the right, many of the genes that are found on mouse chromosome 17 are similar to genes on human chromosomes. Humans may be more closely related to other organisms than previously thought.

Found on human chromosome

6
16
21
6
19
18
2

Mouse chromosome 17

Human hair

DNA

. . . The strands of DNA in the human genome, if unwound and connected end to end, would be more than 1.5 m long—but only about 130 trillionths of a centimeter wide. Even an average human hair is as much as 200,000 times wider than that.

Centriole

Nucleus

Endoplasmic reticulum

Mitochondrion

Cytoplasm

. . . The biggest advance in genetics in years took place in February, 2001. Scientists successfully mapped the human genome. There are about 30,000 genes in the human genome. Genes are in the nucleus of each of the several trillion cells in your body.

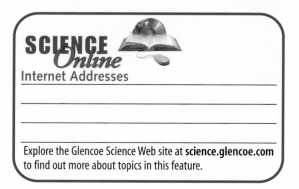

SCIENCE Online
Internet Addresses

_____
_____
_____

Explore the Glencoe Science Web site at **science.glencoe.com** to find out more about topics in this feature.

. . . It would take about nine and one-half years to read aloud without stopping the 3 billion bits of instructions (called base pairs) in your genome.

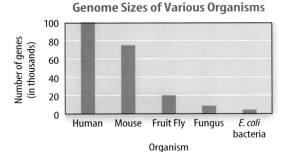

Genome Sizes of Various Organisms

Y axis: Number of genes (in thousands) — 0, 20, 40, 60, 80, 100
X axis: Human, Mouse, Fruit Fly, Fungus, E. coli bacteria — Organism

. . . Not all the DNA in your genes contains useful information. About 90 percent of it is "junk" DNA—meaningless sequences located in and between genes.

Do the Math

1. If one million base pairs of DNA take up 1 megabyte of storage space on a computer, how many gigabytes (1,024 megabytes) would the whole genome fill?
2. Consult the above graph. How many more genes are in the human genome than the genome of the fruit fly?
3. If you wrote the genetic information for each gene in the human genome on a separate sheet of 0.2-mm-thick paper and stacked the sheets, how tall would the stack be?

Go Further

By decoding the human genome scientists hope to identify the location of disease-causing genes. Research a genetic disease and share your results with your class.

Do the Math

Teaching Strategies

- Review place value for millions and billions to help students convert units in the first problem.
- Discuss what units are used to label the Y axis of the graph for the second problem.
- Remind students of the meaning of the metric prefix *milli-* (1/1000) to help them convert units for the third problem.

Answers

1. 3 gigabytes (1 million base pairs = 1 megabyte; 3 billion base pairs = 3,000 megabytes or 3 gigabytes)
2. 80,000 genes
3. 20 m

Go Further

Have students prepare a poster with information about the genetic disease they have chosen to investigate. Children's hospitals are often an excellent source of information about genetic disorders.
IS Visual-Spatial

Visual Learning

Genome Sizes of Various Organisms Have students examine the information in the graph and propose reasons for the large number of genes in the human genome as compared to the number of genes in the *E. coli* genome. As students discuss their ideas, point out the different levels of sophistication in a human body and an *E. coli* bacteria.

Reviewing Main Ideas

Preview

Students can answer the questions in their Science Journals. Discuss the answers as you go through the chapter. **IS Linguistic**

Review

Students can write their answers, then compare them with those of other students. **IS Interpersonal**

Reteach

Students can look at the illustrations and describe details that support the main ideas of the chapter. **IS Visual-Spatial**

Answers to Chapter Review

SECTION 1

4. Punnett squares can help to predict the variations and ratios of offspring.

SECTION 3

4. Accept all reasonable answers. Common examples may include corn, wheat, rice, and various produce.

Reviewing Main Ideas

Section 1 Genetics

1. Genetics is the study of how traits are inherited. Gregor Mendel determined the basic laws of genetics.

2. Traits are controlled by alleles on chromosomes in the nuclei of cells.

3. Some alleles can be dominant and others can be recessive in action.

4. When a pair of chromosomes separates during meiosis, the different alleles for a trait move into separate sex cells. Mendel found that traits followed the laws of probability and that he could predict the outcome of genetic crosses. *How can a Punnett square help predict inheritance of traits?*

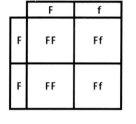

	F	f
F	FF	Ff
F	FF	Ff

Section 2 Genetics Since Mendel

1. Inheritance patterns studied since Mendel include incomplete dominance, multiple alleles, and polygenic inheritance.

2. These inheritance patterns allow a greater variety of phenotypes to be produced than would result from Mendelian inheritance.

3. Some disorders are the results of inheritance and can be harmful, even deadly, to those affected.

4. Pedigree charts help reveal patterns of the inheritance of a trait in a family. Pedigrees show that sex-linked traits are expressed more often in males than in females.

Section 3 Advances in Genetics

1. Genetic engineering uses biological and chemical methods to add or remove genes in an organism's DNA.

2. Recombinant DNA is one way genetic engineering can be performed using bacteria to make useful chemicals, including hormones.

3. Gene therapy shows promise for correcting many human genetic disorders by inserting normal alleles into cells.

4. Breakthroughs in the field of genetic engineering are allowing scientists to do many things, such as producing plants that are resistant to disease. *What types of crops might benefit from advances in genetic engineering? Give examples.*

FOLDABLES Reading & Study Skills

After You Read

How many characteristics listed in your Classify Study Fold are inherited from your parents? How many are not inherited? Why are some not inherited?

FOLDABLES Reading & Study Skills

After You Read

After students have read the chapter and completed the Foldable described in Before You Read, have them do the activity on the student page.

Dinah Zike

Visualizing Main Ideas

Examine the following pedigree for diabetes and explain the inheritance pattern.

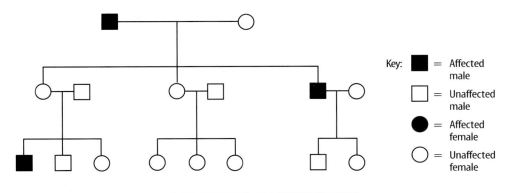

Key:
- ■ = Affected male
- □ = Unaffected male
- ● = Affected female
- ○ = Unaffected female

Vocabulary Review

Vocabulary Words

a. allele
b. dominant
c. genetic engineering
d. genetics
e. genotype
f. heredity
g. heterozygous
h. homozygous
i. hybrid
j. incomplete dominance
k. phenotype
l. polygenic inheritance
m. Punnett square
n. recessive
o. sex-linked gene

Using Vocabulary

Make the sentences to the right true by replacing the underlined word with the correct vocabulary word.

> **THE PRINCETON REVIEW** **Study Tip**
>
> When you encounter new vocabulary, write it down in a sentence. This will help you understand, remember, and use new vocabulary words.

1. Alternate forms of a gene are called <u>genetics</u>.

2. The outward appearance of a trait is a <u>genotype</u>.

3. Human height, eye color, and skin color are all traits controlled by <u>sex-linked genes</u>.

4. An allele that produces a trait in the heterozygous condition is <u>recessive</u>.

5. <u>Polygenic inheritance</u> is the branch of biology that deals with the study of heredity.

6. The actual combination of alleles of an organism is its <u>phenotype</u>.

7. <u>Hybrids</u> are moving fragments of DNA from one organism and inserting them into another organism.

8. A <u>phenotype</u> is a helpful device for predicting the proportions of possible genotypes.

9. <u>Genetics</u> is the passing of traits from parents to offspring.

10. Red-green color blindness and hemophilia are two human genetic disorders that are caused by a <u>genotype</u>.

Chapter **5** Study Guide

Visualizing Main Ideas

See student page.

Vocabulary Review

Using Vocabulary

1. alleles
2. phenotype
3. polygenic inheritance
4. dominant
5. Genetics
6. genotype
7. Genetic engineering
8. Punnett square
9. Heredity
10. sex-linked gene

IDENTIFYING Misconceptions

Assess

Use the assessment as follow-up to page 126F after students have completed the chapter.

Procedure Repeat the question: If brown eyes are dominant over blue eyes, does this mean that someday all people will be brown eyed? Have students write and diagram their answer.

Expected Outcome Students should show that brown-eyed parents can have blue-eyed children if both parents have one blue-eyed allele. Students should show that the allele is passed directly from parent to child. It does not disappear in the parent, then reappear in the child, nor does it disappear from the population. Students should show that they understand that a dominant allele is not stronger or more frequently expressed than a recessive allele.

Checking Concepts

1. A
2. C
3. A
4. C
5. C
6. B
7. D
8. A
9. A
10. B

Thinking Critically

11. DNA is a chemical; a gene contains DNA; an allele is a form of a gene specific for a trait; genes are located on chromosomes.
12. The phenotype will show the dominant trait, whether the genotype is homozygous or heterozygous, because the recessive gene does not show up in the phenotype.
13. The coat colors of some rabbits are affected by temperature differences in the environment.
14. The normal allele is usually inserted only into the cells that cause the disorder. For this reason, the reproductive cells would not be changed by gene therapy.

Chapter 5 Assessment

Checking Concepts

Choose the word or phrase that best answers the question.

1. Which of the following are located in the nuclei on chromosomes?
   A) genes
   C) carbohydrates
   B) pedigrees
   D) zygotes

2. Which of the following describes the allele that causes color blindness?
   A) dominant
   B) carried on the Y chromosome
   C) carried on the X chromosome
   D) present only in males

3. What is it called when the presence of two different alleles results in an intermediate phenotype?
   A) incomplete dominance
   B) polygenic inheritance
   C) multiple alleles
   D) sex-linked genes

4. What separates during meiosis?
   A) proteins
   C) alleles
   B) phenotypes
   D) pedigrees

5. What controls traits in organisms?
   A) cell membrane
   C) genes
   B) cell wall
   D) Punnett squares

6. Which of the following is a use for a Punnett square?
   A) to dominate the outcome of a cross
   B) to predict the outcome of a cross
   C) to assure the outcome of a cross
   D) to number the outcome of a cross

7. What term describes the inheritance of cystic fibrosis?
   A) polygenic inheritance
   B) multiple alleles
   C) incomplete dominance
   D) recessive genes

8. What type of inheritance is eye color?
   A) polygenic inheritance
   B) multiple alleles
   C) incomplete dominance
   D) recessive genes

9. What chromosome(s) did the father contribute if a normal female is produced?
   A) X
   C) Y
   B) XX
   D) XY

10. What type of inheritance is blood type?
    A) polygenic inheritance
    B) multiple alleles
    C) incomplete dominance
    D) recessive genes

Thinking Critically

11. Explain the relationship among DNA, genes, alleles, and chromosomes.

12. Explain how the parents and offspring represented in this Punnett square have the same phenotype.

	F	f
F	FF	Ff
F	FF	Ff

13. Explain why two rabbits with the same genes might not be colored the same if one is raised in Maine and one in Texas.

14. Why would a person who receives genetic therapy for a disorder still be able to pass the disorder to his or her children?

Developing Skills

15. **Predicting** Two organisms were found to have different genotypes but have the same phenotype. Predict what these phenotypes might be. Explain.

Chapter ✔Assessment Planner

Portfolio Encourage students to place in their portfolios one or two items of what they consider to be their best work. Examples include:
- Extension, p. 132
- Science Journal, p. 137
- Assessment, p. 145

Performance Additional performance assessments, Performance Task Assessment Lists, and rubrics for evaluating these activities can be found in Glencoe's **Performance Assessment in the Science Classroom.**

16. Classifying Classify the inheritance pattern for each of the following:

a. many different phenotypes produced by one pair of alleles;

b. many phenotypes produced by more than one pair of alleles; two phenotypes from two alleles; three phenotypes from two alleles.

17. Comparing and Contrasting Compare and contrast Mendelian inheritance with incomplete dominance.

18. Interpreting Scientific Illustrations What were the genotypes of the parents that produced the following Punnett square?

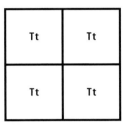

Tt	Tt
Tt	Tt

Performance Assessment

19. Newspaper Article Write a newspaper article to announce a new, genetically engineered plant. Include the method of developing the plant, the characteristic changed, and the terms that you would expect to see. Read your article to the class.

TECHNOLOGY

Go to the Glencoe Science Web site at **science.glencoe.com** or use the **Glencoe Science CD-ROM** for additional chapter assessment.

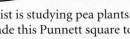
THE PRINCETON REVIEW Test Practice

A scientist is studying pea plants. The scientist made this Punnett square to predict the color traits of the offspring of two parent pea plants.

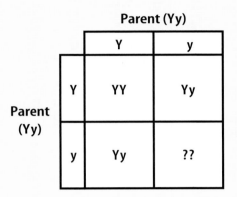

Parent (Yy)

Parent (Yy)	Y	y
Y	YY	Yy
y	Yy	??

Study the Punnett square and answer the following questions.

1. Which of these genotypes will complete this Punnett square?
A) YY
B) Yy
C) yy
D) Yx

2. In peas, the color yellow (Y) is dominant to the color green (y). According to this Punnett square, most of the offspring of the yellow pea plant and the green pea plant probably will be _____.
F) orange
G) green
H) yellow
J) red

THE PRINCETON REVIEW Test Practice

The Test-Taking Tip was written by The Princeton Review, the nation's leader in test preparation.

1. C
2. H

Developing Skills

15. The phenotypes would be the expression of a dominant trait.

16. (a) multiple allele inheritance
(b) polygenic inheritance

17. Mendelian inheritance has two forms of an allele that produce only two phenotypes. Incomplete dominance also has two forms of an allele, but produces three phenotypes.

18. TT and tt; both were purebred, one dominant, one recessive

Performance Assessment

19. Answers will vary, but should explain genetic engineering methods and how the methods can change the traits of organisms. Use **Performance Assessment in the Science Classroom**, p.141.

✓Assessment Resources

📁 **Reproducible Masters**

Chapter Resources Booklet
Chapter Review, pp. 33–34
Chapter Tests, pp. 35–38
Assessment Transparency Activity, p. 45

Glencoe Science Web site
Interactive Tutor
Chapter Quizzes

Glencoe Technology
🖌 Assessment Transparency
💿 Interactive CD-ROM Chapter Quizzes
💿 ExamView Pro Test Bank
💿 Vocabulary PuzzleMaker Software
📼 MindJogger Videoquiz DVD/VHS

Section/Objectives	Standards		Activities/Features
	National	**State/Local**	
Chapter Opener	See p. 6T for a Key to Standards.		**Explore Activity:** Model camouflage, p. 155 **Before You Read,** p. 155
Section 1 Ideas About Evolution 🕐 2 sessions 📦 1 block 1. **Describe** Lamarck's theory of acquired characteristics and Darwin's theory of evolution. 2. **Identify** why variations in organisms are important. 3. **Compare and contrast** gradualism and punctuated equilibrium.	National Content Standards: UCP4, A1, A2, C1, C2, C5, D2, G1, G3		**Science Online,** p. 158 **Problem-Solving Activity:** Does natural selection take place in a fish tank?, p. 159 **MiniLAB:** Relating Evolution to Species, p. 161 **Health Integration,** p. 163 **Activity:** Hidden Frogs, p. 164
Section 2 Clues About Evolution 🕐 2 sessions 📦 1.5 blocks 1. **Identify** the importance of fossils as evidence of evolution. 2. **Explain** how relative and radiometric dating are used to estimate the age of fossils. 3. **List** examples of five types of evidence for evolution.	National Content Standards: UCP4, C1, C2, C5, D2, D1, G2, G3		**Science Online,** p. 166 **Visualizing the Geologic Time Scale,** p. 168 **Earth Science Integration,** p. 169
Section 3 The Evolution of Primates 🕐 3 sessions 📦 2 blocks 1. **Describe** the differences among living primates. 2. **Identify** the adaptations of primates. 3. **Discuss** the evolutionary history of modern primates.	National Content Standards: UCP4, A1, C1, C2, C5, G1, G2, G3		**MiniLAB:** Living Without Thumbs, p. 173 **Activity:** Recognizing Variation in a Population, pp. 176–177 **Science and History:** Fighting the Battle Against HIV, pp. 178–179

Activity Materials	Reproducible Resources	Section Assessment	Technology
Explore Activity: classified ads from the newspaper, white paper, black paper, hole punch, watch or clock with second hand	**Chapter Resources Booklet** Foldables Worksheet, p. 15 Directed Reading Overview, p. 17 Note-taking Worksheets, pp. 31–32	*GLENCOE'S* **ASSESSMENT** *ADVANTAGE*	
MiniLAB: lined paper **Activity:** cardboard form of a frog, colored markers, crayons, colored pencils, glue, beads, sequins, modeling clay	**Chapter Resources Booklet** Transparency Activity, p. 42 MiniLAB, p. 3 Enrichment, p. 28 Reinforcement, p. 25 Directed Reading, p. 18 Lab Activities, pp. 9–10, 11–14 Activity Worksheet, pp. 5–6 **Cultural Diversity,** p. 19 **Earth Science Critical Thinking/ Problem Solving,** p. 14 **Mathematics Skill Activities,** p. 1	Portfolio Curriculum Connection, p. 161 Performance Problem-Solving Activity, p. 159 MiniLAB, p. 161 Skill Builder Activities, p. 163 Content Section Assessment, p. 163	Section Focus Transparency Interactive CD-ROM/DVD Guided Reading Audio Program
Need materials? Contact Science Kit at 1-800-828-7777 or www.sciencekit.com on the Internet.	**Chapter Resources Booklet** Transparency Activity, p. 43 Enrichment, p. 29 Reinforcement, p. 26 Directed Reading, p. 19 Transparency Activity, pp. 45–47 **Physical Science Critical Thinking/Problem Solving,** p. 11 **Life Science Critical Thinking/ Problem Solving,** p. 3	Portfolio Science Journal, p. 166 Performance Skill Builder Activities, p. 171 Content Section Assessment, p. 171	Section Focus Transparency Teaching Transparency Interactive CD-ROM/DVD Guided Reading Audio Program
MiniLAB: tape **Activity:** fruit and seeds from one plant species, metric ruler, hand lens, graph paper	**Chapter Resources Booklet** Transparency Activity, p. 44 MiniLAB, p. 4 Enrichment, p. 30 Reinforcement, p. 27 Directed Reading, pp. 19, 20 Activity Worksheet, pp. 7–8 **Lab Management and Safety,** p. 71	Portfolio MiniLAB Assessment, p. 173 Performance MiniLAB, p. 173 Skill Builder Activities, p. 175 Content Section Assessment, p. 175	Section Focus Transparency Interactive CD-ROM/DVD Guided Reading Audio Program

End of Chapter Assessment

GLENCOE'S **ASSESSMENT** *ADVANTAGE*

Blackline Masters	Technology	Professional Series
Chapter Resources Booklet Chapter Review, pp. 35–36 Chapter Tests, pp. 00–00 **Standardized Test Practice by The Princeton Review,** pp. 27–30	MindJogger Videoquiz CD-ROM Explorations and Quizzes Vocabulary Puzzle Makers ExamView Pro Test Bank Interactive Lesson Planner Interactive Teacher's Edition	Performance Assessment in the Science Classroom (PASC)

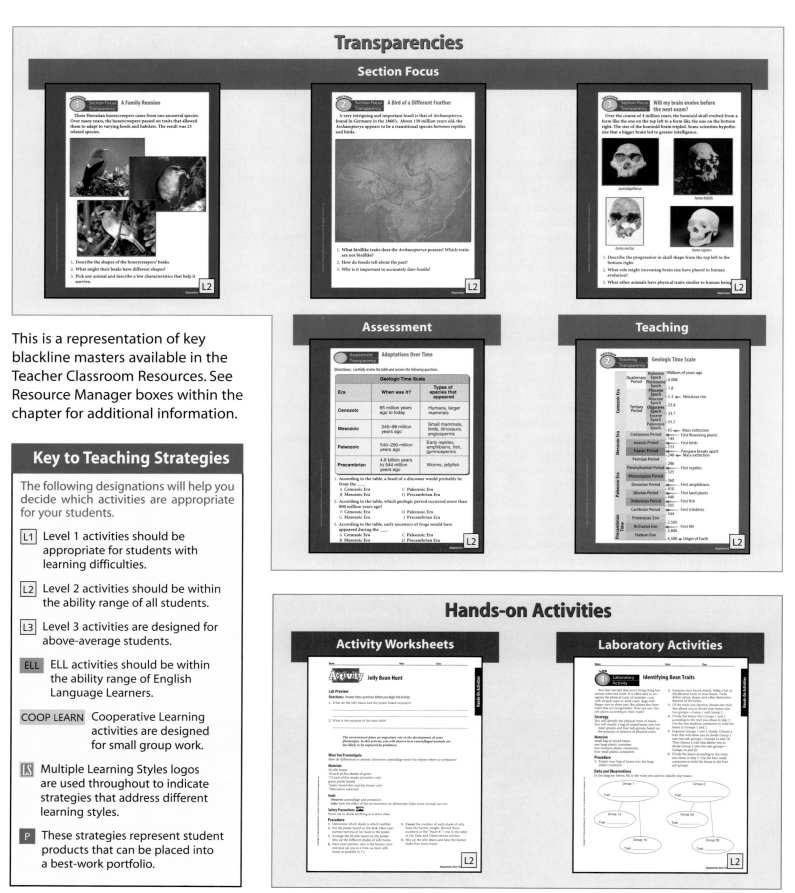

Transparencies

Section Focus

Section Focus Transparency 1 — A Family Reunion

These Hawaiian honeycreepers came from one ancestral species. Over many years, the honeycreepers passed on traits that allowed them to adapt to varying foods and habitats. The result was 23 related species.

1. Describe the shapes of the honeycreepers' beaks.
2. What might their beaks have different shapes?
3. Pick any animal and describe a few characteristics that help it survive.

L2

Section Focus Transparency 2 — A Bird of a Different Feather

A very intriguing and important fossil is that of *Archaeopteryx*, found in Germany in the 1860's. About 150 million years old, the *Archaeopteryx* appears to be a transitional species between reptiles and birds.

1. What birdlike traits does the *Archaeopteryx* possess? Which traits are not birdlike?
2. How do fossils tell about the past?
3. Why is it important to accurately date fossils?

L2

Section Focus Transparency 3 — Will my brain evolve before the next exam?

Over the course of 4 million years, the hominid skull evolved from a form like the one on the top left to a form like the one on the bottom right. The size of the hominid brain tripled. Some scientists hypothesize that a bigger brain led to greater intelligence.

australopithecus   *homo habilis*
homo erectus   *homo sapiens*

1. Describe the progression in skull shape from the top left to the bottom right.
2. What role might increasing brain size have played in human evolution?
3. What other animals have physical traits similar to human beings?

L2

This is a representation of key blackline masters available in the Teacher Classroom Resources. See Resource Manager boxes within the chapter for additional information.

Key to Teaching Strategies

The following designations will help you decide which activities are appropriate for your students.

L1 Level 1 activities should be appropriate for students with learning difficulties.

L2 Level 2 activities should be within the ability range of all students.

L3 Level 3 activities are designed for above-average students.

ELL ELL activities should be within the ability range of English Language Learners.

COOP LEARN Cooperative Learning activities are designed for small group work.

LS Multiple Learning Styles logos are used throughout to indicate strategies that address different learning styles.

P These strategies represent student products that can be placed into a best-work portfolio.

Assessment

Assessment Transparency — Adaptations Over Time

Directions: Carefully review the table and answer the following questions.

Geologic Time Scale		
Era	**When was it?**	**Types of species that appeared**
Cenozoic	65 million years ago to today	Humans, larger mammals
Mesozoic	245–98 million years ago	Small mammals, birds, dinosaurs, angiosperms
Paleozoic	540–290 million years ago	Early reptiles, amphibians, fish, gymnosperms
Precambrian	4.6 billion years to 544 million years ago	Worms, jellyfish

1. According to the table, a fossil of a dinosaur would probably be from the ___.
   A Cenozoic Era   C Paleozoic Era
   B Mesozoic Era   D Precambrian Era
2. According to the table, which geologic period occurred more than 800 million years ago?
   F Cenozoic Era   H Paleozoic Era
   G Mesozoic Era   J Precambrian Era
3. According to the table, early ancestors of frogs would have appeared during the ___.
   A Cenozoic Era   C Paleozoic Era
   B Mesozoic Era   D Precambrian Era

L2

Teaching

Teaching Transparency 2 — Geologic Time Scale

Cenozoic Era	Quaternary Period	Holocene Epoch — Millions of years ago
		Pleistocene Epoch — 0.008
		Pliocene Epoch — 1.8
	Tertiary Period	Miocene Epoch — 5.3 — Himalaya rise
		Oligocene Epoch — 23.8
		Eocene Epoch — 33.7
		Paleocene Epoch — 55.5
Mesozoic Era	Cretaceous Period	— 65 — Mass extinction, First flowering plants
	Jurassic Period	— 145 — First birds
	Triassic Period	— 213 — Pangaea breaks apart, — 248 — Mass extinction
Paleozoic Era	Permian Period	— 286
	Pennsylvanian Period	— 325 — First reptiles
	Mississippian Period	— 360
	Devonian Period	— 410 — First amphibians
	Silurian Period	— 440 — First land plants
	Ordovician Period	— 505 — First fish
	Cambrian Period	— 544 — First trilobites
Precambrian Time	Proterozoic Eon	— 2,500
	Archaean Eon	— 3,800 — First life
	Hadean Eon	— 4,500 — Origin of Earth

L2

Hands-on Activities

Activity Worksheets

Activity — Jelly Bean Hunt

Lab Preview
Directions: Answer these questions before you begin the Activity.
1. What do the jelly beans and the poster board represent?

2. What is the purpose of the data table?

The environment plays an important role in the development of some phenotypes. In this activity, you will observe how camouflaged animals are less likely to be captured by predators.

What You'll Investigate
How do differences in animal coloration camouflage some but expose others to predation?

Materials
50 jelly beans
10 each of five shades of green
*10 each of five shades of another color
green poster board
*poster board that matches chosen color
*Alternative materials

Goals
Observe camouflage and predation.
Infer how the effect of the environment on phenotype helps some animals survive.

Safety Precautions
Never eat or drink anything in science class.

Procedure
1. Determine which shade is which number.
2. Put the poster board on the desk. Have your partner turn his or her back to the poster.
3. Arrange the 50 jelly beans on the poster. Mix up the different shades of jelly beans.
4. Have your partner, who is the hunter, turn and pick up one at a time, as many jelly beans as possible in 3 s.
5. **Count** the number of each shade of jelly bean the hunter caught. Record these numbers in the "Hunt #1" row in the table in the Data and Observations section.
6. Mix up the jelly beans and have the hunter make four more hunts.

L2

Laboratory Activities

Laboratory Activity 1 — Identifying Bean Traits

You have learned that every living thing has certain inherited traits. It is often easy to recognize the physical traits of most beans. Take with striped coats or solid coats; dogs with floppy ears or short ears. But plants also have traits that are recognizable. How can you classify plants according to their traits?

Strategy
You will identify the physical traits of beans. You will classify a bag of mixed beans into two main groups and four sub-groups based on the presence or absence of physical traits.

Materials
small bag of mixed beans
one large plastic container
two medium plastic containers
four small plastic containers

Procedure
1. Empty your bag of beans into the large plastic container.

2. Examine your beans closely. Make a list of the physical traits of your beans. Traits define colors, shape, and other distinctive features of the beans.
3. Of the traits you observe, choose one trait that allows you to divide your beans into two groups—Group 1 and Group 2.
4. Divide the beans into Groups 1 and 2 according to the trait you chose in step 3. Use the two medium containers to hold the beans in Groups 1 and 2.
5. Examine Groups 1 and 2 closely. Choose a trait that will allow you to divide Group 1 into two sub-groups—Groups 1a and 1b. Then choose a trait that allows you to divide Group 2 into two sub-groups—Groups 2a and 2b.
6. Divide the beans according to the traits you chose in step 5. Use the four small containers to hold the beans in the four sub-groups.

Data and Observations
In the diagram below, fill in the traits you used to classify your beans.

Group 1   Group 2
Trait ___   Trait ___
Group 1a   Group 2a
Trait ___   Trait ___
Group 1b   Group 2b
Trait ___   Trait ___

L2

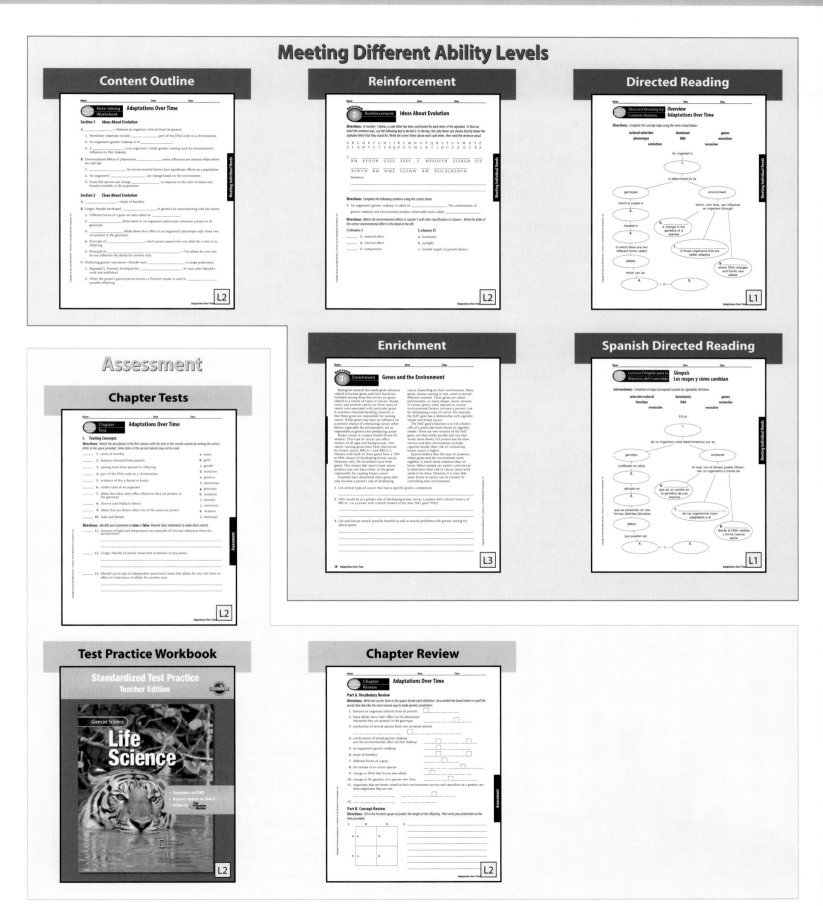

Meeting Different Ability Levels

Content Outline

Note-taking Worksheet — Adaptations Over Time

L2

Reinforcement

Reinforcement — Ideas About Evolution

L2

Directed Reading

Directed Reading for Content Mastery — *Overview* Adaptations Over Time

L1

Assessment

Chapter Tests

Chapter Test — Adaptations Over Time

L2

Enrichment

Enrichment — Genes and the Environment

L3

Spanish Directed Reading

Lectura Dirigida para la Maestría del Contenido — *Sinopsis* Los rasgos y cómo cambian

L1

Test Practice Workbook

Standardized Test Practice Teacher Edition

Glencoe Science — Life Science

L2

Chapter Review

Chapter Review — Adaptations Over Time

L2

Science Content Background

SECTION 1

Ideas About Evolution

Before Evolutionary Theories

Plato and Aristotle, two Greek philosophers, held views that species were essentially perfect. Because species were considered to be well adapted, there was no discussion needed on evolution. Special Creation with all species fixed was the prevailing view. In addition, Carolus Linnaeus, father of taxonomy, organized the diversity of living things into a hierarchy of taxonomic categories that did not imply evolution.

Student Misconception

Environmental changes cause changes in traits that help organisms cope with the new environment.

Refer to the facing page for teaching strategies to address this misconception. Refer to page 163 for content related to this topic.

Evolution by Natural Selection

Charles Darwin and Alfred Wallace provided enough evidence in 1859 to convince many scientists that evolution occurs. Their ideas differed from the prevailing views of their time in two important ways—species change, or evolve, and natural selection is the process by which this evolution occurs.

An important point about the discussions on natural selection and evolution is Darwin's observations were not limited to those made during his trip on

the *HMS Beagle*. Even as a young boy, Darwin was an avid collector of beetles and other information about natural history. By the time he became the ship's naturalist, he was already in agreement with his grandfather, Erasmus Darwin, that organisms evolve.

SECTION 2

Clues About Evolution

The Fossil Record

Some organisms which either lived for only a short time or only in a certain environment, formed fossils called index fossils. Index fossils are used by geologists to correlate rock strata across large areas.

Radioactive isotopes have half-lives that are not affected by environmental factors such as temperature or atmospheric pressure. Because the length of half-lives for radioactive isotopes of elements is known, an age estimate can be assigned to many rocks or fossils.

The evidence of evolution of species from the fossils record is compatible with other types of evidence for evolution. Transitional fossils have been located for some species, and species such as echinoderms have extensive fossil records that appear complete.

SECTION 3

The Evolution of Primates

Ongoing Research

Discoveries regarding primate evolution occur regularly. DNA comparisons have been done in an attempt to establish a date for the evolution of modern humans. Results of these tests are currently being debated, repeated, and extended.

SCIENCE Online

For additional content background on this topic, go to the Glencoe Science Web site at science.glencoe.com.

Tetsu Yamazaki/International Stock

IDENTIFYING ▷ Misconceptions

Find Out What Students Think

Students may think that . . .

- **Environmental changes cause changes in traits that help organisms cope with the new environment.**

Students often form a magical view of natural selection. They know that if pesticides are applied to a crop, some insects will survive and reproduce. However, rather than understanding that the insects that survived did so because of pre-existing traits, students often believe that the pesticide itself caused the insects to become resistant. In the same way they may believe that antibiotics cause bacteria to form antibiotic resistance, or that organisms develop new traits because they need them to survive in a new environment (e.g., giraffes having long necks).

Activity

Have students read the section in the text that describes how bacteria become resistant to penicillin. If possible, bring in an article from a popular science journal describing the problem of antibiotic resistance. Ask students to imagine a situation in which they were required to clean their desks and the counters of the room daily with antibiotic soap to kill *Salmonella* and *Staphylococcus* bacteria. Have students write a paragraph describing what would happen to the bacteria in the room. Students should understand that resistant strains of these bacteria could be selected for and become a problem in the room. Some students, however, may persist in believing that the resistant bacteria form because of the antibacterial soaps.

Promote Understanding

Activity

Divide the class into small groups, and give each group a bowl containing 10 beans of various, distinct colors (i.e., white, black, spotted, red). Only one bean should be red. Supply each group with bags of various colors of beans. Tell students that the beans represent a colony of bacteria, and the colors represent minor genetic variations in the same species.

- On your signal have each group "multiply" their beans. Since bacteria divide to reproduce, have students simply add one new black bean for each black bean in the bowl, one red bean for every red bean in the bowl, and so on. Have students "multiply" their beans twice (for a total of 40 beans in the bowl).

- Next, tell students that an antibiotic has been spilled in the environment. The antibiotic works by degrading the bacterial cell wall. The genes that gave the red bacteria their color also gave them a cell wall that was particularly thick and resists the action of the antibiotic. All other bacteria were killed.

- Have students remove all beans from the bowl except the red beans. Now have them "multiply" the remaining (red) beans for two or three more generations. Point out that because the red "bacteria" already had a feature that allowed them to survive the antibiotic, only red "bacteria" remain.

Assess

After completing the chapter, see *Identifying Misconceptions* in the Study Guide.

Adaptations Over Time

Chapter Vocabulary

species
evolution
natural selection
variation
adaptation
gradualism
punctuated equilibrium
sedimentary rock
radioactive element
embryology
homologous
vestigial structure
primate
hominid
Homo sapiens

What do you think?

Science Journal The calico cat in this picture has a litter of kittens. The variations in offspring are because each kitten is the result of an egg and sperm joining. Fertilization is a random event that creates unique individuals.

Adaptations Over Time

Are today's cockroaches different from those that lived 10,000 years ago? How have these and other organisms survived Earth's changing environments over time? What evidence exists for changes in a species? Theories about how species change over time and some of the evidence for these changes are presented in this chapter. You also will read about primate adaptations over time.

What do you think?

Science Journal Look at the picture below with a classmate. Discuss what might be happening. Here's a hint: *This is one of the reasons species change.* Write your answer or best guess in your Science Journal.

154 ◆ **A**

Theme Connection

Stability and Change Changes that occur during evolution bring about stability by increasing variation within a population.

EXPLORE ACTIVITY

EXPLORE ACTIVITY

The cheetah is one of nature's speediest hunters, but it can run swiftly for only short distances. The cheetah's fur blends in with tall grass, making it almost invisible as it hides and waits for prey to wander close by. Then the cheetah pounces, capturing the prey before it can run away.

Model camouflage

1. Spread a sheet of newspaper classified ads on the floor.
2. Using a hole puncher, punch out 100 circles from each of the following types of paper: white paper, black paper, and classified ads.
3. Scatter all the circles on the newspaper on the floor. For 10 s, pick up as many circles as possible, one at a time. Have a partner time you.
4. Count the number of each kind of paper circle that you picked up. Record your results in your Science Journal.

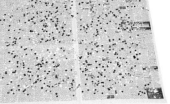

Observe

Which paper circles were most difficult to find? What can you infer about a cheetah's coloring from this activity? Enter your responses to these questions in your Science Journal.

FOLDABLES
Reading & Study Skills

Before You Read

Making a Sequence Study Fold Make the following Foldable to help you predict what might occur next in adaptations over time.

1. Place a sheet of paper in front of you so the long side is at the top. Fold the paper in half from top to bottom.
2. Fold both sides in. Unfold the paper so three sections show.
3. Through the top thickness of paper, cut along each of the fold lines to the top fold, forming three tabs. Label each tab *Past, Present,* and *Future* as shown. Title the middle tab *Primates.*
4. Before you read the chapter, write what primates have in common under the *Present* tab. As you read the chapter, write what primates were like in the past under the *Past* tab.

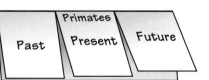

A ◆ 155

EXPLORE ACTIVITY

Purpose Students model camouflage coloration and its role in survival. L1 ELL COOP LEARN
IS Kinesthetic

Preparation Accumulate classified ads from the newspaper. Clear space for partners to work.

Materials newspaper classified ads, black and white paper, stopwatch or clock, hole punch

Teaching Strategies

- Show students photographs of a cheetah crouched in tall grass, and ask them to explain how the animal's markings enable it to blend in with its surroundings.
- If you find that students are picking up most of the circles within the time limit, add more circles or use less time.

Observe

Printed circles are most difficult to find. The cheetah's spotted fur blends in with the shadows and shades of dried vegetation found in tall grass.

Assessment

Process Provide students with photographs of animals that exhibit concealing coloration or patterns and have them describe how these features benefit each animal. Use **Performance Assessment in the Science Classroom,** p. 89.

FOLDABLES
Reading & Study Skills

Before You Read

Dinah Zike Study Fold

Purpose Students make a Foldable to record what they know and learn about adaptations of a species over time. Students describe primates as they exist today and as they were in the past, and they use what they learn to predict what they might be like in the future.

📁 For additional help, see Foldables Worksheet, p. 15 in **Chapter Resources Booklet,** or go to the Glencoe Science Web site at **science.glencoe.com.** See After You Read in the Study Guide at the end of this chapter.

1 Motivate

Bellringer Transparency

Display the Section Focus Transparency for Section 1. Use the accompanying Transparency Activity Master. L2

ELL

Tie to Prior Knowledge

Reinforce the differences between the terms *hypothesis* and *theory*. A hypothesis is a testable prediction based on observations. Explain that a theory is not a guess, but rather an accepted explanation based on a large number of tests. Scientists consider most theories to be true.

SECTION

1 Ideas About Evolution

As You Read

What You'll Learn

Describe Lamarck's theory of acquired characteristics and Darwin's theory of evolution.
Identify why variations in organisms are important.
Compare and contrast gradualism and punctuated equilibrium.

Vocabulary

species
evolution
natural selection
variation
adaptation
gradualism
punctuated equilibrium

Why It's Important

The theory of evolution suggests why there are differences among living things.

Early Models of Evolution

Millions of species of plants, animals, and other organisms live on Earth today. Do you suppose they are exactly the same as they were when they first appeared—or have any of them changed? A **species** is a group of organisms that share similar characteristics and can reproduce among themselves to produce fertile offspring. The characteristics of a species are inherited when they pass from parent to offspring. Change in these inherited characteristics over time is **evolution. Figure 1** shows how the characteristics of the camel have changed over time.

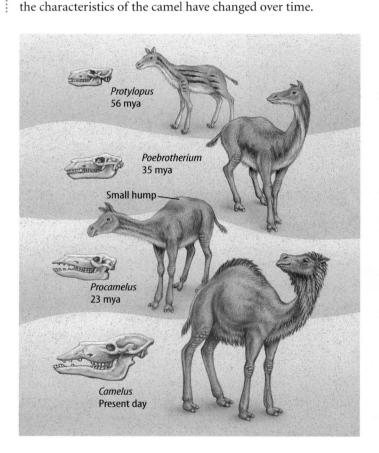

Figure 1
By studying fossils, scientists have traced the evolution of the camel. About 56 million years ago, camels had a small body. Some 33 million years later, species of camels had grown larger and had a small hump. Present-day species are even larger and have a bigger hump.

Protylopus
56 mya

Poebrotherium
35 mya

Small hump

Procamelus
23 mya

Camelus
Present day

Section ✓*Assessment* Planner

PORTFOLIO
Curriculum Connection, p. 161

PERFORMANCE ASSESSMENT
MiniLAB, p. 161
Skill Builder Activities, p. 163
See page 182 for more options.

CONTENT ASSESSMENT
Section, p. 163
Challenge, p. 163
Chapter, pp. 182–183

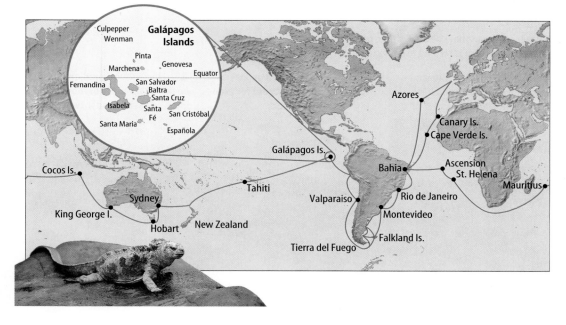

Theory of Acquired Characteristics In 1809, Jean Baptiste de Lamarck proposed a hypothesis to explain how species change over time. He suggested that characteristics, or traits, developed during a parent organism's lifetime are inherited by its offspring. His hypothesis is called the theory of acquired characteristics. Scientists collected data on traits that are passed from parents to children. The data showed that traits developed during a parent's lifetime, such as large muscles built by hard work or exercise, are not passed on to offspring. The evidence did not support Lamarck's theory.

☑ Reading Check *What was Lamarck's explanation of evolution?*

Darwin's Model of Evolution

In December 1831, the HMS *Beagle* sailed from England on a journey to explore the South American coast. On board was a young naturalist named Charles Darwin. During the journey, Darwin recorded observations about the plants and animals he saw. He was amazed by the variety of life on the Galápagos Islands, which are about 1,000 km from the coast of Ecuador. Darwin hypothesized that the plants and animals on the Galápagos Islands originally must have come from Central and South America. But the islands were home to many species he had not seen in South America, including giant cactus trees, huge land tortoises, and the iguana shown in **Figure 2.**

Figure 2
This map shows the route of Darwin's voyage on the HMS *Beagle*. Darwin noticed many species on the Galápagos Islands that he had not seen along the coast of South America, including the marine iguana. This species is the only lizard in the world known to enter the ocean and feed on seaweed.

Visual Learning ——○

Figure 1 Have students list the differences and similarities they observe in the modern camel and its ancestors. Possible answers: differences in teeth and leg bones; overall skull shape is similar. **How might these changes have occurred?** Environmental changes drive organisms to adapt.

☑ Reading Check

Answer Traits developed during a parent organism's lifetime are inherited by its offspring.

IDENTIFYING Misconceptions

Ask students to list the inadequacies of Lamarck's theory. Students may agree with Lamarck until they critically examine the failures of this explanation. The primary failure of Lamarck's explanation is that acquired characteristics are not inherited.

Darwin's Model of Evolution

Visual Learning ——○

Figure 2 Point out that Darwin suspected the process of evolution before he ever began his voyage. Ask students to explain why he was able to use evidence from his voyage to develop his theory of evolution by natural selection. Many of the species in the Galapagos are unique to the islands, but are similar to forms found on the mainland of South America.

Resource Manager

Chapter Resources Booklet
   Transparency Activity, p. 42
   Directed Reading for Content Mastery, pp. 17, 18

Inclusion Strategies

Learning Disabled Allow students to use clay to make impressions of various items such as a comb, a key, etc. Plaster-of-paris can be poured into the impressions to form fossils. Place the plaster casts into a box. Allow students to try to identify the objects by reaching into the box without looking. You may use blindfolds if some students cannot resist the temptation to look.
L1 LS **Kinesthetic**

Darwin's Model of Evolution, continued

Discussion

How are genetics and the theory of evolution related? Genetics provides the mechanism for evolution to work in a population. If traits were not inherited, there could be no evolution.

SCIENCE *Online*
Internet Addresses

_____

_____

_____

_____

Explore the Glencoe Science Web site at **science.glencoe.com** to find out more about topics in this section.

✔ **Reading Check**

Answer Darwin suggested that they all evolved from a common ancestral species in South America.

Natural Selection

Visual Learning

Table 1 Emphasize the importance of the principles of natural selection as mechanisms for evolution. **Why is overproduction of offspring important?** Overproduction assures that at least some of the offspring will survive.

L2 ⬛ **Logical-Mathematical**

Figure 3
Darwin observed that the beak shape of each species of Galápagos finch is related to its eating habits.

A Finches that eat nuts and seeds have short, strong beaks for breaking hard shells.

B Finches that feed on insects have long, slender beaks for probing beneath tree bark.

C Finches with medium-sized beaks eat a variety of foods including seeds and insects.

SCIENCE *Online*

Research Visit the Glencoe Science Web site at **science.glencoe.com** for more information about the finches Darwin observed. In your Science Journal, describe the similarities and differences of any two species of Galápagos finches.

Darwin's Observations Darwin observed 13 species of finches on the Galápagos Islands. He noticed that all 13 species looked similar, except for differences in body size, beak shape, and eating habits, as shown in **Figure 3.** He also noticed that all the Galápagos finches looked similar to a finch species he had seen on the South American coast. Darwin hypothesized that all 13 Galápagos species evolved from South American species.

Competition and Survival All living organisms produce more offspring than survive. Galápagos finches lay several eggs every few months. Darwin realized that, in just a few years, several pairs of finches could produce a large population. A population is made up of all the individuals of a species living in the same area. Members of a large population compete for living space, food, and other resources. Those that are best able to survive are more likely to reproduce and pass on their traits to the next generation.

Darwin reasoned that the Galápagos finches must have had to compete for food. Finches with beak shapes that allowed them to eat available food survived longer and produced more offspring than finches without those beak shapes. After many generations, these groups of finches became separate species.

✔ **Reading Check** *How did Darwin explain the evolution of the different species of Galápagos finches?*

Inclusion Strategies

Gifted Students can invent their own species. They can draw it, describe its habitat and diet, and give the species a history. They should describe evolutionary changes that may have occurred within the species. Have students make a timeline showing major physical changes and ecological events that resulted in changes in the species. The species may be from the past or the future. L3 ⬛ **Visual-Spatial**

Science Journal

Darwin and Wallace Have students research and describe in their Science Journal how the work of Alfred Wallace complemented that of Charles Darwin. Wallace and Darwin came to the same conclusion about evolution. The work of both men was presented at the same time, in 1858. Darwin proposed the mechanism of natural selection to account for the conclusion. L2 ⬛ **Linguistic**

Natural Selection

After the voyage, Charles Darwin returned to England and continued to think about his observations. He collected more evidence on inherited traits by breeding racing pigeons. He also studied breeds of dogs and varieties of flowers. In the mid 1800s, Darwin developed the theory of evolution that is accepted by most scientists today. He described his ideas in a book called *On the Origin of Species,* which was published in 1859.

Darwin's observations led many other scientists to conduct experiments on inherited characteristics. After many years, Darwin's hypothesis became known as the theory of evolution by natural selection. **Natural selection** means that organisms with traits best suited to their environment are more likely to survive and reproduce. Their traits are passed on to more offspring. The principles that describe how natural selection works are listed in **Table 1.**

Over time, as new data has been gathered and reported, some changes have been made to Darwin's original ideas about evolution by natural selection. His theory remains one of the most important ideas in the study of life science.

Table 1 The Principles of Natural Selection

1. Organisms produce more offspring than can survive.

2. Differences, or variations, occur among individuals of a species.

3. Variations are passed on to offspring.

4. Some variations are helpful. Individuals with helpful variations survive and reproduce better than those without these variations.

5. Over time, the offspring of individuals with helpful variations make up more of a population and eventually become a separate species.

Problem-Solving Activity

Does natural selection take place in a fish tank?

Alejandro raises tropical fish as a hobby. Could the observations that he makes over several weeks illustrate the principles of natural selection?

Identifying the Problem

Alejandro keeps a detailed journal of his observations, some of which are given in the table to the right.

Solving the Problem

Refer to **Table 1** and match each of Alejandro's journal entries with the principle(s) it demonstrates. Here's a hint: *Some entries may not match any of the principles of natural selection. Some entries may match more than one principle.*

Fish Tank Observations

Date	Observation
June 6	6 fish are placed in aquarium tank.
July 22	16 new young appear.
July 24	3 young have short or missing tail fins. 13 young have normal tail fins.
July 28	Young with short or missing tail fins die.
August 1	2 normal fish die—from overcrowding?
August 12	30 new young appear.
August 15	5 young have short or missing tail fins. 5 have normal tail fins.
August 18	Young with short or missing tail fins die.
August 20	Tank is overcrowded. Fish are divided equally into two tanks.

SECTION 1 Ideas About Evolution **A ◆ 159**

Variation and Adaptation

Caption Answers

- **Figure 4A** Neither predators nor prey can detect the scorpion fish in its natural environment.
- **Figure 4B** Predators might find it easily. Other lemurs might avoid it, preventing it from reproducing.

Activity

Display photographs of organisms that have unique adaptations such as the eye spots on the wings of moths or the thickness of a coconut husk. Have students identify the usefulness of each adaptation. Eye spots on moth wings may startle predators. Coconut husks protect the seed and allow it to travel by floating in salt water.

L2   LS **Visual-Spatial**

Figure 4
Variations that provide an advantage tend to increase in a population over time. Variations that result in a disadvantage tend to decrease in a population over time.

Variation and Adaptation

Darwin's theory of natural selection emphasizes the differences among individuals of a species. These differences are called variations. A **variation** is an inherited trait that makes an individual different from other members of its species. Variations result from permanent changes, or mutations, in an organism's genes. Some gene changes produce small variations, such as differences in the shape of human hairlines. Other gene changes produce large variations, such as an albino squirrel in a population of gray squirrels or fruit without seeds. Over time, more and more individuals of the species might inherit these variations. If individuals with these variations continue to survive and reproduce over many generations, a new species can evolve. It might take hundreds, thousands, or millions of generations for a new species to evolve.

Some variations are more helpful than others. An **adaptation** is any variation that makes an organism better suited to its environment. The variations that result in an adaptation can involve an organism's color, shape, behavior, or chemical makeup. Camouflage (KA muh flahj) is an adaptation. A camouflaged organism, like the one shown in **Figure 4,** blends into its environment and is more likely to survive and reproduce.

A Camouflage allows organisms to blend into their environment. *How does its coloration give this scorpion fish a survival advantage?*

B Albinism can prevent an organism from blending into its environment. *What might happen to an albino lemur in its natural environment?*

LAB DEMONSTRATION

Purpose to observe variations

Materials pictures of various animal groups (i.e. cows, antelope, horses, wolves, rabbits), overhead projector

Preparation Have pictures made into transparencies. Try to find pictures that contain some obvious differences (for instance, animals of different colors).

Procedure Have students observe the pictures and list variations among the individuals in a group. Repeat for each group of animals.

Expected Outcome Students will observe variations in animals of the same species. Some variations, like size or color, will be obvious. Others, such as differences in the markings of animals, may be more subtle.

✓ Assessment

What causes differences between animals in the same species? genetic variations
Do any of these variations aid in survival? If so, how? Answers will vary. Accept all reasonable answers.

Figure 5
About 600 years ago, European rabbits were introduced to the Canary Islands from a visiting Portuguese ship. The Canary Islands are in the Atlantic Ocean off the northwest coast of Africa. Over time, the Canary Island rabbits became a separate species.

A European rabbits feed during the day and are fairly large.

B Canary Island rabbits feed during the night. *Why might large eyes be considered a helpful adaptation in Canary Island rabbits?*

Changes in the Sources of Gene Over time, the genetic makeup of a species might change its appearance. For example, as the genetic makeup of a species of seed-eating Galápagos finch changes, so does the size and shape of its beak. Many kinds of environmental factors help bring about changes. When individuals of the same species move in to or out of an area, they might bring in or remove genes and variations. Suppose a family from another country moves to your neighborhood. They bring with them different foods, customs, and ways of speaking. In a similar way, when new individuals enter an existing population, they can bring in different genes and variations.

Geographic Isolation Sometimes mountains, lakes, or other geologic features isolate a small number of individuals from the rest of a population. Over several generations, variations that do not exist in the larger population might begin to be more common in the isolated population. Also, gene mutations can occur that add variations to populations. Over time, the two populations can become so different that they no longer breed with each other. The two populations of rabbits shown in **Figure 5** have been isolated from each other geographically for thousands of generations.

Mini LAB

Relating Evolution to Species

Procedure
1. On a piece of **lined paper,** print the alphabet in lower-case letters.
2. Organize the letters into three groups. Put all of the vowels in the first group. Place all of the letters that drop below the line into the second group. Place all of the remaining letters in the third group.

Analysis
1. How are the three groups of letters similar to each other?
2. If the letters were organisms, what traits would indicate to scientists how closely related the letters were to each other?

Caption Answer
Figure 5B Their large eyes help the rabbits see in the dark.

Mini LAB

Purpose Students practice classifying and sequencing. [L2] **N** **Visual-Spatial**
Teaching Strategy Explain to students that the letters of the alphabet have changed over time. You may research and show the evolution of the letters *f* and *s* in particular. Tell how this type of evolution is different from evolution in living things.
Analysis
1. Answers will vary. Possible answers: all are letters of the alphabet; all are lowercase.
2. Letters with a characteristic in common would be the most closely related (i.e. vowels and consonants that do not drop below the line). Letters with similar characteristics would be the next closest relations (i.e. consonants that do drop below the line). Letters with no similar characteristics would be distantly related.

✓ Assessment

Performance To further assess students' understanding of evolution, have them make up and explain another hypothetical evolutionary schema using whatever shapes or materials they choose. Use **Performance Assessment in the Science Classroom,** p. 123.

Resource Manager

Chapter Resources Booklet
    MiniLAB, p. 3

Curriculum Connection

History Direct students to research the mid-nineteenth century to determine what daily life was like for Darwin and his peers. Students should make posters showing technologies used, dress of the period, and religious or political events. [L2] **N** **Visual-Spatial** [P]

Use Science Words

Word Origin Scientists once accepted that organisms evolve according to the gradualism model. *Gradus*, meaning a step, is the Latin word from which gradualism is derived. Ask students why this word is used. Gradualism seems to occur step by step.
L2 ⬚ **Linguistic**

Discussion

Explain to students that punctuated equilibrium caused quite a bit of controversy within the scientific community when it was first postulated. **Why didn't the new evidence for a different rate of evolution destroy acceptance of the theory of evolution?** Theories are adaptable. By incorporating new evidence to explain a greater number of observations, the theory is strengthened.

Visual Learning

Figure 6 Have students use the illustration as they discuss gradualism and punctuated equilibrium. Ask why punctuated equilibrium appears to have been involved in the evolution of the bears. The diagram shows few intermediate forms. L2
⬚ **Visual-Spatial**

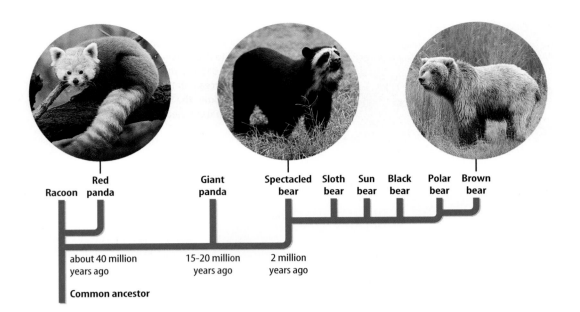

Red Racoon • Red panda • Giant panda • Spectacled bear • Sloth bear • Sun bear • Black bear • Polar bear • Brown bear

about 40 million years ago
15-20 million years ago
2 million years ago

Common ancestor

Figure 6
The evolution of bears illustrates the punctuated equilibrium model of evolution. Six distinct bear species evolved over two million years. The same series of changes would have taken many times longer according to the gradualism model of evolution.

The Speed of Evolution

Scientists do not agree on how quickly evolution occurs. Many scientists hypothesize that evolution occurs slowly, perhaps over tens or hundreds of millions of years. Other scientists hypothesize that evolution can occur quickly. Some scientists propose that evidence supports both of these models.

Gradualism Darwin hypothesized that evolution takes place slowly. The model that describes evolution as a slow, ongoing process by which one species changes to a new species is known as **gradualism.** According to the gradualism model, a continuing series of mutations and variations over time will result in a new species. Look back at **Figure 1,** which shows the evolution of the camel over tens of millions of years. Fossil evidence shows a series of intermediate forms that indicate a gradual change from the earliest camel species to today's species.

Punctuated Equilibrium Gradualism doesn't explain the evolution of all species. For some species, the fossil record shows few intermediate forms—one species suddenly changes to another. According to the **punctuated equilibrium** model, rapid evolution comes about when the mutation of a few genes results in the appearance of a new species over a relatively short period of time. The fossil record gives examples of this type of evolution, as you can see in **Figure 6.**

Resource Manager

Chapter Resources Booklet
Enrichment, p. 28
Reinforcement, p. 26

Curriculum Connection

Art Have students make a piece of art that shows their understanding of gradualism (i.e. a drawing that shows the slow evolution of one organism to another). In art, this process is called morphing.
L2 ⬚ **Visual-Spatial**

Punctuated Equilibrium Today Evolution by the punctuated equilibrium model can occur over a few thousand or million years, and sometimes even faster. For example, many bacteria have changed in a few decades. The antibiotic penicillin originally came from the fungus shown in **Figure 7.** But many bacteria species that were once easily killed by penicillin no longer are harmed by it. These bacteria have developed resistance to the drug. Penicillin has been in use since 1943. Just four years later, in 1947, a species of bacteria that causes pneumonia and other infections already had developed resistance to the drug. By the 1990s, several disease-producing bacteria had become resistant to penicillin and many other antibiotics.

How did penicillin-resistant bacteria evolve so quickly? As in any population, some organisms have variations that allow them to survive unfavorable living conditions when other organisms cannot. When penicillin was used to kill bacteria, those with the penicillin-resistant variation survived, reproduced, and passed this trait to their offspring. Over a period of time, this bacteria population became penicillin-resistant.

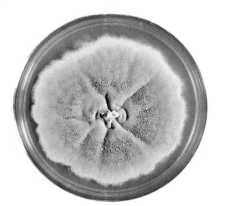

Health INTEGRATION

When a doctor prescribes antibiotics, the patient is told to take the medicine every few hours for a week or more. A patient who feels better after two or three days might stop taking the medicine. But, if any of the disease-causing bacteria remain in the body, the patient could become ill again. In your Science Journal, explain why it is important to take all of the antibiotics the doctor prescribes.

Figure 7
The fungus growing in this petri dish is *Penicillium*, the original source of penicillin. It produces an antibiotic substance that prevents the growth of certain bacteria.

Health INTEGRATION

It's important to kill all of the disease-causing bacteria, because any surviving bacteria could become resistant to the antibiotic.

IDENTIFYING Misconceptions

Many students think that environmental changes cause changes in traits that help organisms cope with the new environment. Refer to page 154F for teaching strategies that address this misconception.

3 Assess

Reteach
Have students list similarities between artificial selection, such as dog breeding, and natural selection. In both, specific traits are selected. L2

Challenge
Have students discuss why Darwin was impressed with the ability of humans to produce new breeds of plants and animals through artificial selection. He saw this as an analogy to the mechanism of evolution by natural selection. L2 COOP LEARN IS Interpersonal

---

Section 1 Assessment

1. Compare Lamarck's and Darwin's ideas about how evolution takes place.

2. Explain why variations are important to the survival of a population.

3. Explain how the gradualism model of evolution differs from the punctuated equilibrium model of evolution.

4. How does geographic isolation contribute to evolution?

5. **Think Critically** What adaptations would be helpful for an animal species that was moved to the arctic?

Skill Builder Activities

6. **Concept Mapping** Use information given in **Figure 6** to make a concept map that shows how raccoons, red pandas, giant pandas, polar bears, and black bears are related to a common ancestor. **For more help, refer to the** Science Skill Handbook.

7. **Using Percentages** The evolution of the camel can be traced back at least 56 million years. Use **Figure 1** to estimate the percent of this time that the modern camel has existed. **For more help, refer to the** Math Skill Handbook.

SECTION 1 Ideas About Evolution **A** ◆ **163**

✓ Assessment

Performance To assess students' abilities to classify organisms by their variations, ask them to classify two species of birds that eat different types of foods. Use **Performance Assessment in the Science Classroom,** p. 121.

Answers to Section Assessment

1. Lamarck thought acquired traits were passed to offspring; Darwin concluded that only certain traits were inherited and passed to offspring.

2. Over time, different variations may become adaptations important for survival and reproduction.

3. Gradualism—an ancestral species slowly evolves to become another species; punctuated equilibrium—species tend to remain constant for millions of years and suddenly become two or more species in a relatively short amount of time.

4. by separating populations with different variations and allowing them to independently evolve, producing greater variation

5. Possible answers: lighter coat color; traits for surviving extreme cold

6. The concept maps should illustrate several species evolving from a common ancestor.

7. Two million years/56 million years × 100% = approximately 4%

Activity
BENCH TESTED

Purpose Students will explore how natural selection equips organisms for survival in their environment.

Process Skills observing, analyzing, inferring, formulating, modeling

Time Required 40 minutes

Teaching Strategies:

- Obtain color photographs of frogs in natural settings to present examples of camouflage to students.
- Obtain color photographs of other camouflaged animals and ask students how natural selection has prepared them for survival in their environment.

Troubleshooting Provide students with pictures of different environments to serve as a reference.

Answers to Questions

1. Answer will vary, but students should consider the colors, patterns, and textures of the habitat.
2. Color patterns, textures, and body shapes that provide the best camouflage in an environment help those frogs avoid predators, and, through natural selection, these characteristics become dominant in a frog population.
3. The frog may not be properly camouflaged from predators in its new environment.

Assessment

Process Ask students to explain why the frog they have modeled would be not be equipped to survive in a different environment. Use **PASC,** p. 89.

Activity

Hidden Frogs

Through natural selection, animals become adapted for survival in their environment. Adaptations include shapes, colors, and even textures that help an animal blend into its surroundings. These adaptations are called camouflage. The red-eyed tree frog's mint green body blends in with tropical forest vegetation as shown in the photo on the right. Could you design camouflage for a desert frog? A temperate forest frog?

What You'll Investigate
What type of camouflage would best suit a frog living in a particular habitat?

Materials (for each group)
cardboard form of a frog	glue
colored markers	beads
crayons	sequins
colored pencils	modeling clay

Goals
■ **Create** a frog model camouflaged to blend in with its surroundings.

Safety Precautions 👓

Procedure

1. Choose one of the following habitats for your frog model: muddy shore of a pond, orchid flowers in a tropical rain forest, multicolored clay in a desert, or the leaves and branches of trees in a temperate forest.
2. **List** the features of your chosen habitat that will determine the camouflage your frog model will need.
3. **Brainstorm** with your group the body shape, coloring, and skin texture that would make the best camouflage for your model. Record your ideas in your Science Journal.

4. **Draw** samples of colors, patterns, texture, and other features your frog model might have in your Science Journal.
5. Show your design ideas to your teacher and ask for further input.
6. **Construct** your frog model.

Conclude and Apply

1. **Explain** how the characteristics of the habitat helped you decide on the specific frog features you chose.
2. **Infer** how the color patterns and other physical features of real frogs develop in nature.
3. **Explain** why it might be harmful to release a frog into a habitat for which it is not adapted.

Communicating
Your Data

Create a poster or other visual display that represents the habitat you chose for this activity. Use your display to show classmates how your design helps camouflage your frog model. **For more help, refer to the** Science Skill Handbook.

Communicating
Your Data

Ask students to access the Glencoe Science Web site to research their information.

Resource Manager

Chapter Resources Booklet
Activity Worksheet, pp. 5–6
Lab Activities, pp. 9–10, 11–14

Clues About Evolution

Clues from Fossils

Imagine going on a fossil hunt in Wyoming. Your companions are paleontologists—scientists who study the past by collecting and examining fossils. As you climb a low hill, you notice a curved piece of stone jutting out of the sandy soil. One of the paleontologists carefully brushes the soil away and congratulates you on your find. You've discovered part of the fossilized shell of a turtle like the one shown in **Figure 8.**

The Green River Formation covers parts of Wyoming, Utah, and Colorado. On your fossil hunt, you learn that about 50 million years ago, during the Eocene Epoch, this region was covered by lakes. The water was home to fish, crocodiles, lizards, and turtles. Palms, fig trees, willows, and cattails grew on the lakeshores. Insects and birds flew through the air. How do scientists know all this? After many of the plants and animals of that time died, they were covered with silt and mud. Over millions of years, they became the fossils that have made the Green River Formation one of the richest fossil deposits in the world.

As You Read

***What* You'll Learn**

Identify the importance of fossils as evidence of evolution.
Explain how relative and radiometric dating are used to estimate the age of fossils.
List examples of five types of evidence for evolution.

Vocabulary
sedimentary rock
radioactive element
embryology
homologous
vestigial structure

***Why* It's Important**
The scientific evidence for evolution helps you understand why this theory is so important to the study of biology.

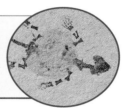

The turtle *Cisternum undatum* is from the same fossil formation.

The most abundant fossils are of a freshwater herring, *Knightia oecaena,* which is Wyoming's state fossil.

Figure 8
The desert of the Green River Formation is home to pronghorn antelope, elks, coyotes, and eagles. Fossil evidence shows that about 50 million years ago the environment was much warmer and wetter than it is today.

SECTION 2 Clues About Evolution **A** **165**

1 Motivate

Bellringer Transparency
Display the Section Focus Transparency for Section 2. Use the accompanying Transparency Activity Master. L2
ELL

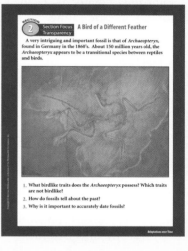

Section Focus Transparency   A Bird of a Different Feather

A very intriguing and important fossil is that of *Archaeopteryx*, found in Germany in the 1860's. About 150 million years old, the *Archaeopteryx* appears to be a transitional species between reptiles and birds.

1. What birdlike traits does the *Archaeopteryx* possess? Which traits are not birdlike?
2. How do fossils tell about the past?
3. Why is it important to accurately date fossils?

Tie to Prior Knowledge

Review the structure and function of DNA with students while they study the evidence for evolution. Emphasize that changes in DNA provide the basis for evolution.

Section ✔*Assessment* Planner

PORTFOLIO
Science Journal, p. 166
PERFORMANCE ASSESSMENT
Skill Builder Activities, p. 171
See page 182 for more options.

CONTENT ASSESSMENT
Section, p. 171
Challenge, p. 171
Chapter, pp. 182–183

2 Teach

Clues from Fossils

Caption Answer

Figure 9 Imprint fossils, mineralized fossils, and cast fossils are the most common.

Earth Science INTEGRATION

Nearly 75 percent of Earth's surface is covered by sedimentary rock. In some places, sedimentary rock layers may be more than a mile thick. Many sedimentary rocks lack radioactive materials needed for radiometric dating.

Activity

Bring in samples of igneous, metamorphic, and sedimentary rocks. Ask students to observe the differences. Explain that igneous rock was once molten, so no organism could have lived in it. Metamorphic rock is a rock that has been reheated, so its structure has changed from the original. Any fossils contained in it are usually lost. Sedimentary rock has the best characteristics for the preservation of a fossil record. L2 ELL IS **Visual-Spatial**

Figure 9
Examples of several different types of fossils are shown here. *Which of these would most likely be found in a layer of sedimentary rock?*

A **Imprint fossils** A leaf, feather, bones, or even the entire body of an organism can leave an imprint on sediment that later hardens to become rock.

B **Mineralized fossils** Minerals can replace wood or bone to create a piece of petrified wood shown to the left or a mineralized bone fossil.

C **Frozen fossils** The remains of organisms like this mammoth can be trapped in ice that remains frozen for thousands or millions of years.

E **Cast Fossils** Minerals can fill in the hollows of animal tracks as shown to the right, mollusk shell, or other parts of an organism to create a cast.

D **Fossils in amber** When the sticky resin of certain cone-bearing plants hardens over time, amber forms. It can contain the remains of trapped insects.

Earth Science INTEGRATION

Types of Fossils

Most of the evidence for evolution comes from fossils. A fossil is the remains, an imprint, or a trace of a prehistoric organism. Several types of fossils are shown in **Figure 9.** Most fossils are found in sedimentary rock. **Sedimentary rock** is formed when layers of sand, silt, clay, or mud are compacted and cemented together, or when minerals are deposited from a solution. Limestone, sandstone, and shale are all examples of sedimentary rock. Fossils are found more often in limestone than in any other kind of sedimentary rock. The fossil record provides evidence that living things have evolved. Other areas of study in addition to fossils also support the theory of evolution.

166 ◆ A CHAPTER 6 Adaptations Over Time

Teacher FYI

The fossil record has always been incomplete because most organisms never become fossils. They are either decomposed or eaten before they have an opportunity to become fossilized.

Science Journal

The Grand Canyon No place on Earth has as many layers of exposed sedimentary rock as the Grand Canyon. Have students research the Grand Canyon by accessing the Glencoe Science Web site and prepare an essay on what they would expect to see if they visited. L2
IS **Linguistic** P

Determining a Fossil's Age

Paleontologists use detective skills to determine the age of dinosaur fossils or the remains of other ancient organisms. They can use clues provided by unique rock layers and the fossils they contain. The clues provide information about the geology, weather, and life-forms that must have been present during each geologic time period. Two basic methods—relative dating and radiometric dating—can be used, alone or together, to estimate the ages of rocks and fossils.

Relative Dating One way to find the approximate age of fossils found within a rock layer is relative dating. Relative dating is based on the idea that in undisturbed areas, younger rock layers are deposited on top of older rock layers, as shown in **Figure 10.** Relative dating provides only an estimate of a fossil's age. The estimate is made by comparing the ages of rock layers found above and below the fossil layer. For example, suppose a 50-million-year-old rock layer lies below a fossil, and a 35-million-year-old layer lies above it. According to relative dating, the fossil is probably between 35 million and 50 million years old.

✔ **Reading Check** *Why can relative dating be used only to estimate the age of a fossil?*

Radiometric Dating Scientists can obtain a more accurate estimate of the age of a rock layer by using radioactive elements. A **radioactive element** gives off a steady amount of radiation as it slowly changes to a nonradioactive element. Each radioactive element gives off radiation at a different rate. Scientists can estimate the age of the rock by comparing the amount of radioactive element with the amount of nonradioactive element in the rock. This method of dating does not always produce exact results, because the original amount of radioactive element in the rock can never be determined for certain.

Data Update Visit the Glencoe Science Web site at **science.glencoe.com** for news about recent fossil discoveries. In your Science Journal, write a brief report describing how one of these discoveries was made and what it reveals about past life on Earth.

Figure 10
In Bryce Canyon, erosion by water and wind has cut through the sedimentary rock, exposing the layers. Fossils found in lower layers of sedimentary rock are usually older than the fossils found in upper layers.

Resource Manager

Chapter Resources Booklet
Transparency Activity, p. 43
Directed Reading for Content Mastery, p. 19

Inclusion Strategies

Visually Impaired You can explain relative dating to visually impaired students by creating layers of different materials that the student can differentiate by touch. Use stiff cardboard or foam board and glue the materials in layers. Glue easily identifiable objects as analogies to fossils.

Activity

Have students research the Scopes trial and other legislation and court cases concerning the teaching of evolution. *The American Biology Teacher* published several articles detailing this history in 1998–1999. Have them report their findings to the class. L2 IS **Linguistic**

Determining a Fossil's Age

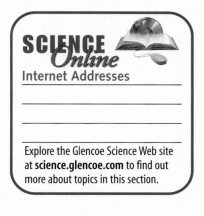

Internet Addresses
_____
_____
_____

Explore the Glencoe Science Web site at **science.glencoe.com** to find out more about topics in this section.

✔ **Reading Check**

Answer Relative dating can only give a range, not an exact age.

Make a Model

Have students make a model showing how relative dating is used. Their model can show layers of sand, dirt, salt, cornmeal, or other materials in a plastic drink bottle or glass container. Several "fossils" should be placed in the model to explain their relative ages. Have each student present his or her model to the group. L2 IS **Kinesthetic and Visual-Spatial**

Activity

Have groups of students collect rocks and fossils from your area. Allow them to research the types of rocks and fossils they find. If students will donate their finds to the school, you can quickly build a school collection of fossils and rocks to display. L2 ELL COOP LEARN IS **Interpersonal**

Visualizing the Geologic Time Scale

Have students examine the pictures and read the captions. Then ask the following questions.

In the geologic time scale, which is longer—an era or a period? Students should note that an era is a longer time than a period.

The names of the geologic eras have Greek roots. *Ceno* means "recent" and *zoic* means "life." *Paleo* means "ancient." Infer the meaning of the Greek prefix *meso*. Meso means "middle", so mesozoic means "middle life."

Activity

Have students work in teams to create a poster about one of the geologic periods shown in the feature. The poster should contain facts about the plants and animals that were alive during the period, as well as illustrations depicting the landforms and bodies of water that were present. The teams of students should present their findings to the class.

Extension

Have interested students research the Precambrian era, which accounts for about 90% of geologic time. Students should use a word processing program to prepare a short report of their findings.

Figure 11

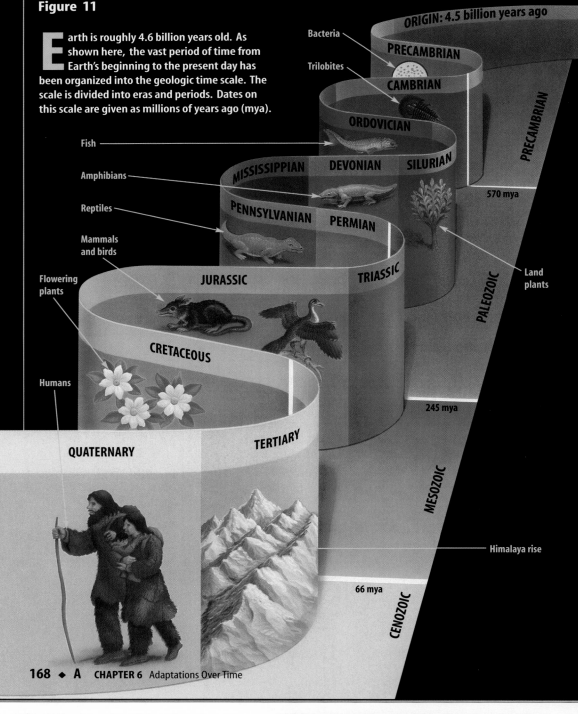

Earth is roughly 4.6 billion years old. As shown here, the vast period of time from Earth's beginning to the present day has been organized into the geologic time scale. The scale is divided into eras and periods. Dates on this scale are given as millions of years ago (mya).

168 ◆ A   CHAPTER 6   Adaptations Over Time

Curriculum Connection

Math Explain the vastness of geological, or "deep" time. A million years is only 0.02 percent of the total. Have students convert the eras and periods into percentages of the entire scale.
L2 LS **Logical-Mathematical**

Resource Manager

Chapter Resources Booklet
Transparency Activity, pp. 45–47

Fossils and Evolution

Fossils provide a record of organisms that lived in the past. However, the fossil record has gaps, much like a book with pages missing. The gaps exist because of an incomplete rock record and most organisms do not become fossils. This means that the fossil record will always be incomplete. By looking at fossils, scientists conclude that many simpler forms of life existed earlier in Earth's history, and more complex forms of life appeared later, as shown in **Figure 11.** Fossils provide direct evidence that evolution has occurred on Earth.

Almost every week, fossil discoveries are made somewhere in the world. When fossils are found, they are used to help scientists understand the past. Scientists can use fossils to make models that show what the organisms could have looked like. From fossils, scientists can sometimes determine whether the organisms lived in family groups or alone, what they ate, what kind of environment they lived in, and many other things about them. Most fossils represent extinct organisms. From a study of the fossil record, scientists have concluded that more than 99 percent of all organisms that have ever existed are extinct now.

More Clues About Evolution

Besides fossils, what other clues do humans have about evolution? Sometimes, evolution can be directly observed. Plant breeders observe evolution when they use cross-breeding to produce genetic changes in plants. The development of antibiotic resistance in bacteria is another direct observation of evolution. Entomologists have noted similar rapid evolution of pesticide-resistant insect species. These observations provide direct evidence that evolution occurs. Also, many examples of indirect evidence for evolution exist. They include similarities in embryo structures, the chemical makeup of organisms, including DNA, and the way organisms develop into adults. Indirect evidence does not provide proof of evolution, but it does support the idea that evolution takes place over time.

Embryology The study of embryos and their development is called **embryology** (em bree AH luh jee). An embryo is the earliest growth stage of an organism. A tail and gills or gill slits are found in the embryos of fish, reptiles, birds, and mammals, as **Figure 12** shows. Fish keep their gills, but the other organisms lose them as their development continues. Fish, birds, and reptiles keep their tails, but many mammals lose theirs. These similarities suggest an evolutionary relationship among all vertebrate species.

Figure 12
Similarities in the embryos of fish, chickens, and rabbits show evidence of evolution.

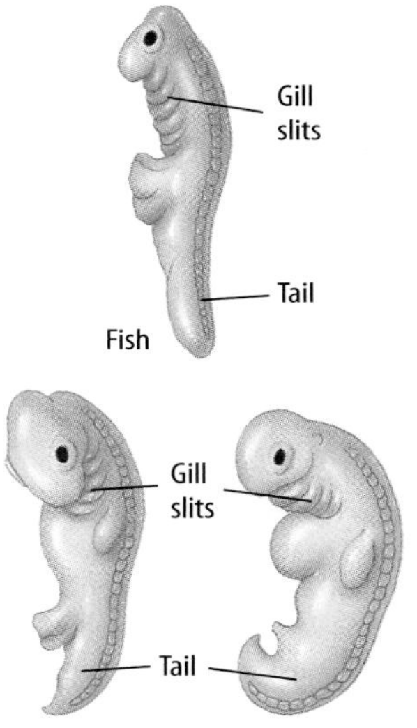

Gill slits

Tail

Fish

Gill slits

Tail

Chicken   Rabbit

SECTION 2 Clues About Evolution   A ◆ 169

Use an Analogy

Use a length of rope or kite string as an analogy for the geologic time scale. Make knots to illustrate where the eras begin and end, and paint sections different colors to illustrate the periods. Another analogy for the geologic time scale is a clock. Use a wall clock and talk about the eras and periods as you advance the clock from 12:00. Make your conversion calculations before you begin.

Fossils and Evolution

Earth Science INTEGRATION

Changes in structures often mirror changes in the environment.

Activity

Have students locate fossils in walls of local buildings and research the locations from which the building materials came. Most of the fossils will be of marine forms in limestone that may have come from other states in the U.S. or from other countries. L2 ELL
IS **Visual-Spatial**

More Clues About Evolution

Teacher FYI

Morphological and molecular studies indicate that marine mammals (e.g., whales, dolphins, porpoises) and even-toed ungulates (e.g., pigs, hippos, camels) share a common ancestor not shared by any other group. This implies that cows and whales are more closely related than cows and horses.

✔ Active Reading

Double Entry Journal In this strategy, the student takes notes and adds his or her own reflections while reading the student text. Students are encouraged to explore ideas, make responses, and take risks in giving opinions about the reading. Have them divide a sheet of paper in half. On the left, have students identify a particular passage or quotation of significance in the reading. The reader record anything luminous, enigmatic, stimulating, or disturbing. On the right, the reader responds, question, elaborates, makes personal connections, evaluates, reflects, analyzes, or interprets. Have students make a Double Entry Journal about evolution.

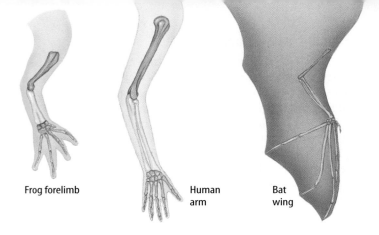

Visual Learning

Figure 13 Have students compare the wing of a bat and the flipper of a porpoise with a human hand. Ask students what similarities they have. Possible answers: number of bones, muscle, and blood vessels; type of bones; they are homologous. L2 IS **Visual-Spatial**

✔ Reading Check

Answer These structures often indicate that two or more species share common ancestors.

Teacher FYI

Pesticide resistance in insects, antibiotic resistance in bacteria, and observed differences in salamanders, frogs, and birds are all examples of direct evidence for evolution.

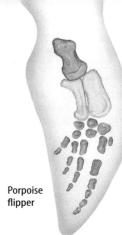

Porpoise flipper   Frog forelimb   Human arm   Bat wing

Figure 13
A porpoise flipper, frog forelimb, human arm, and bat wing are homologous. These structures show different arrangements and shapes of the bones of the forelimb. They have the same number of bones, muscles, and blood vessels, and they developed from similar tissues.

Homologous Structures What do the structures shown in **Figure 13** have in common? Although they have different functions, each of these structures is made up of the same kind of bones. Body parts that are similar in origin and structure are called **homologous** (hoh MAH luh gus). Homologous structures also can be similar in function. They often indicate that two or more species share common ancestors.

✔ Reading Check   *What do homologous structures indicate?*

Vestigial Structures The bodies of some organisms include **vestigial** (veh STIH jee ul) **structures**—structures that don't seem to have a function. Vestigial structures also provide evidence for evolution. For example, manatees, snakes, and whales no longer have back legs, but, like all animals with legs, they still have pelvic bones. The human appendix is a vestigial structure. The appendix appears to be a small version of the cecum, which is an important part of the digestive tract of many mammals. Scientists hypothesize that vestigial structures, like those shown in **Figure 14,** are body parts that once functioned in an ancestor.

Figure 14
Humans have three small muscles around each ear that are vestigial. In some mammals, such as horses, these muscles are large. They allow a horse to turn its ears toward the source of a sound. Humans cannot rotate their ears, but some people can wiggle their ears.

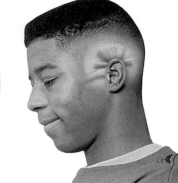

170 ◆ A   **CHAPTER 6** Adaptations Over Time

Resource Manager

Chapter Resources Booklet
Enrichment, p. 29
Reinforcement, p. 26

🌐 Cultural Diversity

Evolving Viruses The flu is an example of a sickness caused by a virus whose DNA evolves in order for it to survive. Every major flu epidemic has come from South China, where ducks, pigs, and humans are brought into daily contact. An avian flu transfers to pigs, as does a human flu variety. The viruses exchange pieces of genetic code to form a new flu strain. When the virus reinfects humans, it is different enough that antibodies made to fight the first form do not stop the new virus. That is why flu shots do not protect against all varieties.

DNA If you enjoy science fiction, you probably have read books or seen movies in which scientists re-create dinosaurs and other extinct organisms from DNA taken from fossils. DNA is the molecule that controls heredity and directs the development of every organism. In a cell with a nucleus, DNA is found in genes that make up the chromosomes. Scientists compare DNA from living organisms to identify similarities among species. Examinations of ancient DNA often provide additional evidence of how some species evolved from their extinct ancestors. By looking at DNA, scientists also can determine how closely related organisms are. For example, DNA studies indicate that dogs are the closest relatives of bears.

Similar DNA also can suggest common ancestry. Apes such as the gorillas shown in **Figure 15,** chimpanzees, and orangutans, have 24 pairs of chromosomes. Humans have 23 pairs. When two of an ape's chromosomes are laid end to end, a match for human chromosome number 2 is formed. Also, similar proteins such as hemoglobin—the oxygen-carrying protein in red blood cells—are found in many primates. This can be further evidence that primates have a common ancestor.

Figure 15
Gorillas have DNA and proteins that are similar to humans and other primates.

③ Assess

Reteach

Show students examples of as many kinds of fossils as possible. Have students identify each type of fossil. L1 IS **Naturalist**

Challenge

Why isn't carbon dating used for all radiometric techniques? Carbon's half-life of approximately 5,000 years is too short.

✓Assessment

Performance Have students prepare a poster showing the time periods in which fish, amphibians, reptiles, birds, and mammals first appeared. Use **Performance Assessment in the Science Classroom,** p. 145.

Section ② Assessment

1. How are relative dating and radiometric dating used by scientists?

2. Why are fossils important evidence of evolution? Describe five different kinds of fossils.

3. Explain how DNA can provide some evidence of evolution.

4. Describe three examples of direct evidence for evolution.

5. **Think Critically** Compare and contrast the five types of evidence that support the theory of evolution.

Skill Builder Activities

6. **Interpreting Scientific Illustrations** According to **Figure 11,** what was the longest geological era? What was the shortest era? During what period did mammals appear? **For more help, refer to the** Science Skill Handbook.

7. **Using Percentages** The Cenozoic Era represents about 66 million years. Approximately what percent of Earth's 4.6-billion-year history does this era represent? **For more help, refer to the** Math Skill Handbook.

SECTION 2 Clues About Evolution **A ◆ 171**

Answers to Section Assessment

1. Relative dating is used to find the approximate age of a rock layer by its position relative to other layers. Radiometric dating is used to date rocks by measuring relative amounts of radioactive and non-radioactive elements.

2. Fossils provide evidence of how simpler forms of life changed over time to more complex forms. Organisms can be frozen in ice or trapped in amber. Minerals can replace wood or bone. There are also cast fossils and imprint fossils.

3. Organisms with similar DNA are closely related.

4. antibiotic resistance in bacteria, pesticide resistance in insects, and genetic changes in plants

5. Students should compare and contrast vestigial structures, DNA, homologous structures, fossils, and embryology.

6. Ordovician; Silurian; Quaternary

7. 66 million years/4,600 million years × 100 = 1.43%

1 Motivate

Bellringer Transparency

Display the Section Focus Transparency for Section 3. Use the accompanying Transparency Activity Master. L2 ELL

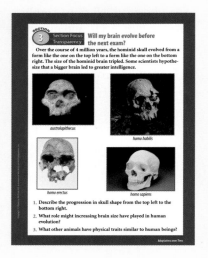

Tie to Prior Knowledge

Students may have questions about the relationship between species of primates. Remind students that species are classified into groups based on similarities, such as structure and DNA sequences.

The Evolution of Primates

As You Read

What **You'll Learn**
Describe the differences among living primates.
Identify the adaptations of primates.
Discuss the evolutionary history of modern primates.

Vocabulary
primate
hominid
Homo sapiens

Why **It's Important**
Studying primate evolution will help you appreciate the differences among primates.

Figure 16
The ability to rotate the shoulder in a complete circle allows humans to swim through water and tree-dwelling primates to travel through treetops.

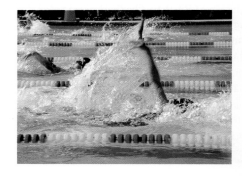

Primates

Humans, monkeys, and apes belong to the group of mammals known as the **primates.** All primates have opposable thumbs, binocular vision, and flexible shoulders that allow the arms to rotate. These shared characteristics could indicate that all primates may have evolved from a common ancestor.

Having an opposable thumb allows you to cross your thumb over your palm and touch your fingers. This means that you can grasp and hold things with your hands. An opposable thumb allows tree-dwelling primates to hold on to branches.

Binocular vision permits you to judge depth or distance with your eyes. In a similar way, it allows tree-dwelling primates to judge the distances as they move between branches. Flexible shoulders and rotating forelimbs also help tree-dwelling primates move from branch to branch. They also allow humans to do the backstroke, as shown in **Figure 16.**

Primates are divided into two major groups. The first group, the prosimians (pro SIH mee uhn), includes lemurs and tarsiers like those shown in **Figure 17.** The second group, anthropoids (AN thruh poydz), includes monkeys, apes, and humans.

Section ✓*Assessment* Planner

PORTFOLIO
MiniLab Assessment, p. 173
PERFORMANCE ASSESSMENT
Try at Home MiniLAB, p. 173
Skill Builder Activities, p. 175
See page 182 for more options.

CONTENT ASSESSMENT
Section, p. 175
Challenge, p. 175
Chapter, pp. 182–183

Figure 17
Tarsiers and lemurs are active at night.
A Tarsiers are commonly found in the rain forests of Southeast Asia.
B Lemurs live on Madagascar and other nearby islands.

2 Teach

Primates

Visual Learning

Figure 16 Have students identify other uses for rotating forelimbs in primates. Possible answers: opening doors, swinging a baseball bat, throwing a football Use the photos to discuss other common characteristics of primates. L2 IS **Visual-Spatial**

Hominids About 4 million to 6 million years ago, humanlike primates appeared that were different from the other primates. These ancestors, called **hominids,** ate both meat and plants and walked upright on two legs. Hominids shared some characteristics with gorillas, orangutans, and chimpanzees, but a larger brain separated them from the apes.

African Origins In the early 1920s, a fossil skull was discovered in a quarry in South Africa. The skull had a small space for the brain, but it had a humanlike jaw and teeth. The fossil, named *Australopithecus,* was one of the oldest hominids discovered. An almost-complete skeleton of *Australopithecus* was found in northern Africa in 1974. This hominid fossil, shown in **Figure 18,** was called Lucy and had a small brain but is thought to have walked upright. This fossil indicates that modern hominids might have evolved from similar ancestors.

Figure 18
The fossil remains of Lucy are estimated to be 2.9 million to 3.4 million years old.

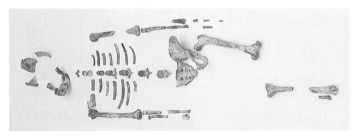

TRY AT HOME
Mini LAB

Living Without Thumbs
Procedure
1. Using **tape,** fasten down each of your thumbs next to the palm of each hand.
2. Leave your thumbs taped down for at least 1 h. During this time, do the following activities: eat a meal, change clothes, and brush your teeth. Be careful not to try anything that could be dangerous.
3. Untape your thumbs, then write about your experiences in your **Science Journal.**

Analysis
1. Did not having use of your thumbs significantly affect the way you did anything? Explain.
2. Infer how having opposable thumbs could have influenced primate evolution.

TRY AT HOME
Mini LAB

Purpose Students observe the function of opposable thumbs, and infer how they may have influenced primate evolution. L1 ELL IS **Kinesthetic**
Materials tape
Teaching Strategy Tell students it will be easier for them to tape both thumbs down if they use a roll of tape, rather than tape from a dispenser.
Safety Precautions Tell students not to try anything that could be dangerous with impaired manual dexterity during this activity.
Analysis
1. Answers should indicate that students were negatively affected.
2. Possible answer: Opposable thumbs would allow for the use of tools, and tools are a foundation of modern civilization and technology.

Assessment

Performance Have students design a house with features that could be easily used by someone without thumbs. Use **PASC,** p. 123. P

SECTION 3 The Evolution of Primates **A ◆ 173**

Teacher FYI
Primates are thought to have evolved during the Eocene epoch. There are presently about 200 species of primates, although there were more in the past. Genetic studies indicate that the bonobo, chimpanzee, and gorilla are more closely related to humans than to any other primates.

Resource Manager

Chapter Resources Booklet
    Transparency Activity, p. 44
    MiniLAB, p. 4
Home and Community Involvement, p. 48

Primates, continued

Teacher FYI

The African Rift Valley is an area of Africa where many human and hominid fossils have been uncovered. A rift valley occurs between geologic faults.

Activity

Using what they know about Neanderthals, have students write and illustrate an advertisement in their Science Journals for a fictional newspaper, *The Neanderthal News*. The ad should be for a modern product that Neanderthals might have been able to use. Student ads may emphasize tools for hammering and cutting. L2
LS Linguistic

✔ Reading Check

Answer Because tools were found near *Homo habilis* fossils, and *Homo habilis* means "handyman."

Humans

Caption Answer

Figure 20 Neanderthal skulls have a heavier brow ridge and thicker bones.

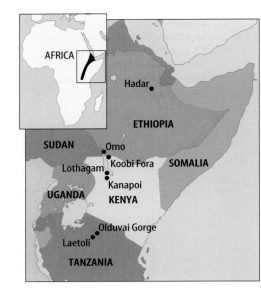

Figure 19
Many of the oldest humanlike skeletons have been found in this area of east Africa.

Early Humans In the 1960s in the region of Africa shown in **Figure 19,** a hominid fossil, which was more like present-day humans than *Australopithecus,* was discovered. The hominid was named *Homo habilis,* the handy man, because simple stone tools were found near him. *Homo habilis* is estimated to be 1.5 million to 2 million years old. Based upon many fossil comparisons, scientists have suggested that *Homo habilis* gave rise to another species, *Homo erectus,* about 1.6 million years ago. This hominid had a larger brain than *Homo habilis. Homo erectus* traveled from Africa to Southeast Asia, China, and possibly Europe. *Homo habilis* and *Homo erectus* are thought to be ancestors of humans because they had larger brains and more human-like features than *Australopithecus.*

✔ Reading Check   *Why was* Homo habilis *given that name?*

Humans

The fossil record indicates that *Homo sapiens* evolved about 400,000 years ago. By about 125,000 years ago, two early human groups, Neanderthals and Cro-Magnon humans, as shown in **Figure 20,** probably lived at the same time in parts of Africa and Europe.

Neanderthals Short, heavy bodies with thick bones, small chins, and heavy browridges were physical characteristics of Neanderthals (nee AN dur tawlz). They lived in family groups in caves and used well-made stone tools to hunt large animals. Neanderthals disappeared from the fossil record about 30,000 years ago. They might represent a side branch of human evolution and are not direct ancestors of modern humans.

Figure 20
The skull of a Neanderthal can be compared with the skull of a Cro-Magnon *What differences can you see between these two skulls?*

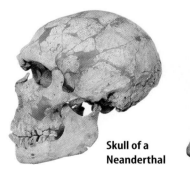

Skull of a Neanderthal

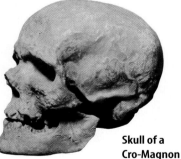

Skull of a Cro-Magnon

174 ◆ A   CHAPTER 6   Adaptations over Time

Cultural Diversity

Tribal Customs Use the information about fossil sites in Africa to increase students' awareness of African geography and the rich cultural heritage found there. Have students research African tribes, such as the Masai, and report on their way of life, customs, and rituals. L2

Resource Manager

Chapter Resources Booklet
   Enrichment, p. 30
   Reinforcement, p. 27
   Directed Reading for Content Mastery, pp. 19, 20

Cro-Magnon Humans Cro-Magnon fossils have been found in Europe, Asia, and Australia and date from 10,000 to about 40,000 years in age. Standing about 1.6 m to 1.7 m tall, the physical appearance of Cro-Magnon people was almost the same as that of modern humans. They lived in caves, made stone carvings, and buried their dead. As shown in **Figure 21,** the oldest recorded art has been found on the walls of caves in France, where Cro-Magnon humans first painted bison, horses, and people carrying spears. Cro-Magnon humans are thought to be direct ancestors of early humans, *Homo sapiens,* which means "wise human." Evidence indicates that modern humans, *Homo sapiens sapiens,* evolved from *Homo sapiens.*

Section 3 Assessment

1. Describe at least three kinds of evidence that suggest all primates might have shared a common ancestor.
2. What is the importance of *Australopithecus?*
3. Describe the differences and similarities among Neanderthals, Cro-Magnon humans, and early humans.
4. Which group do most scientists consider to be direct ancestors of modern humans?
5. **Think Critically** Propose a hypothesis about why teeth are the most abundant fossils of hominids.

Skill Builder Activities

6. **Concept Mapping** Make a concept map to show in what sequence the different groups of hominids appeared. Use the following terms: *Homo sapiens sapiens,* Neanderthal, *Homo habilis, Australopithecus, Homo sapiens,* and Cro-Magnon human. **For more help, refer to the** Science Skill Handbook.
7. **Communicating** Write a story in your Science Journal about what life would be like for you if you did not have thumbs. **For more help, refer to the** Science Skill Handbook.

SECTION 3 The Evolution of Primates **A** ◆ **175**

Section 3 The Evolution of Primates **A** ◆ **175**

Extension

Extension
Show examples of art from the caves of France and other European countries. Ask students to write a paragraph in their Science Journal explaining why this art is important to us today. Art provides insight and understanding of the artists and their lives.
L2 LS **Visual-Spatial**

Reteach
Have students prepare a list on the board of characteristics common to primates. L1 COOP LEARN LS **Interpersonal**

Challenge
What is the difference between *Homo hablis* **and** *Homo erectus?* H. hablis is older and thought to be the ancestor of H. erectus; H. erectus had a larger brain and moved out of Africa 1 million years ago.

Portfolio Have students make a timeline of the sequence of hominid evolution. Use **Performance Assessment in the Science Classroom,** p. 165.

Answers to Section Assessment

1. homologous structures; similar DNA; fossils
2. *Australopithecus,* an early hominid, had a small brain case but humanlike jaws and teeth.
3. Neanderthals had short bodies with massive bones and heavy brow ridges. Cro-Magnon humans were taller, invented art, made stone carvings, and buried their dead. Cro-Magnon humans were very similar to modern humans.
4. Cro-Magnon humans
5. Teeth are the hardest parts of an organism.
6. The concept map should be an events chain in the following order: *Australopithecus, Homo habilis,* Neanderthals, Cro-Magnon humans, *Homo sapiens,* and modern *Homo sapiens sapiens.*
7. Stories should indicate hardships that might result from being maladapted to their environment.

Activity

Recognize the Problem

Purpose

Students design and carry out an experiment showing the variation in a population. L2 ELL COOP LEARN

IS Logical-Mathematical

Process Skills

forming a hypothesis, measuring in SI, using numbers, interpreting data, communicating, making and using tables, designing an experiment

Time Required

45 minutes to plan the investigation, 45 minutes to complete the investigation

Safety Precautions

Caution students not to put any materials into their mouths. Be sure students are not allergic to any plants used.

Form a Hypothesis

Possible Hypotheses

Student hypotheses will vary. Possible hypotheses include: "A sample of peanuts will exhibit variations in numbers of seeds," or "A sample of peanuts will exhibit variations in length of seeds."

Activity *Design Your Own Experiment*

Recognizing Variation in a Population

When you first observe a flock of pigeons, you might think all the birds look alike. However, if you look closer, you will notice minor differences, or variations, among the individuals. Different pigeons might have different color markings, or some might be smaller or larger than others. Individuals of the same species—whether they're birds, plants, or worms—might look alike at first, but some variations undoubtedly exist. According to the principles of natural selection, evolution could not occur without variations. What kinds of variations have you noticed among species of plants or animals?

Recognize the Problem

How can you measure variation in a plant or animal population?

Form a Hypothesis

Make a hypothesis about the amount of variation in the fruit and seeds of one species of plant.

Possible Materials
fruit and seeds from one plant species
metric ruler
magnifying glass
graph paper

Goals
■ **Design** an experiment that will allow you to collect data about variation in a population.
■ **Observe, measure, and analyze** variations in a population.

Safety Precautions

Do not put any fruit or seeds in your mouth. Wash your hands after handling plant parts.

Test Your Hypothesis

Possible Procedures

Procedures will vary. Most students will choose width or length to measure. Others may choose volume, number of seeds, or some other variable. Volume of fruit can be measured by water displacement. Students may want to design color charts to compare differences in fruit coloration.

Resource Manager

Chapter Resources Booklet
   Activity Worksheet, pp. 7–8
Lab Management and Safety, p. 71

Test Your Hypothesis

Plan

1. As a group, agree upon and write out the hypothesis statement.

2. **List** the steps you need to take to test your hypothesis. Be specific. Describe exactly what you will do at each step. List your materials.

3. **Decide** what characteristic of fruit and seeds you will study. For example, you could measure the length of fruit and seeds or count the number of seeds per fruit.

4. **Design** a data table in your Science Journal to collect data about two variations. Use the table to record the data your group collects as you complete the experiment.

5. **Identify** any constants, variables, and controls of the experiment.

6. How many fruit and seeds will you examine? Will your data be more accurate if you examine larger numbers?

7. **Summarize** your data in a graph or chart.

Do

1. Make sure your teacher approves your plan before you start.

2. Carry out the experiment as planned.

3. While the experiment is going on, write down any observations you make and complete the data table in your Science Journal.

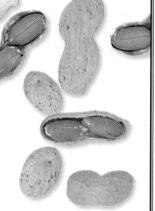

Analyze Your Data

1. **Calculate** the mean and range of variation in your experiment. The range is the difference between the largest and the smallest measurements. The mean is the sum of all the data divided by the sample size.

2. **Graph** your group's results by making a line graph for the variations you measured. Place the range of variation on the x-axis and the number of organisms that had that measurement on the y-axis.

Draw Conclusions

1. **Explain** your results in terms of natural selection.

2. What factors did you use to determine the amount of variation present?

3. Suggest reasons why one or more of the variations you observed in this activity might be helpful to the survival of the individual.

*C*ommunicating
Your Data

Create a poster or other exhibit that illustrates the variations you and your classmates observed.

Performance Ask students to infer the natural selection advantage of fruits producing larger quantities of seeds. Larger seed quantities increase the chances that at least a few seeds will germinate and grow to maturity. Use **Performance Assessment in the Science Classroom,** p. 89.

*C*ommunicating
Your Data

Discuss the variations observed by the class. Have students discuss why some variations are more advantageous than others.

Teaching Strategies

• Guide students as they decide what trait to measure. Length or width of seeds will be most easily measured with the materials suggested.

• For most students, larger seeds will be easier to work with. Peanuts, lima beans, sunflower seeds, pinto beans, and peas are large enough.

• If students are physically incapable of measuring the seeds, have them work with a partner who can help.

Expected Outcome

Most students will collect data that results in a bell-shaped curve when graphed.

Analyze Your Data

1. Mean and range will vary depending on the seeds used and the variables measured.

2. Graphs will be a bell-shaped curve for most variables studied.

Error Analysis

Have students who measure the same trait share their results and explain any differences they observe.

Draw Conclusions

1. Natural selection may result in a variation that is found in many organisms within a population, but variations in the trait may also be found in smaller numbers.

2. by determining what the "norm" is and how often seeds vary from it

3. Answers will vary. Accept all reasonable answers. Possible response: Small, lightweight fruit is more easily dispersed to other areas by birds than heavier fruit.

Content Background

About the time of the 12th International Conference on AIDS in 1998, it had become clear that the powerful new drugs being used to attack AIDS, called the protease inhibitors or the triple cocktail, would not bring the miracle that many had hoped they would. Between 10 and 50 percent of patients with AIDS who took protease inhibitors were seeing a return of the virus in new and more virulent forms. As many as 4.5 percent of newly infected patients were infected with drug-resistant strains of the virus, according to a 1999 study conducted by the Journal of the American Medical Association.

Resistant strains of AIDS, much like resistant strains of other infectious diseases such as strep throat, are caused by patients who miss doses of or quit taking their medication. They then develop drug-resistant infections and may pass the new forms of the disease on to others. If a person contracts HIV from another person with a resistant strain, it could be as if the person got infected in 1983 when there were no anti-retroviral drugs. Physicians could be starting at square one in terms of treatment.

In addition, protease inhibitors are extremely expensive and not available to everyone. This could change the HIV problem from a world problem to a problem of developing countries alone.

TIME

SCIENCE AND HISTORY

Wong-Staal was on one of the two teams that first identified HIV as the virus that causes AIDS.

Fighting

Some people wear a red ribbon as a reminder to fight HIV and AIDS.

The first cases of AIDS, or acquired immune deficiency syndrome, in humans were reported in the early 1980s. AIDS is caused by the human immunodeficiency virus, or HIV. It is most likely that HIV first occurred in nonhuman primates, evolving into a form that could infect humans. For the first two decades of the battle against HIV and AIDS, it looked like the virus might win. Teams of scientists from many fields, and in many parts of the world, are part of the ongoing counterattack.

A major problem in AIDS research is the rapid evolution of HIV. When HIV multiplies inside a host cell, new versions of the virus are produced as well as identical copies of the virus that invaded the cell. New versions of the virus can soon outnumber the original version. That's why HIV is so hard to fight—a treatment that works against today's HIV might not work against tomorrow's version.

178 ◆ A

Resources for Teachers and Students

AIDS in the World II: Global Dimensions, Social Roots, and Responses: The Global AIDS Policy Coalition, 2nd edition, edited by Jonathan Mann and Daniel J.M. Tarantola, Oxford University Press, New York and London, 1996.

AIDS and STDs: Global Perspectives, Rachel Donatelle, Pearson Custom Publishing, New York, 1999.

Confronting AIDS: Public Priorities in a Global Epidemic, edited by The World Bank, Oxford University Press, New York and London, 1999

Global Responses to AIDS, by Cristiana Bestos, Indiana University Press, Bloomington, Indiana, 1999.

These rapid changes in HIV also mean that different strains of the virus exist in different places around the world. That means most vaccines, which are still in the experimental stage, and treatments developed in the United States work only for AIDS patients who contracted the virus in the United States. This leaves AIDS sufferers in some parts of the world without effective treatments. Also, treatments might work for only a short period of time. Traditional vaccines quickly become useless. So, researchers such as geneticist Flossie Wong-Staal at the University of California in San Diego, must look for new ways to fight the evolving virus.

Working Backwards

Flossie Wong-Staal is taking a new approach. Her research focuses on how HIV uses host human cells. First, her team identifies the parts of a human cell that HIV depends on. Next, the team looks for parts of the human cell that HIV needs but the human cell doesn't need. Then the team looks for a way to remove—or inactivate—that unneeded part. This technique limits the virus's ability to multiply.

Wong-Staal's research combines three important aspects of science—a deep understanding of how cells and genes operate, great skill in the techniques of genetics, and great ideas. Understanding, skill, and great ideas are the best weapons so far in the fight to conquer HIV.

Discussion

How would Wong-Stall's research avoid the pitfalls of the new drugs and vaccines to treat HIV and AIDS? Possible answer: Instead of depending on suppressing the virus with drugs, this new research would prevent the virus from multiplying by changing existing cell structure. This could eliminate the daily regiment of taking multiple drugs.

Historical Significance

Even though the outbreak and spread of the HIV virus and AIDS have a unique history, students might find useful an examination of other diseases that have had a world-wide impact and that have been "cured." Tell students that they will research the disease tuberculosis, or TB, in an effort to map the history of the disease. Provide students with copies of a world map. Then have students record on their maps the answers to these questions:

- When and where was the first known outbreak of TB?
- At the height of the TB epidemic, in what countries was the disease known to occur?
- At the height of the disease, how many people were infected with the disease?
- When did the numbers of infected people began to decline?
- When was the TB vaccine introduced?

Explain that even though there is a TB vaccine, new drug-resistant strains of TB have recently been discovered.

the Battle Against HIV

Scientists around the world are trying to keep up with a constantly changing virus

Adults and children living with HIV/AIDS - total: 34.3 million

NORTH AMERICA 900,000

WESTERN EUROPE 520,000

CARIBBEAN 360,000

NORTH AFRICA & MIDDLE EAST 220,000

SUB-SAHARAN AFRICA 24.5 million

SOUTH AMERICA 1.3 million

EASTERN EUROPE & CENTRAL ASIA 420,000

EAST & ASIA PACIFIC 530,000

SOUTH & SOUTH-EAST ASIA 5.6 million

AUSTRALIA & NEW ZEALAND 15,000

SOURCE: JOINT UNITED NATIONS PROGRAM ON HIV/AIDS, 1999

CONNECTIONS Research Use the Glencoe Science Web site and other sources to determine which nations have the highest rates of AIDS infection. Which nation has the highest rate? Where does the U.S. rank? Next, find data from ten years ago. Have the rankings changed?

SCIENCE *Online*

For more information, visit science.glencoe.com

CONNECTIONS What might account for the difference in numbers of people infected in different countries? Possible answers: The rates vary with the availability of medicine and access to health care and with education about how HIV is transmitted. Explain that the largest number of new infections of HIV in the U.S. are among young people. Have students discuss possible reasons for this.

SCIENCE *Online*

Internet Addresses

_____

_____

_____

Explore the Glencoe Science Web site at **science.glencoe.com** to find out more about topics in this feature.

Reviewing Main Ideas

Preview

Students can answer the questions in their Science Journals. Discuss the answers as you go through the chapter. **Linguistic**

Review

Students can write their answers, then compare them with those of other students. **Interpersonal**

Reteach

Students can look at the illustrations and describe details that support the main ideas of the chapter. **Visual-Spatial**

Answers to Chapter Review

SECTION 1

4. spear-shaped bill for catching fish; long legs for wading in shallow water; eyes adapted for peering into the water

SECTION 2

1. Imprint fossils form when the outline of an organism is left on sediment that later becomes rock.
4. Similarities in DNA and proteins suggest ancestral relationships.

SECTION 3

1. opposable thumbs, binocular vision, flexible shoulders, rotating forelimbs

Reviewing Main Ideas

Section 1 Ideas About Evolution

1. Evolution is one of the central ideas of biology. It is an explanation of how living things have changed in the past and a basis for predicting how they might change in the future.

2. Charles Darwin developed the theory of evolution by natural selection to explain how evolutionary changes account for the diversity of organisms on Earth.

3. Natural selection includes concepts of variation, overproduction, and competition.

4. According to natural selection, organisms with traits best suited to their environment are more likely to survive and reproduce. *What traits make this organism suited to its watery environment?*

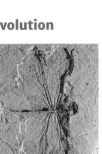

Section 2 Clues About Evolution

1. Fossils provide evidence for evolution. *How are imprint fossils like the ones to the right formed?*

2. Relative dating and radiometric dating can be used to estimate the age of fossils.

3. The evolution of antibiotic-resistant bacteria, pesticide-resistant insects, and rapid genetic changes in plant species provide direct evidence that evolution occurs.

4. Homologous structures, vestigial structures, comparative embryology, and chemical similarities in DNA and other substances provide indirect evidence of evolution. *How does DNA provide evidence of evolution?*

Section 3 The Evolution of Primates

1. Primates include monkeys, apes, and humans. Hominids are humanlike primates. *What are the common characteristics of primates?*

2. The earliest known hominid fossil is *Australopithecus.*

3. *Homo sapiens* are thought to have evolved from Cro-Magnon humans at least 400,000 years ago.

FOLDABLES
Reading & Study Skills

After You Read

Using what you learned, predict how primates might change and write your ideas under the *Future* tab of your Foldable.

FOLDABLES
Reading & Study Skills

After You Read

After students have read the chapter and completed the Foldable described in Before You Read, have them do the activity on the student page.

Dinah Zike

Visualizing Main Ideas

Complete the following spider map on evolution.

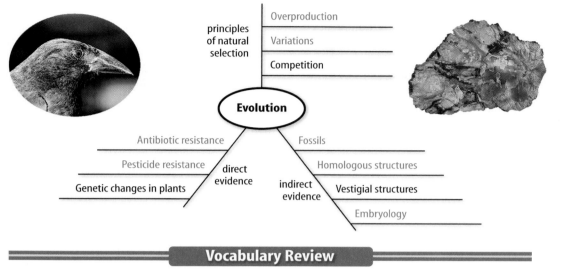

- principles of natural selection
  - Overproduction
  - Variations
  - Competition

Evolution

- direct evidence
  - Antibiotic resistance
  - Pesticide resistance
  - Genetic changes in plants
- indirect evidence
  - Fossils
  - Homologous structures
  - Vestigial structures
  - Embryology

Visualizing Main Ideas

See student page.

Vocabulary Review

Using Vocabulary

1. Sedimentary rock
2. vestigial structures
3. homologous
4. primates
5. embryology
6. natural selection
7. *Homo sapiens*

Vocabulary Review

Vocabulary Words

a. adaptation
b. embryology
c. evolution
d. gradualism
e. hominid
f. *Homo sapiens*
g. homologous
h. natural selection
i. primate
j. punctuated equilibrium
k. radioactive element
l. sedimentary rock
m. species
n. variation
o. vestigial structure

Using Vocabulary

Replace each underlined phrase with the correct vocabulary words.

1. <u>Layers of deposition</u> might contain many different kinds of fossils.

2. The muscles that move the human ear appear to be <u>of no obvious use</u>.

3. Forelimbs of bats, humans, and seals are <u>similar in origin</u>.

4. Opposable thumbs are a characteristic of <u>this group of mammals</u>.

5. The study of <u>early development of species</u> can provide evidence of evolution.

6. The principles of <u>this mechanism of evolution</u> include variation and competition.

7. <u>Early humans</u> likely evolved directly from Cro-Magnons.

THE PRINCETON REVIEW **Study Tip**

Make a plan. Before you start your homework, write a checklist of what you need to do for each subject. As you finish each item, check it off.

IDENTIFYING ▷ Misconceptions

Assess

Use the assessment as follow-up to page 154F after students have completed the chapter.

Discussion After students complete the bean/bacteria activity, ask the following questions. Have students respond first in writing, and then discuss the answers as a class.

- Why did the red "bacteria" survive?
- Did the antibiotic cause the bacteria to have a thicker cell wall?
- When did the red bacteria's thick cell wall develop—before or after the introduction of the antibiotic?

Expected Outcome Students should understand that the red bacteria's trait of a thicker cell wall existed before the antibiotic was introduced. In the activity, genes that gave the bacterium its color also resulted in the thickened cell wall. The trait gave the bacterium an advantage that helped it survive.

Checking Concepts

1. C
2. B
3. D
4. D
5. A
6. D
7. D
8. A
9. C
10. D

Thinking Critically

11. Lamarck: Owls hunt at night and their eyes grow larger with use. The trait is passed on. Darwin: A variation in the size of owls' eyes was an advantage to survival. This inherited feature was passed on to offspring over many generations until owls became adapted for seeing prey at night with large eyes.

12. Answers will vary. Possible answer: Geographical isolation as a result of a volcanic eruption can divide a population. Two species may evolve.

13. Chameleons blend into their environment. This ability to change color helps protect them from predators.

14. The layer of rock where it was formed would be noted. Radiometric dating would be done. Comparisons to other fossils would be made.

15. Protective coloration is an adaptation. A white rabbit living in a cold climate will survive better than a brown rabbit.

Chapter 6 Assessment

Checking Concepts

Choose the word or phrase that best answers the question.

1. What is an example of adaptation?
   - A) a fossil
   - B) gradualism
   - C) camouflage
   - D) embryo

2. What method provides the most accurate estimate of a fossil's age?
   - A) natural selection
   - B) radiometric dating
   - C) relative dating
   - D) camouflage

3. What do homologous structures, vestigial structures, and fossils provide evidence of?
   - A) gradualism
   - B) food choice
   - C) populations
   - D) evolution

4. Which model of evolution shows change over a relatively short period of time?
   - A) embryology
   - B) adaptation
   - C) gradualism
   - D) punctuated equilibrium

5. What might a series of helpful variations in a species result in?
   - A) adaptation
   - B) fossils
   - C) embryology
   - D) climate change

6. What describes organisms that are adapted to their environment?
   - A) homologous
   - B) not reproducing
   - C) forming fossils
   - D) surviving and reproducing

7. What is the study of an organism's early development called?
   - A) adaptation
   - B) relative dating
   - C) natural selection
   - D) embryology

8. What animal group(s) have opposable thumbs and binocular vision?
   - A) all primates
   - B) hominids
   - C) humans only
   - D) monkeys only

9. Which of the following is a principle of natural selection?
   - A) inheritance of acquired traits
   - B) Unused traits become smaller.
   - C) Organisms produce more offspring than can survive.
   - D) the size of an organism

10. A hominid fossil has the same number of bones in its hand as a gorilla. What type of evidence for evolution does this represent?
    - A) DNA
    - B) embryology
    - C) vestigial structures
    - D) homologous structures

Thinking Critically

11. How would Lamarck and Darwin have explained the large eyes of an owl?

12. Using an example, explain how a new species of organism could evolve.

13. How is the color-changing ability of chameleons an adaptation?

14. Describe the processes a scientist would use to figure out the age of a fossil.

15. Explain how a species could adapt to its environment. Give an example.

Developing Skills

16. **Predicting** Predict what type of bird the foot pictured below would belong to. Explain your reasoning.

Chapter ✓Assessment Planner

Portfolio Encourage students to place in their portfolios one or two items of what they consider to be their best work. Examples include:
- Curriculum Connection, p. 161
- Science Journal, p. 166
- Assessment, p. 173

Performance Additional performance assessments, Performance Task Assessment Lists, and rubrics for evaluating these activities can be found in Glencoe's **Performance Assessment in the Science Classroom.**

17. Interpreting Data Each letter below represents a chemical found in different species of bacteria. Which species are closely related?

Chemicals Present in Bacteria Species	
Species 1	A, G, T, C, L, E, S, H
Species 2	A, G, T, C, L, D, H
Species 3	A, G, T, C, L, D, P, U, S, R, I, V
Species 4	A, G, T, C, L, D, H

18. Forming Hypotheses Frog eggs are common in ponds in spring. Make a hypothesis as to why ponds are not overpopulated by frogs in summer. Use the concept of natural selection to help you.

19. Comparing and Contrasting Compare and contrast Cro-Magnon humans and modern humans *Homo sapiens sapiens.*

20. Concept Mapping Make an events chain of the events that led Charles Darwin to his theory of evolution by natural selection.

Performance Assessment

21. Collection With permission, collect fossils from your area and identify them. Show your collection to your class.

22. Brochure Assume that you are head of an advertising company hired by Charles Darwin. Develop a brochure to explain Darwin's theory of evolution by natural selection.

TECHNOLOGY

Go to the Glencoe Science Web site at **science.glencoe.com** or use the **Glencoe Science CD-ROM** for additional chapter assessment.

THE PRINCETON REVIEW **Test Practice**

A scientist studied a genetic variation in a large family of birds. She made the pedigree below to show how the variations within the family appeared.

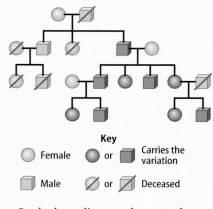

Key

○ Female   ● or ■ Carries the variation

▢ Male   ⊘ or ⊠ Deceased

Study the pedigree and answer the following questions.

1. Which of the following is most likely the scientist's conclusion from this data?
  A) Female birds of this species die more often than the males.
  B) The variation helps the birds survive and reproduce.
  C) Birds of this species lay one or two eggs.
  D) The genetic variation only helps one of the two sexes.

2. To which offspring is this genetic variation most often passed along?
  F) all offspring
  G) some females and all males
  H) only the father's daughters
  J) males only

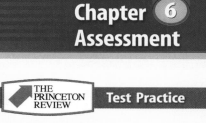
THE PRINCETON REVIEW **Test Practice**

The Test-Taking Tip was written by The Princeton Review, the nation's leader in test preparation.
1. B
2. F

Developing Skills

16. The foot is from an aquatic bird with webbed feet for swimming.
17. Species 2 and 4 are the closest in relation; they have the same chemicals.
18. Predators and competition for resources will eliminate many frogs. Only the most adapted will survive.
19. Cro-Magnon and humans are similar in almost every respect. Cro-Magnon humans are thought to be the direct ancestors of early humans, who are the direct ancestors of modern humans. Differences were mainly in culture and language.
20. Darwin did amateur studies in natural history as a boy. He became a naturalist aboard the *Beagle* and gathered information for five years. After returning to England, Darwin worked for the rest of his life to develop his theory.

Performance Assessment

21. Fossil collections will vary, depending on location. Students may get help from experts at a nearby university. Use **PASC**, p. 121.
22. The brochures should include the principles of natural selection, as found in **Table 1.** Use **PASC**, p. 129.

Assessment **Resources**

📁 Reproducible Masters

Chapter Resources Booklet
  Chapter Review, pp. 35–36
  Chapter Tests, pp. 37–40
  Assessment Transparency Activity, p. 47

Glencoe Science Web site
  Interactive Tutor
  Chapter Quizzes

Glencoe Technology

  🖱 Assessment Transparency
  💿 Interactive CD-ROM Chapter Quizzes
  💿 ExamView Pro Test Bank
  💿 Vocabulary PuzzleMaker Software
  📼 MindJogger Videoquiz DVD/VHS

Reading Comprehension

Reading Comprehension

QUESTION 1: C

Students must use the information in the passage in order to identify the best-supported conclusion.

- **Choice A** No; this is not supported by the passage.
- **Choice B** No; this is not supported by the passage.
- **Choice C** Yes; this is supported by the passage.
- **Choice D** No; this is not supported by the passage.

QUESTION 2: H

Students must use information from the passage to identify the correct cause. Students should use the clue *important to human health*.

- **Choice F** No; this is not supported by the passage.
- **Choice G** No; although this is a detail from the passage, it is not the reason enzymes are important to human health.
- **Choice H** Yes; this is the reason enzymes are important to human health.
- **Choice J** No; although this is a detail from the passage, it is not the reason enzymes are important to human health.

Read the passage. Then read each question that follows the passage. Decide which is the best answer to each question.

Enzymes in Humans

A catalyst is a substance that makes a chemical reaction happen faster than it would happen by itself. Interestingly, it affects the rate of the reaction without permanently entering into the reaction. More than 2,000 catalysts are necessary for the human body to function well. These catalysts are called enzymes.

Enzymes are a kind of protein. How an enzyme works depends on what shape it has. A special place on an enzyme attaches to chemicals. This site is called the active site. Enzyme activity can be compared to a lock and a key. Only the correct chemicals, or keys, will fit into the enzyme, or lock. The enzyme brings chemicals together so they can react. This is how enzymes speed up reactions—by making the reactants come together in a more direct way than if they were left to just bump into each other randomly. One enzyme can be used over and over to activate the same reaction. Some enzymes can help reactions go in either direction. In order for an enzyme to work properly, the temperature and pH must be within a certain range. Enough energy and enough reactants also must be present.

The three types of enzymes are metabolic, digestive, and food. Metabolic enzymes catalyze the reactions within cells. They help phosphorus turn into bone, iron attach to red blood cells, and wounds to heal. Digestive enzymes help with the breakdown of foods, allowing nutrients to be absorbed into the bloodstream and used by the body. Food enzymes are supplied through foods that are eaten, and they help with digestion.

Enzymes are essential for many reactions within the human body. Amylase is an enzyme found in saliva. It starts digesting your food before you even swallow!

An enzyme called carbonic anhydrase (kar BAH nihk ´ an HI drays) helps remove carbon dioxide from your cells. You breathe the carbon dioxide out and replace it with oxygen. Carbonic anhydrase enzyme makes the reaction 107 times faster than if it had to happen on its own! You can see how people depend on enzyme catalysts to maintain health.

Enzymes can be found in all living things. Enzymes also have been used in industry for nearly 100 years. Some of the products that depend on the action of enzymes are leather, alcohol, medications, baking products, detergents, and even fruit juice!

Test-Taking Tip Make sure that you understand what you are reading as you read a passage. If you are confused by something, stop and read the information again.

1. Based on the information in the passage, it can be concluded that _____.
   A) enzymes are found only in humans
   B) amylase is an enzyme that removes oxygen
   C) humans have more than 2,000 enzymes
   D) another word for the locks found in doors is enzyme

2. Enzymes are important to human health because they _____.
   F) are used to help open locks
   G) are used to make leather and fruit juice
   H) speed up the reactions in human bodies
   J) are found in all living things

Standardized Test Practice

Reasoning and Skills

Read each question and select the best answer.

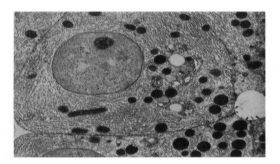

1. The object shown here is a(n) _____ because it contains structures surrounded by membranes.

A) prokaryotic cell
B) mitochondrion
C) Golgi body
D) eukaryotic cell

Test-Taking Tip Think about the way cells are classified into groups.

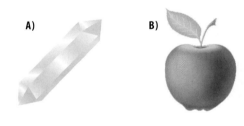

A)   B)

2. Item A above is different from item B because it _____.

F) is not organized
G) does not require energy for its formation
H) is not composed of cells
J) does not respond to changes in temperature or pressure

Test-Taking Tip Review the characteristics common to all living things.

3. Cattails and some other plant species can produce new plants without using seeds. What is this process called?

A) sexual reproduction
B) variation
C) asexual reproduction
D) mutation

Test-Taking Tip Think about the two types of reproduction.

Consider this question carefully before writing your answer on a separate sheet of paper.

4. The virus particle pictured above is not inside a host cell. Give at least one good reason why it could be considered a living organism and one good reason why it could not.

Test-Taking Tip Compare the characteristics of a virus with the characteristics of living organisms.

STANDARDIZED TEST PRACTICE   A ◆ 185

Reasoning and Skills

QUESTION 1: D
Students need to understand that the structures in a *eukaryotic cell* are surrounded by membranes.

QUESTION 2: H
Students need to use their understanding of cells in order to identify the difference between Item A and Item B. Only choice H, *is not composed of cells*, correctly identifies an attribute held by Item A but not Item B.

QUESTION 3: C
Students must understand that vegetative propagation is a form of asexual reproduction.

QUESTION 4: Answers will vary.
Students should mention that viruses are not made up of cells. Furthermore, viruses cannot reproduce outside a host. On the other hand, they do have genetic material (DNA or RNA) and can multiply inside a host cell.

Teaching Tip

Suggest that students make an outline of their essays before they begin writing.

Student Resources

Student Resources

About the Field Guide

- This field guide contains representative photos of some breeds of cats and descriptions of the traits characteristic of each breed.
- In using a field guide, students will apply steps of a scientific method as they observe, investigate, analyze data and draw conclusions.
- Encourage students to use this field guide outside the classroom.

Tie to Prior Knowledge

Most students will be familiar with cats as house pets. Have students name traits that are present in the cats with which they are familiar. List their responses on the board. **What traits are common to all cats, and which are present only in a particular cat or breed of cats?** Students should conclude that there are certain traits common to all cats, other traits are present only in some cats.

Student responses to the questions in this activity will vary. Encourage students to use specific and detailed notes when recording the traits present in each cat. Have each student make a Venn diagram that shows the traits of two or three of the cats on their list.

IS Logical-Mathematical

For centuries, humans have lived with cats. They have kept cats in their homes and on their properties. Cats hunt mice and other rodents that eat stored grains and other human foods. Cats also are companions and family pets. Today, the cat is the most popular pet in the United States.

When animals mate, they pass their genetic traits to their offspring. Occasionally, a natural mutation results in a new breed. Sometimes animal scientists try to create new breeds through selective breeding. They study the pedigree, or family history, of several animals of the same species to see what genetic traits they carry. Then they mate the animals that are most likely to pass the desired traits to their offspring. Over time, a new breed can be developed.

The Cat Fancier's Association recognizes 37 breeds of cats. This field guide describes the traits of 14 of these recognized breeds. None of these breeds has come about by recent selective breeding. Some of these breeds have ancient histories, and others have resulted from natural mutations.

Most cats that people adopt today have a mixed ancestry of several breeds. Read about different breeds on the next few pages. Do you know a cat that has one or more of the described traits?

Feline Traits

Feline Breeds

Siamese

Siamese

This is an ancient breed from Siam, which is now called Thailand. Siamese have long bodies and tails, and their fur is short. They are easy to recognize because they have light-colored bodies and dark ears, masks, tails, and legs. Their eyes are blue.

Devon Rex

Devon Rex

This breed is a natural mutation that first appeared in Devonshire, England, in 1960. Their eyes and batlike ears look huge against their tiny faces. When you stroke a Devon Rex's coat, its fur ripples.

Field Activity

For a week, use this field guide to observe the cats in your neighborhood. What traits do they have? What breeds might be part of their pedigree? Go to the Glencoe Science Web site at **science. glencoe.com** to find more photographs of felines. In your Science Journal, record each cat's name, the traits you noticed, and the breeds that have those traits.

Resources for Teachers and Students

ASPCA Complete Guide to Cats, by James R. Richards, Chronicle Books, 1999.

Cat Breeds of the World, by Paddy Cutts, Lorenz, 1999.

Cats!, by Kate Zentall, BowTie Press, 1998.

Field GUIDE

Cornish Rex

This natural mutation first appeared in Cornwall, England, in about 1950. Cornish Rex cats remind some people of a skinny breed of dog called a whippet. They have arched backs, small waists, and long legs. Their ears are large, and they have small, egg-shaped heads. Their short, curly fur is soft.

Chartreux

Chartreux [shahr-TROOZ]

This breed dates back at least to the sixteenth century. Their name comes from a type of Spanish wool, but they are considered French cats. Chartreux cats are large and powerful, but they tend to be gentle. They are known for their woolly, bluish coats.

British Shorthair

This breed descends from ancient Roman house cats. They are large, powerful animals with broad chests and round faces. They have short legs and short, thick fur. You might have seen these calm, intelligent cats in TV commercials.

British Shorthair

American Wirehair

This breed is a natural mutation that first appeared in New York in 1966. The feature that makes them special is their unusual coat. Each hair is stiff and crimped, which makes the coat hard. Their whiskers also are wiry.

American Wirehair

FIELD GUIDE   A ◆ 189

Use Science Words

Word Usage Remind students that the term *feline* refers to all members of the cat family, not only the domesticated cats shown in this field guide. See how many types of felines students can list. Then have students research library sources for information on types of wild or extinct felines.

Teacher FYI

Purebred cats sometimes are shown competitively. Cats entered in shows sponsored by the Cat Fancier's Association are judged against a list of traits considered desirable for each breed. These traits are determined by a breed council, and are developed to promote healthy and beautiful cats. The Household Pet class is the only group not compared with a set of written standards.

Fun Fact

Siamese kittens are completely white when they are born. The markings that are distinctive to their breed develop during the first year of life.

SCIENCE *Online*
Internet Addresses

Explore the Glencoe Science Web site at **science.glencoe.com** to find out more about topics in this field guide.

Field GUIDE

Field Guide

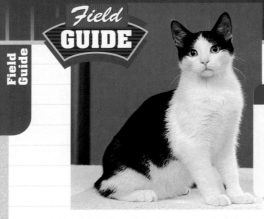

American Shorthair

American Shorthair

This breed came to America with the English Puritans in the 1600s. As the name suggests, they have short fur. They come in many colors, but most are silver with black bands.

Abyssinian (a buh SIH nee un)

In the mid-1800s, this breed was brought to England from Ethiopia, which was then called Abyssinia. However, some scientists believe these cats might have originated in Asia. Abyssinians have arched necks, muscular bodies, large ears, and almond-shaped eyes. Their coats can be ruddy, fawn, auburn, or bluish, and they are marked with several dark bands.

Abyssinian

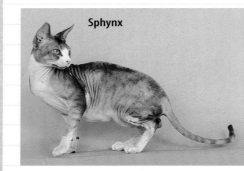

Sphynx

Sphynx

The Sphynx is a natural mutation. It first appeared in Canada in 1966. At first glance, these cats appear to be totally bald. In fact, their bodies are covered with a soft, fuzzy, downlike hair. They have short whiskers or none at all, and their skin is often wrinkled.

Selkirk Rex

This breed first appeared as a natural mutation in Wyoming. Selkirk Rexs are large and powerful like the British Shorthair, and they have curly hair and whiskers. Unlike Devon Rex and Cornish Rex, their hair can be long or short. They come in many colors.

Selkirk Rex

190 ◆ A STUDENT RESOURCES

Norwegian Forest Cat

These green-eyed cats came to North America with the Viking explorers. In the winter, their hair is thick and a plush mane grows around their necks and chests. The long hair of their inner ears stays with them all year. They come in many colors.

Norwegian Forest Cat

Manx

Manx

This breed first appeared on the Isle of Man. Manx cats are best known as the cats without tails, but some have stubby tails called rises. They have arched backs, round heads, and round bodies. Their hair can be long or short.

Maine Coon

This breed developed in North America and was first recognized in Maine. Maine Coons are large, sturdy cats. Long hair and the tufts of hair in their ears help them tolerate extreme cold. Their coats are shaggy, but they feel silky.

Maine Coon cats

Egyptian Mau

Egyptian Mau

The ancient Egyptians loved to draw this breed, which descends from the African wildcat. Egyptian Maus have green eyes, and their fur can be silver, bronze, black, bluish, or smoke colored. They differ from all other domestic cats because they are the only natural breed with a spotted coat.

FIELD GUIDE   A ◆ 191

Visual Learning

Manx The breeding of purebred cats can magnify their undesirable traits as well as their desirable ones. The Manx is an example of a breed that is sometimes subject to health problems due to its unique characteristics. The back legs of this breed are long in proportion to its body, causing these cats to walk with an unusual gait, more like a hobble than a walk. This breed can also have trouble with incontinence. Stillbirths in litters are common as well. **IS Visual-Spatial**

Make a Model

Have students make models of fictional cat breeds that incorporate traits they find appealing. Students should use the information in this field guide and additional reference sources for ideas. Depending on the materials that are available, the models can be two-dimensional, three dimensional, or computer generated. L2 **IS Kinesthetic**

Discussion

How does the environment in which a cat breed originated affect its traits? Possible answer: Cat breeds that originated in cold climates often have long, thick hair, while those that originated in warmer climates often have shorter hair.

Inclusion Strategies

Gifted Have especially able students research the "personalities" that are characteristic to selected breeds of cat. Instruct students to research whether there is a genetic component contributing to each breed's unique personality. Have students present their findings to the class. L3 **IS Linguistic**

Organizing Information

As you study science, you will make many observations and conduct investigations and experiments. You will also research information that is available from many sources. These activities will involve organizing and recording data. The quality of the data you collect and the way you organize it will determine how well others can understand and use it. In **Figure 1,** the student is obtaining and recording information using a microscope.

Putting your observations in writing is an important way of communicating to others the information you have found and the results of your investigations and experiments.

Researching Information

Scientists work to build on and add to human knowledge of the world. Before moving in a new direction, it is important to gather the information that already is known about a subject. You will look for such information in various reference sources. Follow these steps to research information on a scientific subject:

Step 1 Determine exactly what you need to know about the subject. For instance, you might want to find out what happened to local plant life when Mount St. Helens erupted in 1980.

Step 2 Make a list of questions, such as: When did the eruption begin? How long did it last? How large was the area in which plant life was affected?

Step 3 Use multiple sources such as textbooks, encyclopedias, government documents, professional journals, science magazines, and the Internet.

Step 4 List where you found the sources. Make sure the sources you use are reliable and the most current available.

Figure 1
Making an observation is one way to gather information directly.

Evaluating Print and Nonprint Sources

Not all sources of information are reliable. Evaluate the sources you use for information, and use only those you know to be dependable. For example, suppose you want information about the digestion of fats and proteins. You might find two Websites on digestion. One Web site contains "Fat Zapping Tips" written by a company that sells expensive, high-protein supplements to help your body eliminate excess fat. The other is a Web page on "Digestion and Metabolism" written by a well-respected medical school. You would choose the second Web site as the more reliable source of information.

In science, information can change rapidly. Always consult the most current sources. A 1985 source about the human genome would not reflect the most recent research and findings.

Interpreting Scientific Illustrations

As you research a science topic, you will see drawings, diagrams, and photographs. Illustrations help you understand what you read. Some illustrations are included to help you understand an idea that you can't see easily by yourself. For instance, you can't see the bones of a blue whale, but you can look at a diagram of a whale skeleton as labeled in **Figure 2** that helps you understand them. Visualizing a drawing helps many people remember details more easily. Illustrations also provide examples that clarify difficult concepts or give additional information about the topic you are studying.

Most illustrations have a label or a caption. A label or caption identifies the illustration or provides additional information to better explain it. Can you find the caption or labels in **Figure 2?**

Figure 2
A labeled diagram of the skeletal structure of a blue whale.

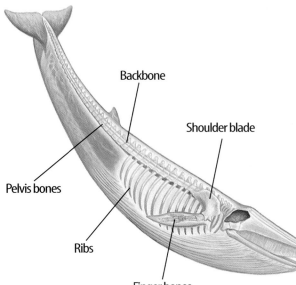

Backbone

Shoulder blade

Pelvis bones

Ribs

Finger bones

Concept Mapping

If you were taking a car trip, you might take some sort of road map. By using a map, you begin to learn where you are in relation to other places on the map.

A concept map is similar to a road map, but a concept map shows relationships among ideas (or concepts) rather than places. It is a diagram that visually shows how concepts are related. Because a concept map shows relationships among ideas, it can make the meanings of ideas and terms clear and help you understand what you are studying.

Overall, concept maps are useful for breaking large concepts down into smaller parts, making learning easier.

Venn Diagram

Although it is not a concept map, a Venn diagram illustrates how two subjects compare and contrast. In other words, you can see the characteristics that the subjects have in common and those that they do not.

The Venn diagram in **Figure 3** shows the relationship between two categories of organisms, plants and animals. Both share some basic characteristics as living organisms. However, there are differences in the ways they carry out various life processes, such as obtaining nourishment, that distinguish one from the other.

Figure 3
A Venn diagram shows how objects or concepts are alike and how they are different.

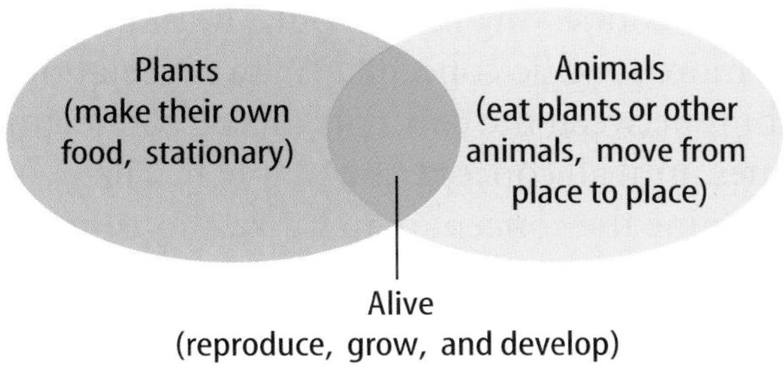

Plants
(make their own food, stationary)

Animals
(eat plants or other animals, move from place to place)

Alive
(reproduce, grow, and develop)

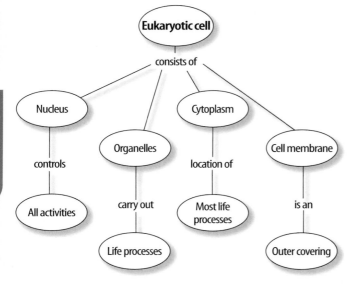

Figure 4
A network tree shows how concepts or objects are related.

Network Tree Look at the concept map in **Figure 4,** that shows details about a eukaryotic cell. This is called a network tree concept map. Notice how some words are in ovals while others are written across connecting lines. The words inside the ovals are science terms or concepts. The words written on the connecting lines describe the relationships between the concepts.

When constructing a network tree, write the topic on a note card or piece of paper. Write the major concepts related to that topic on separate note cards or pieces of paper. Then arrange them in order from general to specific. Branch the related concepts from the major concept and describe the relationships on the connecting lines. Continue branching to more specific concepts. Write the relationships between the concepts on the connecting lines until all concepts are mapped. Then examine the concept map for relationships that cross branches, and add them to the concept map.

Events Chain An events chain is another type of concept map. It models the order of items or their sequence. In science, an events chain can be used to describe a sequence of events, the steps in a procedure, or the stages of a process.

When making an events chain, first find the one event that starts the chain. This event is called the *initiating event.* Then, find the next event in the chain and continue until you reach an outcome. Suppose you are asked to describe the main stages in the growth of a plant from a seed. You might draw an events chain such as the one in **Figure 5.** Notice that connecting words are not necessary in an events chain.

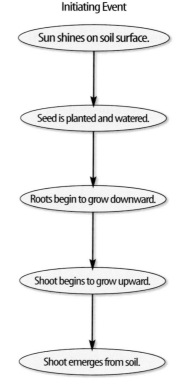

Figure 5
Events chains show the order of steps in a process or event.

Cycle Map A cycle concept map is a specific type of events chain map. In a cycle concept map, the series of events does not produce a final outcome. Instead, the last event in the chain relates back to the beginning event.

You first decide what event will be used as the beginning event. Once that is decided, you list events in order that occur after it. Words are written between events that describe what happens from one event to the next. The last event in a cycle concept map relates back to the beginning event. The number of events in a cycle concept varies, but is usually three or more. Look at the cycle map, as shown in **Figure 6.**

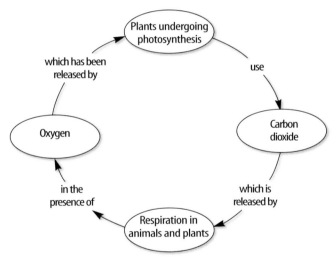

Figure 6
A cycle map shows events that occur in a cycle.

Spider Map A type of concept map that you can use for brainstorming is the spider map. When you have a central idea, you might find you have a jumble of ideas that relate to it but may not clearly relate to each other. The circulatory system spider map in **Figure 7** shows that if you write these ideas outside the main concept, then you can begin to separate and group unrelated terms so they become more useful.

Figure 7
A spider map allows you to list ideas that relate to a central topic but not necessarily to one another.

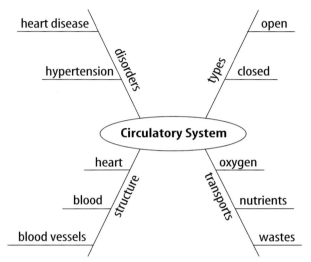

Writing a Paper

You will write papers often when researching science topics or reporting the results of investigations or experiments. Scientists frequently write papers to share their data and conclusions with other scientists and the public. When writing a paper, use these steps.

Step 1 Assemble your data by using graphs, tables, or a concept map. Create an outline.

Step 2 Start with an introduction that contains a clear statement of purpose and what you intend to discuss or prove.

Step 3 Organize the body into paragraphs. Each paragraph should start with a topic sentence, and the remaining sentences in that paragraph should support your point.

Step 4 Position data to help support your points.

Step 5 Summarize the main points and finish with a conclusion statement.

Step 6 Use tables, graphs, charts, and illustrations whenever possible.

Investigating and Experimenting

You might say the work of a scientist is to solve problems. When you decide to find out why one corner of your yard is always soggy, you are problem solving, too. You might observe the corner is lower than the surrounding area and has less vegetation growing in it. You might decide to see if planting some grass will keep the corner drier.

Scientists use orderly approaches to solve problems. The methods scientists use include identifying a question, making observations, forming a hypothesis, testing a hypothesis, analyzing results, and drawing conclusions.

Scientific investigations involve careful observation under controlled conditions. Such observation of an object or a process can suggest new and interesting questions about it. These questions sometimes lead to the formation of a hypothesis. Scientific investigations are designed to test a hypothesis.

Identifying a Question

The first step in a scientific investigation or experiment is to identify a question to be answered or a problem to be solved. You might be interested in knowing why an animal like the one in **Figure 8** look the way they do.

Figure 8
When you see a bird, you might ask yourself, "How does the shape of this bird's beak help it feed?"

Forming Hypotheses

Hypotheses are based on observations that have been made. A hypothesis is a possible explanation based on previous knowledge and observations.

Perhaps a scientist has observed that bean plants grow larger if they are fertilized than if not. Based on these observations, the scientist can make a statement that he or she can test. The statement is a hypothesis. The hypothesis could be: *Fertilizer makes bean plants grow larger.* A hypothesis has to be something you can test by using an investigation. A testable hypothesis is a valid hypothesis.

Predicting

When you apply a hypothesis, or general explanation, to a specific situation, you predict something about that situation. First, you must identify which hypothesis fits the situation you are considering. People use predictions to make everyday decisions. Based on previous observations and experiences, you might form a prediction that if fertilizer makes bean plants grow larger, then fertilized plants will yield more beans than plants not fertilized. Someone could use this prediction to plan to grow fewer plants.

Testing a Hypothesis

To test a hypothesis, you need a procedure. A procedure is the plan you follow in your experiment. A procedure tells you what materials to use, as well as how and in what order to use them. When you follow a procedure, data are generated that support or do not support the original hypothesis statement.

For example, suppose you notice that your guppies don't seem as active as usual when your aquarium heater is not working. You wonder how water temperature affects guppy activity level. You decide to test the hypothesis, "If water temperature increases, then guppy activity should increase." Then you write the procedure shown in **Figure 9** for your experiment and generate the data presented in the table below.

Procedure
1. Fill five identical glass containers with equal amounts of aquarium water.
2. Measure and record the temperature of the water in the first container.
3. Heat and cool the other containers so that two have higher and two have lower water temperatures.
4. Place a guppy in each container; count and record the number of movements each guppy makes in 5 minutes.

Figure 9
A procedure tells you what to do step by step.

Number of Guppy Movements		
Container	Temperature (°C)	Movements
1	38	56
2	40	61
3	42	70
4	36	46
5	34	42

Are all investigations alike? Keep in mind as you perform investigations in science that a hypothesis can be tested in many ways. Not every investigation makes use of all the ways that are described on these pages, and not all hypotheses are tested by investigations. Scientists encounter many variations in the methods that are used when they perform experiments. The skills in this handbook are here for you to use and practice.

Identifying and Manipulating Variables and Controls

In any experiment, it is important to keep everything the same except for the item you are testing. The one factor you change is called the independent variable. The factor that changes as a result of the independent variable is called the dependent variable. Always make sure you have only one independent variable. If you allow more than one, you will not know what causes the changes you observe in the dependent variable. Many experiments also have controls—individual instances or experimental subjects for which the independent variable is not changed. You can then compare the test results to the control results.

For example, in the guppy experiment, you made everything the same except the temperature of the water. The glass containers were identical. The volume of aquarium water in each container and beginning water temperature were the same. Each guppy was like the others, as much as possible. In this way, you could be sure that any difference in the number of guppy movements was caused by the temperature change—the independent variable. The activity level of the guppy was measured as the number of guppy movements—the dependent variable. The guppy in the container in which the water temperature was not changed was the control.

Collecting Data

Whether you are carrying out an investigation or a short observational experiment, you will collect data, or information. Scientists collect data accurately as numbers and descriptions and organize it in specific ways.

Observing Scientists observe items and events, then record what they see. When they use only words to describe an observation, it is called qualitative data. For example, a scientist might describe the color of a bird or the shape of a bird's beak as seen through binoculars. Scientists' observations also can describe how much there is of something. These observations use numbers, as well as words, in the description and are called quantitative data. For example, if a particular dog is described as being "furry, yellow, and short-haired," the data are clearly qualitative. Quantitative data for this dog might include "a mass of 14 kg, a height of 46 cm, and an age of 150 days." Quantitative data often are organized into tables. Then, from information in the table, a graph can be drawn. Graphs can reveal relationships that exist in experimental data.

When you make observations in science, you should examine the entire object or situation first, then look carefully for details. If you're looking at a plant, for instance, check general characteristics such as size and overall structure before using a hand lens to examine the leaves and other smaller structures such as flowers or fruits. Remember to record accurately everything you see.

Scientists try to make careful and accurate observations. When possible, they use instruments such as microscopes, metric rulers, graduated cylinders, thermometers, and balances. Measurements provide numerical data that can be repeated and checked.

Sampling When working with large numbers of objects or a large population, scientists usually cannot observe or study every one of them. Instead, they use a sample or a portion of the total number. To *sample* is to take a small, representative portion of the objects or organisms of a population for research. By making careful observations or manipulating variables within a portion of a group, information is discovered and conclusions are drawn that might apply to the whole population.

Estimating Scientific work also involves estimating. To *estimate* is to make a judgment about the size or the number of something without measuring or counting every object or member of a population. Scientists first count the number of objects in a small sample. Looking through a microscope lens, for example, a scientist can count the number of bacterial colonies in the 1-cm^2 frame shown in **Figure 10.** Then the scientist can multiply that number by the number of cm^2 in the petri dish to get an estimate of the total number of bacterial colonies present.

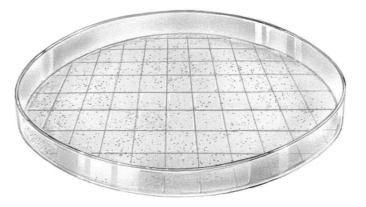

Figure 10
To estimate the total number of bacterial colonies that are present on a petri dish, count the number of bacterial colonies within a 1-cm^2 frame and multiply that number by the number of frames on the dish.

Measuring in SI

The metric system of measurement was developed in 1795. A modern form of the metric system, called the International System, or SI, was adopted in 1960. SI provides standard measurements that all scientists around the world can understand.

The metric system is convenient because unit sizes vary by multiples of 10. When changing from smaller units to larger units, divide by a multiple of 10. When changing from larger units to smaller, multiply by a multiple of 10. To convert millimeters to centimeters, divide the millimeters by 10. To convert 30 mm to centimeters, divide 30 by 10 (30 mm equal 3 cm).

Prefixes are used to name units. Look at the table below for some common metric prefixes and their meanings. Do you see how the prefix *kilo-* attached to the unit *gram* is *kilogram*, or 1,000 g?

Metric Prefixes			
Prefix	**Symbol**	**Meaning**	
kilo-	k	1,000	thousand
hecto-	h	100	hundred
deka-	da	10	ten
deci-	d	0.1	tenth
centi-	c	0.01	hundredth
milli-	m	0.001	thousandth

Now look at the metric ruler shown in **Figure 11.** The centimeter lines are the long, numbered lines, and the shorter lines are millimeter lines.

When using a metric ruler, line up the 0-cm mark with the end of the object being measured, and read the number of the unit where the object ends, in this instance it would be 4.5 cm.

Figure 11
This metric ruler shows centimeters and millimeter divisions.

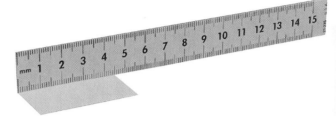

Liquid Volume In some science activities, you will measure liquids. The unit that is used to measure liquids is the liter. A liter has the volume of 1,000 cm³. The prefix *milli-* means "thousandth (0.001)." A milliliter is one thousandth of 1 L and 1 L has the volume of 1,000 mL. One milliliter of liquid completely fills a cube measuring 1 cm on each side. Therefore, 1 mL equals 1 cm³.

You will use beakers and graduated cylinders to measure liquid volume. A graduated cylinder, as illustrated in **Figure 12,** is marked from bottom to top in milliliters. This graduated cylinder contains 79 mL of a liquid.

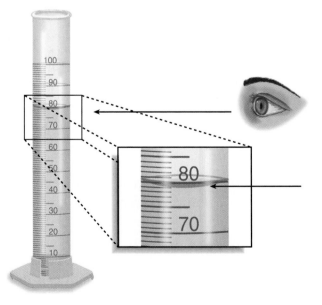

Figure 12
Graduated cylinders measure liquid volume.

Mass Scientists measure mass in grams. You might use a beam balance similar to the one shown in **Figure 13.** The balance has a pan on one side and a set of beams on the other side. Each beam has a rider that slides on the beam.

Before you find the mass of an object, slide all the riders back to the zero point. Check the pointer on the right to make sure it swings an equal distance above and below the zero point. If the swing is unequal, find and turn the adjusting screw until you have an equal swing.

Place an object on the pan. Slide the largest rider along its beam until the pointer drops below zero. Then move it back one notch. Repeat the process on each beam until the pointer swings an equal distance above and below the zero point. Sum the masses on each beam to find the mass of the object. Move all riders back to zero when finished.

Figure 13
A triple beam balance is used to determine the mass of an object.

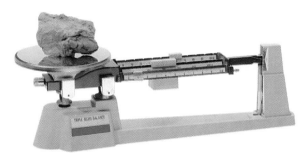

You should never place a hot object on the pan or pour chemicals directly onto the pan. Instead, find the mass of a clean container. Remove the container from the pan, then place the chemicals in the container. Find the mass of the container with the chemicals in it. To find the mass of the chemicals, subtract the mass of the empty container from the mass of the filled container.

Making and Using Tables

Browse through your textbook and you will see tables in the text and in the activities. In a table, data, or information, are arranged so that they are easier to understand. Activity tables help organize the data you collect during an activity so results can be interpreted.

Making Tables To make a table, list the items to be compared in the first column and the characteristics to be compared in the first row. The title should clearly indicate the content of the table, and the column or row heads should tell the reader what information is found in there. The table below lists materials collected for recycling on three weekly pick-up days. The inclusion of kilograms in parentheses also identifies for the reader that the figures are mass units.

Recyclable Materials Collected During Week			
Day of Week	Paper (kg)	Aluminum (kg)	Glass (kg)
Monday	5.0	4.0	12.0
Wednesday	4.0	1.0	10.0
Friday	2.5	2.0	10.0

Using Tables How much paper, in kilograms, is being recycled on Wednesday? Locate the column labeled "Paper (kg)" and the row "Wednesday." The information in the box where the column and row intersect is the answer. Did you answer "4.0"? How much aluminum, in kilograms, is being recycled on Friday? If you answered "2.0," you understand how to read the table. How much glass is collected for recycling each week? Locate the column labeled "Glass (kg)" and add the figures for all three rows. If you answered "32.0," then you know how to locate and use the data provided in the table.

Recording Data

To be useful, the data you collect must be recorded carefully. Accuracy is key. A well-thought-out experiment includes a way to record procedures, observations, and results accurately. Data tables are one way to organize and record results. Set up the tables you will need ahead of time so you can record the data right away.

Record information properly and neatly. Never put unidentified data on scraps of paper. Instead, data should be written in a notebook like the one in **Figure 14.** Write in pencil so information isn't lost if your data gets wet. At each point in the experiment, record your data and label it. That way, your information will be accurate and you will not have to determine what the figures mean when you look at your notes later.

Figure 14
Record data neatly and clearly so it is easy to understand.

Recording Observations

It is important to record observations accurately and completely. That is why you always should record observations in your notes immediately as you make them. It is easy to miss details or make mistakes when recording results from memory. Do not include your personal thoughts when you record your data. Record only what you observe to eliminate bias. For example, when you record that a plant grew 12 cm in one day, you would note that this was the largest daily growth for the week. However, you would not refer to the data as "the best growth spurt of the week."

Making Models

You can organize the observations and other data you collect and record in many ways. Making models is one way to help you better understand the parts of a structure you have been observing or the way a process for which you have been taking various measurements works.

Models often show things that are very large or small or otherwise would be difficult to see and understand. You can study blood vessels and know that they are hollow tubes. The size and proportional differences among arteries, veins, and capillaries can be explained in words. However, you can better visualize the relative sizes and proportions of blood vessels by making models of them. Gluing different kinds of pasta to thick paper so the openings can be seen can help you see how the differences in size, wall thickness, and shape among types of blood vessels affect their functions.

Other models can be devised on a computer. Some models, such as disease control models used by doctors to predict the spread of the flu, are mathematical and are represented by equations.

Skill Handbooks

Making and Using Graphs

After scientists organize data in tables, they might display the data in a graph that shows the relationship of one variable to another. A graph makes interpretation and analysis of data easier. Three types of graphs are the line graph, the bar graph, and the circle graph.

Line Graphs A line graph like in **Figure 15** is used to show the relationship between two variables. The variables being compared go on two axes of the graph. For data from an experiment, the independent variable always goes on the horizontal axis, called the *x*-axis. The dependent variable always goes on the vertical axis, called the *y*-axis. After drawing your axes, label each with a scale. Next, plot the data points.

A data point is the intersection of the recorded value of the dependent variable for each tested value of the independent variable. After all the points are plotted, connect them.

Bar Graphs Bar graphs compare data that do not change continuously. Vertical bars show the relationships among data.

To make a bar graph, set up the *y*-axis as you did for the line graph. Draw vertical bars of equal size from the *x*-axis up to the point on the *y*-axis that represents value of *x*.

Figure 16
The number of wing vibrations per second for different insects can be shown as a bar graph or circle graph.

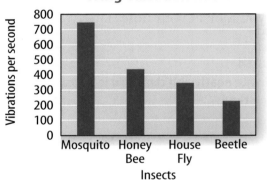

Circle Graphs A circle graph uses a circle divided into sections to display data as parts (fractions or percentages) of a whole. The size of each section corresponds to the fraction or percentage of the data that the section represents. So, the entire circle represents 100 percent, one-half represents 50 percent, one-fifth represents 20 percent, and so on.

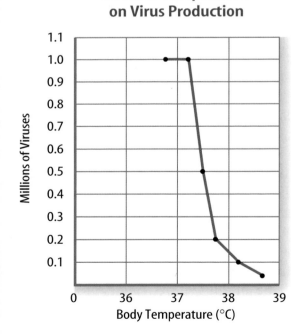

Figure 15
This line graph shows the relationship between body temperature and the millions of infecting viruses present in a human body.

Analyzing Results

To determine the meaning of your observations and investigation results, you will need to look for patterns in the data. You can organize your information in several of the ways that are discussed in this handbook. Then you must think critically to determine what the data mean. Scientists use several approaches when they analyze the data they have collected and recorded. Each approach is useful for identifying specific patterns in the data.

Forming Operational Definitions

An operational definition defines an object by showing how it functions, works, or behaves. Such definitions are written in terms of how an object works or how it can be used; that is, they describe its job or purpose.

For example, a ruler can be defined as a tool that measures the length of an object (how it can be used). A ruler also can be defined as something that contains a series of marks that can be used as a standard when measuring (how it works).

Classifying

Classifying is the process of sorting objects or events into groups based on common features. When classifying, first observe the objects or events to be classified. Then select one feature that is shared by some members in the group but not by all. Place those members that share that feature into a subgroup. You can classify members into smaller and smaller subgroups based on characteristics.

How might you classify a group of animals? You might first classify them by putting all of the dogs, cats, lizards, snakes, and birds into separate groups. Within each group,

you could then look for another common feature by which to further classify members of the group, such as size or color.

Remember that when you classify, you are grouping objects or events for a purpose. For example, classifying animals can be the first step in identifying them. You might know that a cardinal is a red bird. To find it in a large group of animals, you might start with the classification scheme mentioned above. You'll locate a cardinal within the red grouping of the birds that you separate from the rest of the animals. A male ruby-throated hummingbird could be located within the birds by its tiny size and the bright red color of its throat. Keep your purpose in mind as you select the features to form groups and subgroups.

Figure 17
Color is one of many characteristics that are used to classify animals.

Science Skill Handbook

Comparing and Contrasting

Observations can be analyzed by noting the similarities and differences between two or more objects or events that you observe. When you look at objects or events to see how they are similar, you are comparing them. Contrasting is looking for differences in objects or events. The table below compares and contrasts the nutritional value of two cereals.

Nutritional Values		
	Cereal A	**Cereal B**
Calories	220	160
Fat	10 g	10 g
Protein	2.5 g	2.6 g
Carbohydrate	30 g	15 g

Recognizing Cause and Effect

Have you ever gotten a cold and then suggested that you probably caught it from a classmate who had one recently? If so, you have observed an effect and inferred a cause. The event is the effect, and the reason for the event is the cause.

When scientists are unsure of the cause of a certain event, they design controlled experiments to determine what caused it.

Interpreting Data

The word *interpret* means "to explain the meaning of something." Look at the problem originally being explored in an experiment and figure out what the data show. Identify the control group and the test group so you can see whether or not changes in the independent variable have had an effect. Look for differences in the dependent variable between the control and test groups.

These differences you observe can be qualitative or quantitative. You would be able to describe a qualitative difference using only words, whereas you would measure a quantitative difference and describe it using numbers. If there are qualitative or quantitative differences, the independent variable that is being tested could have had an effect. If no qualitative or quantitative differences are found between the control and test groups, the variable that is being tested apparently had no effect.

For example, suppose that three pepper plants are placed in a garden and two of the plants are fertilized, but the third is left to grow without fertilizer. Suppose you are then asked to describe any differences in the plants after two weeks. A qualitative difference might be the appearance of brighter green leaves on fertilized plants but not on the unfertilized plant. A quantitative difference might be a difference in the height of the plants or the number of flowers on them.

Inferring Scientists often make inferences based on their observations. An inference is an attempt to explain, or interpret, observations or to indicate what caused what you observed. An inference is a type of conclusion.

When making an inference, be certain to use accurate data and accurately described observations. Analyze all of the data that you've collected. Then, based on everything you know, explain or interpret what you've observed.

Drawing Conclusions

When scientists have analyzed the data they collected, they proceed to draw conclusions about what the data mean. These conclusions are sometimes stated using words similar to those found in the hypothesis formed earlier in the process.

Conclusions

To analyze your data, you must review all of the observations and measurements that you made and recorded. Recheck all data for accuracy. After your data are rechecked and organized, you are almost ready to draw a conclusion such as "Plants need sunlight in order to grow."

Before you can draw a conclusion, however, you must determine whether the data allow you to come to a conclusion that supports a hypothesis. Sometimes that will be the case, other times it will not.

If your data do not support a hypothesis, it does not mean that the hypothesis is wrong. It means only that the results of the investigation did not support the hypothesis. Maybe the experiment needs to be redesigned, but very likely, some of the initial observations on which the hypothesis was based were incomplete or biased. Perhaps more observation or research is needed to refine the hypothesis.

Avoiding Bias

Sometimes drawing a conclusion involves making judgments. When you make a judgment, you form an opinion about what your data mean. It is important to be honest and to avoid reaching a conclusion if there were no supporting evidence for it or if it were based on a small sample. It also is important not to allow any expectations of results to bias your judgments. If possible, it is a good idea to collect additional data. Scientists do this all the time.

For example, animal behaviorist Katharine Payne made an important observation about elephant communication. While visiting a zoo, Payne felt the air vibrating around her. At the same time, she also noticed that the skin on an elephant's forehead was fluttering. She suspected that the elephants were generating the vibrations and that they might be using the low-frequency sounds to communicate.

Payne conducted an experiment to record these sounds and simultaneously observe the behavior of the elephants in the zoo. She later conducted a similar experiment in Namibia in southwest Africa, where elephant herds roam. The additional data she collected supported the judgment Payne had made, which was that these low-frequency sounds were a form of communication between elephants.

Evaluating Others' Data and Conclusions

Sometimes scientists have to use data that they did not collect themselves, or they have to rely on observations and conclusions drawn by other researchers. In cases such as these, the data must be evaluated carefully.

How were the data obtained? How was the investigation done? Has it been duplicated by other researchers? Did they come up with the same results? Look at the conclusion, as well. Would you reach the same conclusion from these results? Only when you have confidence in the data of others can you believe it is true and feel comfortable using it.

Communicating

The communication of ideas is an important part of the work of scientists. A discovery that is not reported will not advance the scientific community's understanding or knowledge. Communication among scientists also is important as a way of improving their investigations.

Scientists communicate in many ways, from writing articles in journals and magazines that explain their investigations and experiments, to announcing important discoveries on television and radio, to sharing ideas with colleagues on the Internet or presenting them as lectures.

Computer Skills

People who study science rely on computers to record and store data and to analyze results from investigations. Whether you work in a laboratory or just need to write a lab report with tables, good computer skills are a necessity.

Using a Word Processor

Suppose your teacher has assigned a written report. After you've completed your research and decided how you want to write the information, you need to put all that information on paper. The easiest way to do this is with a word processing application on a computer.

A computer application that allows you to type your information, change it as many times as you need to, and then print it out so that it looks neat and clean is called a word processing application. You also can use this type of application to create tables and columns, add bullets or cartoon art to your page, include page numbers, and even check your spelling.

Helpful Hints

- If you aren't sure how to do something using your word processing program, look in the help menu. You will find a list of topics there to click on for help. After you locate the help topic you need, just follow the step-by-step instructions you see on your screen.
- Just because you've spell checked your report doesn't mean that the spelling is perfect. The spell check feature can't catch misspelled words that look like other words. If you've accidentally typed *wind* instead of *wing*, the spell checker won't know the difference. Always reread your report to make sure you didn't miss any mistakes.

Figure 18
You can use computer programs to make graphs and tables.

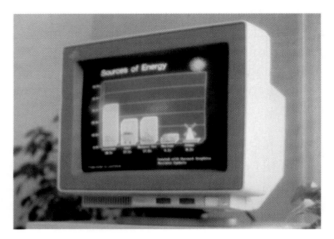

Using a Database

Imagine you're in the middle of a research project busily gathering facts and information. You soon realize that it's becoming more difficult to organize and keep track of all the information. The tool to use to solve information overload is a database. Just as a file cabinet organizes paper records, a database organizes computer records. However, a database is more powerful than a simple file cabinet because at the click of a mouse, the contents can be reshuffled and reorganized. At computer-quick speeds, databases can sort information by any characteristics and filter data into multiple categories.

Helpful Hints

- Before setting up a database, take some time to learn the features of your database software by practicing with established database software.
- Periodically save your database as you enter data. That way, if something happens such as your computer malfunctions or the power goes off, you won't lose all of your work.

Doing a Database Search

When searching for information in a database, use the following search strategies to get the best results. These are the same search methods used for searching Internet databases.

- Place the word *and* between two words in your search if you want the database to look for any entries that have both the words. For example, "fox *and* mink" would give you information that mentions both fox and mink.
- Place the word *or* between two words if you want the database to show entries that have at least one of the words. For example "fox *or* mink" would show you information that mentions either fox or mink.
- Place the word *not* between two words if you want the database to look for entries that have the first word but do not have the second word. For example, "canine *not* fox" would show you information that mentions the term canine but does not mention the fox.

In summary, databases can be used to store large amounts of information about a particular subject. Databases allow biologists, Earth scientists, and physical scientists to search for information quickly and accurately.

Using an Electronic Spreadsheet

Your science fair experiment has produced lots of numbers. How do you keep track of all the data, and how can you easily work out all the calculations needed? You can use a computer program called a spreadsheet to record data that involve numbers. A spreadsheet is an electronic mathematical worksheet.

Type in your data in rows and columns, just as in a data table on a sheet of paper. A spreadsheet uses simple math to do data calculations. For example, you could add, subtract, divide, or multiply any of the values in the spreadsheet by another number. You also could set up a series of math steps you want to apply to the data. If you want to add 12 to all the numbers and then multiply all the numbers by 10, the computer does all the calculations for you in the spreadsheet. Below is an example of a spreadsheet that records data from an experiment with mice in a maze.

Helpful Hints

- Before you set up the spreadsheet, identify how you want to organize the data. Include any formulas you will need to use.
- Make sure you have entered the correct data into the correct rows and columns.
- You also can display your results in a graph. Pick the style of graph that best represents the data with which you are working.

Figure 19
A spreadsheet allows you to display large amounts of data and do calculations automatically.

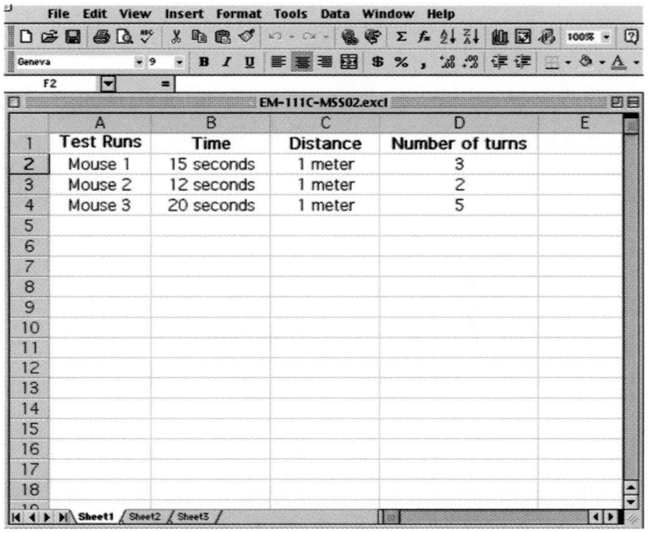

	A	B	C	D	E
1	Test Runs	Time	Distance	Number of turns	
2	Mouse 1	15 seconds	1 meter	3	
3	Mouse 2	12 seconds	1 meter	2	
4	Mouse 3	20 seconds	1 meter	5	

Skill Handbooks

Using a Computerized Card Catalog

When you have a report or paper to research, you probably go to the library. To find the information you need in the library, you might have to use a computerized card catalog. This type of card catalog allows you to search for information by subject, by title, or by author. The computer then will display all the holdings the library has on the subject, title, or author requested.

A library's holdings can include books, magazines, databases, videos, and audio materials. When you have chosen something from this list, the computer will show whether an item is available and where in the library to find it.

Helpful Hints

- Remember that you can use the computer to search by subject, author, or title. If you know a book's author but not the title, you can search for all the books the library has by that author.
- When searching by subject, it's often most helpful to narrow your search by using specific search terms, such as *and, or,* and *not.* If you don't find enough sources, you can broaden your search.
- Pay attention to the type of materials found in your search. If you need a book, you can eliminate any videos or other resources that come up in your search.
- Knowing how your library is arranged can save you a lot of time. The librarian will show you where certain types of materials are kept and how to find specific holdings.

Using Graphics Software

Are you having trouble finding that exact piece of art you're looking for? Do you have a picture in your mind of what you want but can't seem to find the right graphic to represent your ideas? To solve these problems, you can use graphics software. Graphics software allows you to create and change images and diagrams in almost unlimited ways. Typical uses for graphics software include arranging clip art, changing scanned images, and constructing pictures from scratch. Most graphics software applications work in similar ways. They use the same basic tools and functions. Once you master one graphics application, you can use any other graphics application relatively easily.

Figure 20
Graphics software can use your data to draw bar graphs.

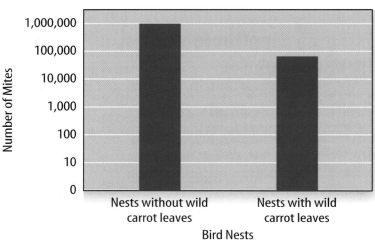

Number of Mites per Bird Nest

Figure 21
Graphics software can use your data to draw circle graphs.

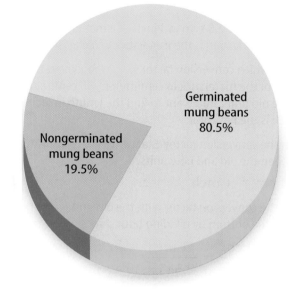

Germinated mung beans 80.5%

Nongerminated mung beans 19.5%

Helpful Hints
- As with any method of drawing, the more you practice using the graphics software, the better your results will be.
- Start by using the software to manipulate existing drawings. Once you master this, making your own illustrations will be easier.
- Clip art is available on CD-ROMs and the Internet. With these resources, finding a piece of clip art to suit your purposes is simple.
- As you work on a drawing, save it often.

Developing Multimedia Presentations

It's your turn—you have to present your science report to the entire class. How do you do it? You can use many different sources of information to get the class excited about your presentation. Posters, videos, photographs, sound, computers, and the Internet can help show your ideas.

First, determine what important points you want to make in your presentation. Then, write an outline of what materials and types of media would best illustrate those points. Maybe you could start with an outline on an overhead projector, then show a video, followed by something from the Internet or a slide show accompanied by music or recorded voices. You might choose to use a presentation builder computer application that can combine all these elements into one presentation. Make sure the presentation is well constructed to make the most impact on the audience.

Figure 22
Multimedia presentations use many types of print and electronic materials.

Helpful Hints
- Carefully consider what media will best communicate the point you are trying to make.
- Make sure you know how to use any equipment you will be using in your presentation.
- Practice the presentation several times.
- If possible, set up all of the equipment ahead of time. Make sure everything is working correctly.

Math Skill Handbook

Use this Math Skill Handbook to help solve problems you are given in this text. You might find it useful to review topics in this Math Skill Handbook first.

Converting Units

In science, quantities such as length, mass, and time sometimes are measured using different units. Suppose you want to know how many miles are in 12.7 km?

Conversion factors are used to change from one unit of measure to another. A conversion factor is a ratio that is equal to one. For example, there are 1,000 mL in 1 L, so 1,000 mL equals 1 L, or:

$$1{,}000 \text{ mL} = 1 \text{ L}$$

If both sides are divided by 1 L, this equation becomes:

$$\frac{1{,}000 \text{ mL}}{1 \text{ L}} = 1$$

The **ratio** on the left side of this equation is equal to one and is a conversion factor. You can make another conversion factor by dividing both sides of the top equation by 1,000 mL:

$$1 = \frac{1 \text{ L}}{1{,}000 \text{ mL}}$$

To **convert units,** you multiply by the appropriate conversion factor. For example, how many milliliters are in 1.255 L? To convert 1.255 L to milliliters, multiply 1.255 L by a conversion factor.

Use the **conversion factor** with new units (mL) in the numerator and the old units (L) in the denominator.

$$1.255 \text{ L} \times \frac{1{,}000 \text{ mL}}{1 \text{ L}} = 1{,}255 \text{ mL}$$

The unit L divides in this equation, just as if it were a number.

Example 1 There are 2.54 cm in 1 inch. If a meterstick has a length of 100 cm, how long is the meterstick in inches?

Step 1 Decide which conversion factor to use. You know the length of the meterstick in centimeters, so centimeters are the old units. You want to find the length in inches, so inch is the new unit.

Step 2 Form the conversion factor. Start with the relationship between the old and new units.

$$2.54 \text{ cm} = 1 \text{ inch}$$

Step 3 Form the conversion factor with the old unit (centimeter) on the bottom by dividing both sides by 2.54 cm.

$$1 = \frac{2.54 \text{ cm}}{2.54 \text{ cm}} = \frac{1 \text{ inch}}{2.54 \text{ cm}}$$

Step 4 Multiply the old measurement by the conversion factor.

$$100 \text{ cm} \times \frac{1 \text{ inch}}{2.54 \text{ cm}} = 39.37 \text{ inches}$$

The meter stick is 39.37 inches long.

Example 2 There are 365 days in one year. If a person is 14 years old, what is his or her age in days? (Ignore leap years)

Step 1 Decide which conversion factor to use. You want to convert years to days.

Step 2 Form the conversion factor. Start with the relation between the old and new units.

$$1 \text{ year} = 365 \text{ days}$$

Step 3 Form the conversion factor with the old unit (year) on the bottom by dividing both sides by 1 year.

$$1 = \frac{1 \text{ year}}{1 \text{ year}} = \frac{365 \text{ days}}{1 \text{ year}}$$

Step 4 Multiply the old measurement by the conversion factor:

$$14 \text{ years} \times \frac{365 \text{ days}}{1 \text{ year}} = 5{,}110 \text{ days}$$

The person's age is 5,110 days.

Practice Problem A cat has a mass of 2.31 kg. If there are 1,000 g in 1 kg, what is the mass of the cat in grams?   2,310 g

Using Fractions

A **fraction** is a number that compares a part to the whole. For example, in the fraction $\frac{2}{3}$, the 2 represents the part and the 3 represents the whole. In the fraction $\frac{2}{3}$, the top number, 2, is called the numerator. The bottom number, 3, is called the denominator.

Sometimes fractions are not written in their simplest form. To determine a fraction's **simplest form,** you must find the greatest common factor (GCF) of the numerator and denominator. The greatest common factor is the largest common factor of all the factors the two numbers have in common.

For example, because the number 3 divides into 12 and 30 evenly, it is a common factor of 12 and 30. However, because the number 6 is the largest number that evenly divides into 12 and 30, it is the **greatest common factor.**

After you find the greatest common factor, you can write a fraction in its simplest form. Divide both the numerator and the denominator by the greatest common factor. The number that results is the fraction in its **simplest form.**

Example Twelve of the 20 corn plants in a field are over 1.5 m tall. What fraction of the corn plants in the field are over 1.5 m tall?

Step 1 Write the fraction.

$$\frac{\text{part}}{\text{whole}} = \frac{12}{20}$$

Step 2 To find the GCF of the numerator and denominator, list all of the factors of each number.

Factors of 12: 1, 2, 3, 4, 6, 12 (the numbers that divide evenly into 12)

Factors of 20: 1, 2, 4, 5, 10, 20 (the numbers that divide evenly into 20)

Step 3 List the common factors.

1, 2, 4.

Step 4 Choose the greatest factor in the list of common factors.

The GCF of 12 and 20 is 4.

Step 5 Divide the numerator and denominator by the GCF.

$$\frac{12 \div 4}{20 \div 4} = \frac{3}{5}$$

In the field, $\frac{3}{5}$ of the corn plants are over 1.5 m tall.

Practice Problem There are 90 duck eggs in a population. Of those eggs, 66 hatch over a one-week period. What fraction of the eggs hatch over a one-week period? Write the fraction in simplest form. $\frac{11}{15}$

Math Skill Handbook

Calculating Ratios

A **ratio** is a comparison of two numbers by division.

Ratios can be written 3 to 5 or 3:5. Ratios also can be written as fractions, such as $\frac{3}{5}$. Ratios, like fractions, can be written in simplest form. Recall that a fraction is in **simplest form** when the greatest common factor (GCF) of the numerator and denominator is 1.

Example From a package of sunflower seeds, 40 seeds germinated and 64 did not. What is the ratio of germinated to not germinated seeds as a fraction in simplest form?

Step 1 Write the ratio as a fraction.

$$\frac{\text{germinated}}{\text{not germinated}} = \frac{40}{64}$$

Step 2 Express the fraction in simplest form. The GCF of 40 and 64 is 8.

$$\frac{40}{64} = \frac{40 \div 8}{64 \div 8} = \frac{5}{8}$$

The ratio of germinated to not germinated seeds is $\frac{5}{8}$.

Practice Problem Two children measure 100 cm and 144 cm in height. What is the ratio of their heights in simplest fraction form? $\frac{25}{36}$

Using Decimals

A **decimal** is a fraction with a denominator of 10, 100, 1,000, or another power of 10. For example, 0.854 is the same as the fraction $\frac{854}{1,000}$.

In a decimal, the decimal point separates the ones place and the tenths place. For example, 0.27 means twenty-seven hundredths, or $\frac{27}{100}$, where 27 is the **number of units** out of 100 units. Any fraction can be written as a decimal using division.

Example Write $\frac{5}{8}$ as a decimal.

Step 1 Write a division problem with the numerator, 5, as the dividend and the denominator, 8, as the divisor. Write 5 as 5.000.

Step 2 Solve the problem.

$$\begin{array}{r} 0.625 \\ 8\overline{)5.000} \\ \underline{48} \\ 20 \\ \underline{16} \\ 40 \\ \underline{40} \\ 0 \end{array}$$

Therefore, $\frac{5}{8} = 0.625$.

Practice Problem Write $\frac{19}{25}$ as a decimal. 0.76

Using Percentages

The word *percent* means "out of one hundred." A **percent** is a ratio that compares a number to 100. Suppose you read that 77 percent of all fish on Earth live in the Pacific Ocean. That is the same as reading that the Earth's fish that live in the Pacific Ocean is $\frac{77}{100}$. To express a fraction as a percent, first find an equivalent decimal for the fraction. Then, multiply the decimal by 100 and add the percent symbol. For example, $\frac{1}{2} = 1 \div 2 = 0.5$. Then $0.5 = 0.50 = 50\%$.

Example Express $\frac{13}{20}$ as a percent.

Step 1 Find the equivalent decimal for the fraction.

$$\begin{array}{r} 0.65 \\ 20\overline{)13.00} \\ \underline{120} \\ 100 \\ \underline{100} \\ 0 \end{array}$$

Step 2 Rewrite the fraction $\frac{13}{20}$ as 0.65.

Step 3 Multiply 0.65 by 100 and add the % sign.

$$0.65 \cdot 100 = 65 = 65\%$$

So, $\frac{13}{20} = 65\%$.

Practice Problem In an experimental population of 365 sheep, 73 were brown. What percent of the sheep were brown? 20%

Using Precision and Significant Digits

When you make a **measurement,** the value you record depends on the precision of the measuring instrument. When adding or subtracting numbers with different precision, the answer is rounded to the smallest number of decimal places of any number in the sum or difference. When multiplying or dividing, the answer is rounded to the smallest number of significant figures of any number being multiplied or divided. When counting the number of **significant figures,** all digits are counted except zeros at the end of a number with no decimal such as 2,500, and zeros at the beginning of a decimal such as 0.03020.

Example The lengths 5.28 and 5.2 are measured in meters. Find the sum of these lengths and report the sum using the least precise measurement.

Step 1 Find the sum.

5.28 m	2 digits after the decimal
+ 5.2 m	1 digit after the decimal
10.48 m	

Step 2 Round to one digit after the decimal because the least number of digits after the decimal of the numbers being added is 1.

The sum is 10.5 m.

Practice Problem Multiply the numbers in the example using the rule for multiplying and dividing. Report the answer with the correct number of significant figures. 27.5 m²

Math Skill Handbook

Solving One-Step Equations

An **equation** is a statement that two things are equal. For example, $A = B$ is an equation that states that A is equal to B.

Sometimes one side of the equation will contain a **variable** whose value is not known. In the equation $3x = 12$, the variable is x.

The equation is solved when the variable is replaced with a value that makes both sides of the equation equal to each other. For example, the solution of the equation $3x = 12$ is $x = 4$. If the x is replaced with 4, then the equation becomes $3 \cdot 4 = 12$, or $12 = 12$.

To solve an equation such as $8x = 40$, divide both sides of the equation by the number that multiplies the variable.

$$8x = 40$$
$$\frac{8x}{8} = \frac{40}{8}$$
$$x = 5$$

You can check your answer by replacing the variable with your solution and seeing if both sides of the equation are the same.

$$8x = 8 \cdot 5 = 40$$

The left and right sides of the equation are the same, so $x = 5$ is the solution.

Sometimes an equation is written in this way: $a = bc$. This also is called a **formula.** The letters can be replaced by numbers, but the numbers must still make both sides of the equation the same.

Example 1 Solve the equation $10x = 35$.

Step 1 Find the solution by dividing each side of the equation by 10.

$$10x = 35 \qquad \frac{10x}{10} = \frac{35}{10} \qquad x = 3.5$$

Step 2 Check the solution.

$$10x = 35 \qquad 10 \times 3.5 = 35 \qquad 35 = 35$$

Both sides of the equation are equal, so $x = 3.5$ is the solution to the equation.

Example 2 In the formula $a = bc$, find the value of c if $a = 20$ and $b = 2$.

Step 1 Rearrange the formula so the unknown value is by itself on one side of the equation by dividing both sides by b.

$$a = bc$$
$$\frac{a}{b} = \frac{bc}{b}$$
$$\frac{a}{b} = c$$

Step 2 Replace the variables a and b with the values that are given.

$$\frac{a}{b} = c$$
$$\frac{20}{2} = c$$
$$10 = c$$

Step 3 Check the solution.

$$a = bc$$
$$20 = 2 \times 10$$
$$20 = 20$$

Both sides of the equation are equal, so $c = 10$ is the solution when $a = 20$ and $b = 2$.

Practice Problem In the formula $h = gd$, find the value of d if $g = 12.3$ and $h = 17.4$. $d = 1.4$

A **proportion** is an equation that shows that two ratios are equivalent. The ratios $\frac{2}{4}$ and $\frac{5}{10}$ are equivalent, so they can be written as $\frac{2}{4} = \frac{5}{10}$. This equation is an example of a proportion.

When two ratios form a proportion, the **cross products** are equal. To find the cross products in the proportion $\frac{2}{4} = \frac{5}{10}$, multiply the 2 and the 10, and the 4 and the 5. Therefore $2 \cdot 10 = 4 \cdot 5$, or $20 = 20$.

Because you know that both proportions are equal, you can use cross products to find a missing term in a proportion. This is known as **solving the proportion.** Solving a proportion is similar to solving an equation.

Example The heights of a tree and a pole are proportional to the lengths of their shadows. The tree casts a shadow of 24 m at the same time that a 6-m pole casts a shadow of 4 m. What is the height of the tree?

Step 1 Write a proportion.

$$\frac{\text{height of tree}}{\text{height of pole}} = \frac{\text{length of tree's shadow}}{\text{length of pole's shadow}}$$

Step 2 Substitute the known values into the proportion. Let h represent the unknown value, the height of the tree.

$$\frac{h}{6} = \frac{24}{4}$$

Step 3 Find the cross products.

$$h \cdot 4 = 6 \cdot 24$$

Step 4 Simplify the equation.

$$4h = 144$$

Step 5 Divide each side by 4.

$$\frac{4h}{4} = \frac{144}{4}$$

$$h = 36$$

The height of the tree is 36 m.

Practice Problem The proportions of bluefish are stable by the time they reach a length of 30 cm. The distance from the tip of the mouth to the back edge of the gill cover in a 35-cm bluefish is 15 cm. What is the distance from the tip of the mouth to the back edge of the gill cover in a 59-cm bluefish?   25.3 cm

Math Skill Handbook

● ● ● ● ● ● ● ● ● ● ● ● ● ● **Using Statistics** ● ● ● ● ● ● ● ● ● ● ● ● ● ●

Statistics is the branch of mathematics that deals with collecting, analyzing, and presenting data. In statistics, there are three common ways to summarize the data with a single number—the mean, the median, and the mode.

The **mean** of a set of data is the arithmetic average. It is found by adding the numbers in the data set and dividing by the number of items in the set.

The **median** is the middle number in a set of data when the data are arranged in numerical order. If there were an even number of data points, the median would be the mean of the two middle numbers.

The **mode** of a set of data is the number or item that appears most often.

Another number that often is used to describe a set of data is the range. The **range** is the difference between the largest number and the smallest number in a set of data.

A **frequency table** shows how many times each piece of data occurs, usually in a survey. The frequency table below shows the results of a student survey on favorite color.

Color	Tally	Frequency
red	||||	4
blue	||||	5
black	||	2
green	|||	3
purple	|||| ||	7
yellow	|||| |	6

Based on the frequency table data, which color is the favorite?

Example The high temperatures (in °C) on five consecutive days in a desert habitat under study are 39°, 37°, 44°, 36°, and 44°. Find the mean, median, mode, and range of this set.

To find the mean:
Step 1 Find the sum of the numbers.

$$39 + 37 + 44 + 36 + 44 = 200$$

Step 2 Divide the sum by the number of items, which is 5.

$$200 \div 5 = 40$$

The mean high temperature is 40°C.

To find the median:
Step 1 Arrange the temperatures from least to greatest.

$$36, \ 37, \ \underline{39}, \ 44, \ 44$$

Step 2 Determine the middle temperature.

The median high temperature is 39°C.

To find the mode:
Step 1 Group the numbers that are the same together.

44, 44, 36, 37, 39

Step 2 Determine the number that occurs most in the set.

$\underline{44, 44}$, 36, 37, 39

The mode measure is 44°C.

To find the range:
Step 1 Arrange the temperatures from largest to smallest.

44, 44, 39, 37, 36

Step 2 Determine the largest and smallest temperature in the set.

$\underline{44}$, 44, 39, 37, $\underline{36}$

Step 3 Find the difference between the largest and smallest temperatures.

$$44 - 36 = 8$$

The range is 8°C.

Practice Problem Find the mean, median, mode, and range for the data set 8, 4, 12, 8, 11, 14, 16.

mean, 10; median, 11; mode, 8; range 12

Safety in the Science Classroom

1. Always obtain your teacher's permission to begin an investigation.

2. Study the procedure. If you have questions, ask your teacher. Be sure you understand any safety symbols shown on the page.

3. Use the safety equipment provided for you. Goggles and a safety apron should be worn during most investigations.

4. Always slant test tubes away from yourself and others when heating them or adding substances to them.

5. Never eat or drink in the lab, and never use lab glassware as food or drink containers. Never inhale chemicals. Do not taste any substances or draw any material into a tube with your mouth.

6. Report any spill, accident, or injury, no matter how small, immediately to your teacher, then follow his or her instructions.

7. Know the location and proper use of the fire extinguisher, safety shower, fire blanket, first aid kit, and fire alarm.

8. Keep all materials away from open flames. Tie back long hair and tie down loose clothing.

9. If your clothing should catch fire, smother it with the fire blanket, or get under a safety shower. NEVER RUN.

10. If a fire should occur, turn off the gas then leave the room according to established procedures.

Follow these procedures as you clean up your work area

1. Turn off the water and gas. Disconnect electrical devices.

2. Clean all pieces of equipment and return all materials to their proper places.

3. Dispose of chemicals and other materials as directed by your teacher. Place broken glass and solid substances in the proper containers. Make sure never to discard materials in the sink.

4. Clean your work area. Wash your hands thoroughly after working in the laboratory.

First Aid	
Injury	**Safe Response ALWAYS NOTIFY YOUR TEACHER IMMEDIATELY**
Burns	Apply cold water.
Cuts and Bruises	Stop any bleeding by applying direct pressure. Cover cuts with a clean dressing. Apply ice packs or cold compresses to bruises.
Fainting	Leave the person lying down. Loosen any tight clothing and keep crowds away.
Foreign Matter in Eye	Flush with plenty of water. Use eyewash bottle or fountain.
Poisoning	Note the suspected poisoning agent.
Any Spills on Skin	Flush with large amounts of water or use safety shower.

Care and Use of a Microscope

Eyepiece Contains magnifying lenses you look through.

Arm Supports the body tube.

Low-power objective Contains the lens with the lowest power magnification.

Stage clips Hold the microscope slide in place.

Fine adjustment Sharpens the image under high magnification.

Coarse adjustment Focuses the image under low power.

Body tube Connects the eyepiece to the revolving nosepiece.

Revolving nosepiece Holds and turns the objectives into viewing position.

High-power objective Contains the lens with the highest magnification.

Stage Supports the microscope slide.

Light source Provides light that passes upward through the diaphragm, the specimen, and the lenses.

Base Provides support for the microscope.

Caring for a Microscope

1. Always carry the microscope holding the arm with one hand and supporting the base with the other hand.

2. Don't touch the lenses with your fingers.

3. The coarse adjustment knob is used only when looking through the lowest-power objective lens. The fine adjustment knob is used when the high-power objective is in place.

4. Cover the microscope when you store it.

Using a Microscope

1. Place the microscope on a flat surface that is clear of objects. The arm should be toward you.

2. Look through the eyepiece. Adjust the diaphragm so light comes through the opening in the stage.

3. Place a slide on the stage so the specimen is in the field of view. Hold it firmly in place by using the stage clips.

4. Always focus with the coarse adjustment and the low-power objective lens first. After the object is in focus on low power, turn the nosepiece until the high-power objective is in place. Use ONLY the fine adjustment to focus with the high-power objective lens.

Making a Wet-Mount Slide

1. Carefully place the item you want to look at in the center of a clean, glass slide. Make sure the sample is thin enough for light to pass through.

2. Use a dropper to place one or two drops of water on the sample.

3. Hold a clean coverslip by the edges and place it at one edge of the water. Slowly lower the coverslip onto the water until it lies flat.

4. If you have too much water or a lot of air bubbles, touch the edge of a paper towel to the edge of the coverslip to draw off extra water and draw out unwanted air.

Diversity of Life: Classification of Living Organisms

A six-kingdom system of classification of organisms is used today. Two kingdoms—Kingdom Archaebacteria and Kingdom Eubacteria—contain organisms that do not have a nucleus and that lack membrane-bound structures in the cytoplasm of their cells. The members of the other four kingdoms have a cell or cells that contain a nucleus and structures in the cytoplasm, some of which are surrounded by membranes. These kingdoms are Kingdom Protista, Kingdom Fungi, Kingdom Plantae, and Kingdom Animalia.

Kingdom Archaebacteria

one-celled; some absorb food from their surroundings; some are photosynthetic; some are chemosynthetic; many found in extremely harsh environments including salt ponds, hot springs, swamps, and deep-sea hydrothermal vents

Kingdom Eubacteria

one-celled; most absorb food from their surroundings; some are photosynthetic; some are chemosynthetic; many are parasites; many are round, spiral, or rod-shaped; some form colonies

Kingdom Protista

Phylum Euglenophyta one-celled; photosynthetic or take in food; most have one flagellum; euglenoids

Phylum Bacillariophyta one-celled; photosynthetic; have unique double shells made of silica; diatoms

Phylum Dinoflagellata one-celled; photosynthetic; contain red pigments; have two flagella; dinoflagellates

Phylum Chlorophyta one-celled, many-celled, or colonies; photosynthetic; contain chlorophyll; live on land, in freshwater, or salt water; green algae

Phylum Rhodophyta most are many-celled; photosynthetic; contain red pigments; most live in deep, saltwater environments; red algae

Phylum Phaeophyta most are many-celled; photosynthetic; contain brown pigments; most live in saltwater environments; brown algae

Phylum Rhizopoda one-celled; take in food; are free-living or parasitic; move by means of pseudopods; amoebas

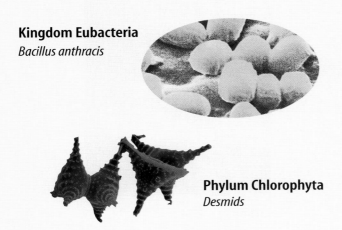

Kingdom Eubacteria
Bacillus anthracis

Phylum Chlorophyta
Desmids

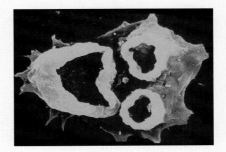

Amoeba

Phylum Zoomastigina one-celled; take in food; free-living or parasitic; have one or more flagella; zoomastigotes

Phylum Ciliophora one-celled; take in food; have large numbers of cilia; ciliates

Phylum Sporozoa one-celled; take in food; have no means of movement; are parasites in animals; sporozoans

Phylum Myxomycota
Slime mold

Phyla Myxomycota and Acrasiomycota one- or many-celled; absorb food; change form during life cycle; cellular and plasmodial slime molds

Phylum Oomycota many-celled; are either parasites or decomposers; live in freshwater or salt water; water molds, rusts and downy mildews

Kingdom Fungi

Phylum Zygomycota many-celled; absorb food; spores are produced in sporangia; zygote fungi; bread mold

Phylum Ascomycota one- and many-celled; absorb food; spores produced in asci; sac fungi; yeast

Phylum Basidiomycota many-celled; absorb food; spores produced in basidia; club fungi; mushrooms

Phylum Deuteromycota members with unknown reproductive structures; imperfect fungi; *Penicillium*

Mycophycota organisms formed by symbiotic relationship between an ascomycote or a basidiomycote and green alga or cyanobacterium; lichens

Phylum Oomycota
Phytophthora infestans

Lichens

Kingdom Plantae

Divisions Bryophyta (mosses), **Anthocerophyta** (hornworts), **Hepatophytal** (liverworts), **Psilophytal** (whisk ferns) many-celled nonvascular plants; reproduce by spores produced in capsules; green; grow in moist, land environments

Division Lycophyta many-celled vascular plants; spores are produced in conelike structures; live on land; are photosynthetic; club mosses

Division Sphenophyta vascular plants; ribbed and jointed stems; scalelike leaves; spores produced in conelike structures; horsetails

Division Pterophyta vascular plants; leaves called fronds; spores produced in clusters of sporangia called sori; live on land or in water; ferns

Division Ginkgophyta deciduous trees; only one living species; have fan-shaped leaves with branching veins and fleshy cones with seeds; ginkgoes

Division Cycadophyta palmlike plants; have large, featherlike leaves; produces seeds in cones; cycads

Division Coniferophyta deciduous or evergreen; trees or shrubs; have needlelike or scalelike leaves; seeds produced in cones; conifers

Division Anthophyta
Tomato plant

Phylum Platyhelminthes
Flatworm

Division Gnetophyta shrubs or woody vines; seeds are produced in cones; division contains only three genera; gnetum

Division Anthophyta dominant group of plants; flowering plants; have fruits with seeds

Kingdom Animalia

Phylum Porifera aquatic organisms that lack true tissues and organs; are asymmetrical and sessile; sponges

Phylum Cnidaria radially symmetrical organisms; have a digestive cavity with one opening; most have tentacles armed with stinging cells; live in aquatic environments singly or in colonies; includes jellyfish, corals, hydra, and sea anemones

Phylum Platyhelminthes bilaterally symmetrical worms; have flattened bodies; digestive system has one opening; parasitic and free-living species; flatworms

Division Bryophyta
Liverwort

Phylum Chordata

Phylum Nematoda round, bilaterally symmetrical body; have digestive system with two openings; free-living forms and parasitic forms; roundworms

Phylum Mollusca soft-bodied animals, many with a hard shell and soft foot or footlike appendage; a mantle covers the soft body; aquatic and terrestrial species; includes clams, snails, squid, and octopuses

Phylum Annelida bilaterally symmetrical worms; have round, segmented bodies; terrestrial and aquatic species; includes earthworms, leeches, and marine polychaetes

Phylum Arthropoda largest animal group; have hard exoskeletons, segmented bodies, and pairs of jointed appendages; land and aquatic species; includes insects, crustaceans, and spiders

Phylum Echinodermata marine organisms; have spiny or leathery skin and a water-vascular system with tube feet; are radially symmetrical; includes sea stars, sand dollars, and sea urchins

Phylum Chordata organisms with internal skeletons and specialized body systems; most have paired appendages; all at some time have a notochord, nerve cord, gill slits, and a postanal tail; include fish, amphibians, reptiles, birds, and mammals

This glossary defines each key term that appears in bold type in the text. It also shows the chapter, section, and page number where you can find the words used.

A

active transport: energy-requiring process in which transport proteins bind with particles and move them through a cell membrane. (Chap. 3, Sec. 2, p. 79)

adaptation: any variation that makes an organism better suited to its environment. (Chap. 6, Sec. 1, p. 160)

allele (uh LEEL): an alternate form that a gene may have for a single trait; can be dominant or recessive. (Chap. 5, Sec. 1, p. 129)

asexual reproduction: a type of reproduction—fission, budding, and regeneration—in which a new organism is produced from one parent and has DNA identical to the parent organism. (Chap. 4, Sec. 1, p. 103)

B

binomial nomenclature (bi NOH mee ul · NOH mun klay chur): two-word naming system that gives all organisms their scientific name. (Chap. 1, Sec. 4, p. 22)

biogenesis (bi oh JEN uh suhs): theory that living things come only from other living things. (Chap. 1, Sec. 3, p. 17)

C

cell: smallest unit of an organism that can carry on life functions. (Chap. 1, Sec. 2, p. 12)

cell membrane: protective outer covering of all cells that is made up of a double layer of fatlike molecules and regulates the interaction between the cell and the environment. (Chap. 2, Sec. 1, p. 40)

cell theory: states that all organisms are made up of one or more cells, the cell is the basic unit of life, and all cells come from other cells. (Chap. 2, Sec. 2, p. 53)

cell wall: rigid structure that encloses, supports, and protects the cells of plants, algae, fungi, and most bacteria. (Chap. 2, Sec. 1, p. 41)

chloroplast: green, chlorophyll-containing, plant-cell organelle that converts sunlight, carbon dioxide, and water into sugar. (Chap. 2, Sec. 1, p. 44)

chromosome: structure in a cell's nucleus that contains genetic material. (Chap. 4, Sec. 1, p. 100)

control: standard to which the outcome of a test is compared. (Chap. 1, Sec. 1, p. 7)

cytoplasm: constantly moving gel-like mixture inside the cell membrane that contains heredity material and is the location of most of a cell's life processes. (Chap. 2, Sec. 1, p. 40)

D

diffusion: a type of passive transport in cells in which molecules move from areas where there are more of them to areas where there are fewer of them. (Chap. 3, Sec. 2, p. 77)

diploid (DIHP loyd): cell whose chromosomes occur in pairs. (Chap. 4, Sec. 2, p. 106)

DNA: deoxyribonucleic acid, which is the genetic material of all organisms, made up of two twisted strands of sugar-phosphate molecules and nitrogen bases. (Chap. 4, Sec. 3, p. 112)

dominant (DAHM uh nunt): describes a trait that covers over, or dominates, another form of that trait. (Chap. 5, Sec. 1, p. 131)

English Glossary

E

egg: haploid sex cell formed in the female reproductive organs. (Chap. 4, Sec. 2, p. 106)

embryology (em bree AHL uh jee): study of embryos and their development. (Chap. 6, Sec. 2, p. 169)

endocytosis (en duh si TOH sus): process by which a cell takes in a substance by surrounding it with the cell membrane. (Chap. 3, Sec. 2, p. 80)

endoplasmic reticulum (ER): cytoplasmic organelle that moves materials around in a cell and is made up of a complex series of folded membranes; can be rough (with attached ribosomes) or smooth (without attached ribosomes). (Chap. 2, Sec. 1, p. 45)

enzyme: a type of protein that regulates nearly all chemical reactions in cells. (Chap. 3, Sec. 1, p. 73)

equilibrium: occurs when molecules of one substance are spread evenly throughout another substance. (Chap. 3, Sec. 2, p. 14)

evolution: change in inherited characteristics over time. (Chap. 6, Sec. 1, p. 156)

exocytosis (ek soh si TOH sus): process by which vesicles release their contents outside the cell. (Chap. 3, Sec. 2, p. 80)

F

fermentation: process by which oxygen-lacking cells and some one-celled organisms release small amounts of energy from glucose molecules and produce wastes such as alcohol, carbon dioxide, and lactic acid. (Chap. 3, Sec. 3, p. 86)

fertilization: in sexual reproduction, the joining of a sperm and egg. (Chap. 4, Sec. 2, p. 106)

G

gene: section of DNA on a chromosome that contains instructions for making specific proteins. (Chap. 4, Sec. 3, p. 114)

genetic engineering: biological and chemical methods to change the arrangement of a gene's DNA to improve crop production, produce large volumes of medicine, and change how cells perform their normal functions. (Chap. 5, Sec. 3, p. 144)

genetics (juh NET ihks): the study of how traits are inherited through the actions of alleles. (Chap. 5, Sec. 1, p. 129)

genotype (JEE nuh tipe): an organism's genetic makeup. (Chap. 5, Sec. 1, p. 133)

genus: first word of the two-word scientific name used to identify a group of similar species. (Chap. 1, Sec. 4, p. 22)

Golgi bodies: organelles that package cellular materials and transport them within the cell or out of the cell. (Chap. 2, Sec. 1, p. 45)

gradualism: model describing evolution as a slow process by which one species changes into a new species through a continuing series of mutations and variations over time. (Chap. 6, Sec. 1, p. 162)

H

haploid (HAP loyd): cell that has only one of each type of chromosome. (Chap. 4, Sec. 2, p. 107)

heredity (huh RED ut ee): the passing of traits from parent to offspring. (Chap. 5, Sec. 1, p. 129)

heterozygous (het uh roh ZI gus): describes an organism with two different alleles for a trait. (Chap. 5, Sec. 1, p. 133)

homeostasis: ability of an organism to keep proper internal conditions no matter what external stimuli are occurring. (Chap. 1, Sec. 2, p. 13)

hominid: humanlike primate that appeared about 4 million to 6 million years ago, ate both plants and meat, and walked upright on two legs. (Chap. 6, Sec. 3, p. 173)

homologous (huh MAHL uh gus): body parts that are similar in structure and origin and can be similar in function. (Chap. 6, Sec. 2, p. 170)

Homo sapiens: early humans that likely evolved from Cro-Magnons. (Chap. 6, Sec. 3, p. 175)

homozygous (hoh muh ZI gus): describes an organism with two alleles that are the same for a trait. (Chap. 5, Sec. 1, p. 133)

host cell: living cell in which a virus can actively reproduce or in which a virus can hide until activated by environmental stimuli. (Chap. 2, Sec. 3, p. 54)

hybrid (HI brud): an offspring that was given different genetic information for a trait from each parent. (Chap. 5, Sec. 1, p. 131)

hypothesis: prediction that can be tested. (Chap. 1, Sec. 1, p. 6)

I

incomplete dominance: production of a phenotype that is intermediate between the two homozygous parents. (Chap. 5, Sec. 2, p. 137)

inorganic compound: compound, such as H_2O, that is made from elements other than carbon and whose atoms can usually be arranged in only one structure. (Chap. 3, Sec. 1, p. 73)

K

kingdom: first and largest category used to classify organisms. (Chap. 1, Sec. 4, p. 21)

L

law: statement about how things work in nature that seems to be true consistently. (Chap. 1, Sec. 1, p. 8)

M

meiosis (mi OH sus): reproductive process that produces four haploid sex cells from one diploid cell and ensures offspring will have the same number of chromosomes as the parent organisms. (Chap. 4, Sec. 2, p. 107)

metabolism: the total of all chemical reactions in an organism. (Chap. 3, Sec. 3, p. 83)

mitochondrion: cell organelle that breaks down lipids and carbohydrates and releases energy. (Chap. 2, Sec. 1, p. 44)

mitosis (mi TOH sus): cell process in which the nucleus divides to form two nuclei identical to each other, and identical to the original nucleus, in a series of steps (prophase, metaphase, anaphase, and telophase). (Chap. 4, Sec. 1, p. 100)

mixture: a combination of substances in which the individual substances do not change or combine chemically but instead retain their own individual properties; can be gases, solids, liquids, or any combination of them. (Chap. 3, Sec. 1, p. 71)

mutation: any permanent change in a gene or chromosome of a cell; may be beneficial, harmful, or have little effect on an organism. (Chap. 4, Sec. 3, p. 116)

N

natural selection: organisms with traits best suited to their environment are more likely to survive and reproduce; includes concepts of variation, overproduction, and competition. (Chap. 6, Sec. 1, p. 159)

nucleus: organelle that controls all the activities of a cell and contains hereditary material made of proteins and DNA. (Chap. 2, Sec. 1, p. 42)

O

organ: structure, such as the heart, made up of different types of tissues that all work together. (Chap. 2, Sec. 1, p. 47)

organelle: structure in the cytoplasm of a eukaryotic cell that can act as a storage site, process energy, move materials, or manufacture substances. (Chap. 2, Sec. 1, p. 42)

organic compounds: compounds that always contain hydrogen and carbon; carbohydrates, lipids, proteins, and nucleic acids are organic compounds found in living things. (Chap. 3, Sec. 1, p. 72)

organisms: any living things that are made of cells, use energy, reproduce, respond, and grow and develop. (Chap. 1, Sec. 2, p. 12)

osmosis: a type of passive transport that occurs when water diffuses through a cell membrane. (Chap. 3, Sec. 2, p. 78)

P

passive transport: movement of substances through a cell membrane without the use of cellular energy; includes diffusion, osmosis, and facilitated diffusion. (Chap. 3, Sec. 2, p. 76)

phenotype (FEE nuh tipe): outward physical appearance and behavior of an organism. (Chap. 5, Sec. 1, p. 133)

photosynthesis: process by which plants and many other producers use light energy from the Sun to make sugars, which can be used as food. (Chap. 3, Sec. 3, p. 84)

phylogeny (fi LAH juh nee): evolutionary history of an organism; used today to group organisms into six kingdoms. (Chap. 1, Sec. 4, p. 21)

polygenic (pahl ih JEHN ihk) **inheritance:** occurs when a group of gene pairs acts together and produces a specific trait, such as human eye color, skin color, or height. (Chap. 5, Sec. 2, p. 139)

primates: group of mammals including humans, monkeys, and apes that share characteristics such as opposable thumbs, binocular vision, and flexible shoulders. (Chap. 6, Sec. 3, p. 172)

punctuated equilibrium: model describing the rapid evolution that occurs when mutation of a few genes results in a species suddenly changing into a new species. (Chap. 6, Sec. 1, p. 162)

Punnett (PUN ut) **square:** a tool to predict the probability of certain traits in offspring that shows the different ways alleles can combine. (Chap. 5, Sec. 1, p. 133)

R

radioactive element: element that gives off a steady amount of radiation as it slowly changes to a nonradioactive element. (Chap. 6, Sec. 2, p. 167)

recessive (rih SES ihv): describes a trait that is covered over, or dominated, by another form of that trait and seems to disappear. (Chap. 5, Sec. 1, p. 131)

respiration: process by which producers and consumers release stored energy from food molecules. (Chap. 3, Sec. 3, p. 85)

ribosome: small structure on which cells make their own proteins. (Chap. 2, Sec. 1, p. 44)

RNA: ribonucleic acid, which carries codes for making proteins from the nucleus to the ribosomes. (Chap. 4, Sec. 3, p. 114)

S

scientific methods: procedures used to solve problems and answer questions that can include stating the problem, gathering information, forming a hypothesis, testing the hypothesis with an experiment, analyzing data, and drawing conclusions. (Chap. 1, Sec. 1, p. 5)

sedimentary rock: a type of rock, such as limestone, that is most likely to contain fossils and is formed when layers of sand, silt, clay, or mud are cemented and compacted together or when minerals are deposited from a solution. (Chap. 6, Sec. 2, p. 166)

sex-linked gene: an allele inherited on a sex chromosome and that can cause human genetic disorders such as color blindness and hemophilia. (Chap. 5, Sec. 2, p. 142)

English Glossary

sexual reproduction: a type of reproduction in which two sex cells, usually an egg and a sperm, join to form a zygote, which will develop into a new organism with a unique identity. (Chap. 4, Sec. 2, p. 106)

species: group of organisms that share similar characteristics and can reproduce among themselves. (Chap. 6, Sec. 1, p. 156)

sperm: haploid sex cells formed in the male reproductive organs. (Chap. 4, Sec. 2, p. 106)

spontaneous generation: idea that living things come from nonliving things. (Chap. 1, Sec. 3, p. 17)

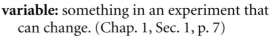

theory: explanation of things or events based on scientific knowledge resulting from many observations and experiments. (Chap. 1, Sec. 1, p. 8)

tissue: group of similar cells that work together to do one job. (Chap. 2, Sec. 1, p. 47)

variable: something in an experiment that can change. (Chap. 1, Sec. 1, p. 7)

variation: inherited trait that makes an individual different from other members of the same species and results from a mutation in the organism's genes. (Chap. 6, Sec. 1, p. 160)

vestigial (veh STIHJ ee ul) **structure:** structure, such as the human appendix, that doesn't seem to have a function and may once have functioned in the body of an ancestor. (Chap. 6, Sec. 2, p. 170)

virus: a strand of hereditary material surrounded by a protein coating. (Chap. 2, Sec. 3, p. 54)

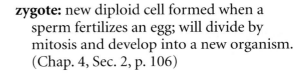

zygote: new diploid cell formed when a sperm fertilizes an egg; will divide by mitosis and develop into a new organism. (Chap. 4, Sec. 2, p. 106)

English Glossary

Este glosario define cada término clave que aparece en negrillas en el texto. También muestra el capítulo, la sección y el número de página en donde se usa dicho término.

A

active transport / transporte activo: proceso que requiere energía en el cual las proteínas de transporte se enlazan con partículas y se mueven a través de la membrana celular. (Cap. 3, Sec. 2, pág. 79)

adaptation / adaptación: toda variación que le permite a un organismo adaptarse mejor a su ambiente. (Cap. 6, Sec. 1, pág. 160)

allele / alelo: formas alternas que un gene puede tener para un sólo rasgo; puede ser dominante o recesivo. (Cap. 5, Sec. 1, pág. 129)

asexual reproduction / reproducción asexual: tipo de reproducción que comprende la fisión, la gemación y la regeneración, en el cual un progenitor produce un nuevo organismo que tiene el DNA idéntico al del organismo progenitor. (Cap. 4, Sec. 1, pág. 103)

B

binomial nomenclature / nomenclatura binaria: sistema que se usa para nombrar organismos y que está basado en dos palabras, la primera palabra indica el género y la segunda palabra indica la especie. (Cap. 1, Sec. 4, pág. 22)

biogenesis / biogénesis: teoría que establece que todo ser vivo proviene de otros seres vivos. (Cap. 1, Sec. 3, pág. 17)

C

cell / célula: unidad básica de los seres vivos que puede realizar las funciones vitales; tiene una estructura ordenada y contiene material hereditario (Cap. 1, Sec. 2, pág. 12)

cell membrane / membrana celular: cubierta externa protectora de todas las células; formada por una capa doble de moléculas adiposas y controla la interacción entre la célula y el medio ambiente. (Cap. 2, Sec. 1, pág. 40)

cell theory / teoría celular: establece que todos los organismos están formados por una o más células, la célula es la unidad básica de la vida y todas las células provienen de otras células. (Cap. 2, Sec. 2, pág. 53)

cell wall / pared celular: estructura rígida que encierra, sostiene y protege las células vegetales, las células de las algas, de los hongos y de la mayoría de las bacterias. (Cap. 2, Sec. 1, pág. 41)

chloroplast / cloroplasto: organelo de las células vegetales, de color verde y que contiene clorofila, que convierte la luz solar, el dióxido de carbono y el agua en azúcar. (Cap. 2, Sec. 1. pág. 44)

chromosome / cromosoma: estructura en el núcleo de una célula que contiene el material genético. (Cap. 4, Sec. 1, pág. 100)

control / control: el estándar que sirve para comparar los resultados obtenidos en un experimento. (Cap. 1, Sec. 1, pág. 7)

cytoplasm / citoplasma: mezcla gelatinosa en continuo movimiento dentro de la membrana celular que contiene material hereditario y en la cual se lleva a cabo la

mayoría de los procesos de una célula.
(Cap. 2, Sec. 1, pág. 40)

diffusion / difusión: tipo de transporte
pasivo celular en el que las moléculas se
mueven desde áreas de mayor concentración a áreas de menor concentración.
(Cap. 3, Sec. 2, pág. 77)

diploid / diploide: célula cuyos cromosomas
se dan en pares. (Cap. 4, Sec. 2, pág. 106)

DNA / DNA: ácido desoxirribonucleico;
material genético de todos los organismos
y compuesto de dos hebras retorcidas de
moléculas de fosfato de azúcar y bases
nitrogenadas. (Cap. 4, Sec. 3, pág. 112)

dominant / dominante: describe un rasgo
que cubre o domina otra forma de dicho
rasgo. (Cap. 5, Sec. 1, pág. 131)

egg / óvulo: célula haploide formada en los
órganos reproductores femeninos.
(Cap. 4, Sec. 2, pág. 106)

embryology / embriología: estudio de los
embriones y su desarrollo. (Cap. 6, Sec. 2,
pág. 169)

endocytosis / endocitosis: proceso que permite que una célula deje pasar una sustancia al rodearla con la membrana
celular. (Cap. 3, Sec. 2, pág. 80)

**endoplasmic reticulum (ER) / retículo
endoplásmico:** organelo citoplásmico que
mueve materiales dentro de una célula y
que está formado por una serie compleja
de membranas plegadas; puede ser áspero
(con ribosomas adheridos) o liso (sin
ribosomas adheridos). (Cap. 2, Sec. 1,
pág. 45)

enzyme / enzima: tipo de proteína que regu-
la casi todas las reacciones químicas de las
células. (Cap. 3, Sec. 1, pág. 73)

equilibrium / equilibrio: ocurre cuando las
moléculas de una sustancia se esparcen
uniformemente en otra sustancia. (Cap. 3,
Sec. 2, pág. 14)

evolution / evolución: cambio, con el
tiempo, en las características heredadas.
(Cap. 6, Sec. 1, pág. 156)

exocytosis / exocitosis: proceso a través
del cual las vesículas liberan sus con-
tenidos fuera de la célula. (Cap. 3, Sec. 2,
pág. 80)

fermentation / fermentación: proceso en
que las células carentes de oxígeno y
algunos organismos unicelulares liberan
pequeñas cantidades de energía de las
moléculas de glucosa y producen dese-
chos como el alcohol, el dióxido de carbono y el ácido láctico. (Cap. 3, Sec. 3,
pág. 86)

fertilization / fecundación: en la reproducción sexual, la unión del espermatozoide y
del óvulo. (Cap. 4, Sec. 2, pág. 106)

gene / gene: sección de DNA en un cromosoma que contiene las instrucciones para
la elaboración de proteínas específicas.
(Cap. 4, Sec. 3, pág. 114)

genetic engineering / ingeniería genética:
métodos biológicos y químicos que se
usan para cambiar el arreglo del DNA de
un gene con el propósito de mejorar la
producción de cosechas, producir grandes
volúmenes de medicamentos y cambiar el

Spanish Glossary

funcionamiento normal de células. (Cap. 5, Sec. 3, pág. 144)

genetics / genética: estudia la manera en que se heredan los rasgos a través de las acciones de los alelos. (Cap. 5, Sec. 1, pág. 129)

genotype / genotipo: la composición genética de un organismo. (Cap. 5, Sec. 1, pág. 133)

genus / género: grupo de especies similares. (Cap. 1, Sec. 4, pág. 22)

Golgi bodies / cuerpos de Golgi: organelos que almacenan materiales celulares y los transportan dentro o fuera de la célula. (Cap. 2, Sec. 1, pág. 45)

gradualism / gradualismo: modelo que describe la evolución como un proceso lento mediante el cual una especie se transforma en otra especie, a través de una serie continua de mutaciones y variaciones que ocurren con el paso del tiempo. (Cap. 6, Sec. 1, pág. 162)

haploid / haploide: célula que sólo tiene uno de cada tipo de cromosoma. (Cap. 4, Sec. 2, pág. 107)

heredity / herencia: el traspaso de rasgos de los progenitores a la progenie. (Cap. 5, Sec. 1, pág. 129)

heterozygous / heterocigoto: describe al organismo que presenta dos alelos distintos para un rasgo. (Cap. 5, Sec. 1, pág. 133)

homeostasis / homeostasis: característica de los seres vivos que les permite mantener las condiciones internas adecuadas, a pesar de los cambios en su ambiente. (Cap. 1, Sec. 2, pág. 13)

hominid / homínido: primate de aspecto humano que apareció entre hace 4 millones y 6 millones de años, se alimentaba de plantas y animales y

caminaba derecho en dos piernas. (Cap. 6, Sec. 3, pág. 173)

homologous / homólogo: partes corporales semejantes en estructura y origen y que pueden ser semejantes en cuanto a su función. (Cap. 6, Sec. 2, pág. 170)

Homo sapiens / Homo sapiens: los primeros humanos que probablemente evolucionaron de los hombres de Cro-Magnon. (Cap. 6, Sec. 3, pág. 175)

homozygous / homocigoto: describe un organismo con dos alelos idénticos para el mismo rasgo. (Cap. 5, Sec. 1, pág. 133)

host cell / célula huésped: célula viva en la cual un virus se puede reproducir activamente o en la cual un virus puede ocultarse hasta que los estímulos ambientales lo activen. (Cap. 2, Sec. 3, pág. 54)

hybrid / híbrido: progenie que ha obtenido información genética distinta para un rasgo de cada progenitor. (Cap. 5, Sec. 1, pág. 131)

hypothesis / hipótesis: predicción que se puede poner a prueba. (Cap. 1, Sec. 1, pág. 6)

incomplete dominance / dominancia incompleta: la producción de un fenotipo intermedio al de los dos progenitores homocigotos. (Cap. 5, Sec. 2, pág. 137)

inorganic compound / compuesto orgánico: compuesto cuyos constituyentes son otros elementos, en vez del carbono y cuyos átomos por lo general pueden arreglarse en sólo una estructura, como por ejemplo, el H_2O, (Cap. 3, Sec. 1, pág. 73)

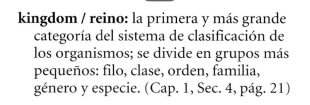

kingdom / reino: la primera y más grande categoría del sistema de clasificación de los organismos; se divide en grupos más pequeños: filo, clase, orden, familia, género y especie. (Cap. 1, Sec. 4, pág. 21)

law / ley: enunciado científico que describe cómo ocurren ciertos fenómenos en la naturaleza y que parece ser cierto en todo momento. (Cap. 1, Sec. 1, pág. 8)

meiosis / meiosis: proceso reproductor que produce cuatro células sexuales haploides a partir de una célula diploide y asegura que la progenie tenga el mismo número de cromosomas que el organismo progenitor. (Cap. 4, Sec. 2, pág. 107)

metabolism / metabolismo: el total de todas las reacciones químicas en un organismo. (Cap. 3, Sec. 3, pág. 83)

mitochondrion / mitocondria: organelo celular que descompone lípidos y carbohidratos y libera energía. (Cap. 2, Sec. 1, pág. 44)

mitosis / mitosis: proceso celular en que el núcleo se divide para formar dos núcleos idénticos uno al otro e idénticos al núcleo original, en una serie de pasos (profase, metafase, anafase y telofase). (Cap. 4, Sec. 1, pág. 100)

mixture / mezcla: combinación de sustancias en que las sustancias individuales no cambian ni se combinan químicamente, sino que retienen sus propiedades individuales; pueden ser gases, líquidos o cualquier combinación de estos dos. (Cap. 3, Sec. 1, pág. 71)

mutation / mutuación: cualquier cambio permanente en un gene o en un cromosoma de una célula; puede ser beneficioso, perjudicial o puede tener un efecto mínimo en un organismo. (Cap. 4, Sec. 3, pág. 116)

natural selection / selección natural: significa que los organismos con rasgos mejor adaptados a su ambiente están más propensos a sobrevivir y reproducirse; incluye conceptos de variación, sobreproducción y competencia. (Cap. 6, Sec. 1, pág. 159)

nucleus / núcleo: organelo que controla todas las actividades de una célula y contiene material hereditario compuesto por proteínas y DNA. (Cap. 2, Sec. 1, pág. 42)

organ / órgano: estructura, como el corazón, compuesta por tipos diferentes de tejidos que funcionan en conjunto. (Cap. 2, Sec. 1, pág. 47)

organelle / organelo: estructura en el citoplasma de una célula eucariota que puede actuar como un lugar de almacenamiento, puede procesar energía, mover materiales o elaborar sustancias. (Cap. 2, Sec. 1, pág. 42)

organic compounds / compuestos orgánicos: compuestos que siempre contienen hidrógeno y carbono; los lípidos, las proteínas y los ácidos nucleicos son compuestos orgánicos que se encuentran en los seres vivos. (Cap. 3, Sec. 1, pág. 72)

organisms / organismo: cualquier ser vivo; usa energía, está formado por células, se reproduce, responde a estímulos, crece y se desarrollan. (Cap. 1, Sec. 2, pág. 12)

osmosis / ósmosis: tipo de transporte pasivo que se lleva a cabo cuando el agua se difunde a través de la membrana celular. (Cap. 3, Sec. 2, pág. 78)

passive transport / transporte pasivo: movimiento de sustancias a través de la membrana celular que no involucra el uso de energía celular; incluye la difusión, la ósmosis y la difusión facilitada. (Cap. 3, Sec. 2, pág. 76)

phenotype / fenotipo: apariencia física externa y comportamiento de un organismo. (Cap. 5, Sec. 1, pág. 133)

photosynthesis / fotosíntesis: proceso mediante el cual las plantas y muchos otros productores utilizan la energía luminosa del Sol para elaborar azúcares que pueden usar como alimento. (Cap. 3, Sec. 3, pág. 84)

phylogeny / filogenia: historia evolutiva de un organismo, sirve para que los científicos puedan clasificar los organismos en reinos. (Cap. 1, Sec. 4, pág. 21)

polygenic inheritance / herencia poligénica: tipo de herencia que ocurre cuando un grupo de pares de genes actúan en conjunto y producen un rasgo específico; por ejemplo el color de los ojos, cabello, piel o estatura de los humanos. (Cap. 5, Sec. 2, pág. 139)

primates / primates: grupo de mamíferos que incluye, entre otros, a los seres humanos, los monos y los simios, los cuales comparten características como pulgares oponibles, visión binocular y hombros flexibles. (Cap. 6, Sec. 3, pág. 172)

punctuated equilibrium / equilibrio puntuado: modelo que describe la evolución rápida que ocurre cuando la mutación de unos cuantos genes da como resultado una especie que repentinamente se transforma en otra especie. (Cap. 6, Sec. 1, pág. 162)

Punnett square / cuadrado de Punnett: instrumento que se usa para predecir ciertos rasgos en la progenie, que muestra las distintas maneras en que los alelos se pueden combinar. (Cap. 5, Sec. 1, pág. 133)

radioactive element / elemento radiactivo: elemento que emite una cantidad constante de radiación a medida que se transforma lentamente en un elemento no radiactivo. (Cap. 6, Sec. 2, pág. 167)

recessive / recesivo: describe un rasgo que es cubierto o dominado por otra forma de ese rasgo y, por lo tanto, parece desaparecer. (Cap. 5, Sec. 1, pág. 131)

respiration / respiración: proceso en que los productores y los consumidores liberan la energía almacenada en las partículas de alimento. (Cap. 3, Sec. 3, pág. 85)

ribosome / ribosoma: estructura pequeña en la cual las células producen sus propias proteínas. (Cap. 2, Sec. 1, pág. 44)

RNA / RNA: ácido ribonucleico que lleva consigo los códigos para la elaboración de proteínas del núcleo a los ribosomas. (Cap. 4, Sec. 3, pág. 114)

scientific method / método científico: técnicas para solucionar problemas que sirven para investigar observaciones realizadas acerca de seres vivos o materia inerte; incluye los siguientes pasos: reconocer un problema, recoger información, formular y poner a prueba una hipótesis, analizar datos y sacar conclusiones. (Cap. 1, Sec. 1, pág. 5)

sedimentary rock / roca sedimentaria: tipo de roca, como la piedra caliza, que está más propensa a contener fósiles y que se forma cuando se cementan o compactan las capas de arena, lodo, arcilla o fango o cuando los minerales se depositan de una solución. (Cap. 6, Sec. 2, pág. 166)

sex-linked gene / gene ligado al sexo: un alelo heredado en un cromosoma del sexo y que puede causar trastornos genéticos, como por ejemplo, el daltonismo o la hemofilia. (Cap. 5, Sec. 2, pág. 142)

sexual reproduction / reproducción sexual: tipo de reproducción en que dos células sexuales, por lo general un óvulo y un espermatozoide, se unen formando un cigoto, el cual se desarrolla en un nuevo organismo con su propia identidad. (Cap. 4, Sec. 2, pág. 106)

species / especies: grupo de organismos que comparten características semejantes y que pueden procrear entre sí. (Cap. 6, Sec. 1, pág. 156)

sperm / espermatozoide: célula sexual haploide formada en los órganos reproductores masculinos. (Cap. 4, Sec. 2, pág. 106)

spontaneous generation / generación espontánea: teoría que dice que los seres vivos pueden originarse a partir de la materia inerte. (Cap. 1, Sec. 3, pág. 17)

theory / teoría: explicación de fenómenos o cosas basada en el conocimiento científico generado a partir de múltiples observaciones y pruebas. (Cap. 1, Sec. 1, pág. 8)

tissue / tejido: grupo de células semejantes que funcionan juntas para efectuar una tarea. (Cap. 2, Sec. 1, pág. 47)

variable / variable: cada una de las condiciones que pueden cambiar durante un experimento. (Cap. 1, Sec. 1, pág. 7)

variation / variación: rasgo heredado que diferencia a un individuo de otros miembros de la misma especie y que resulta de una mutación de los genes del organismo. (Cap. 6, Sec. 1, pág. 160)

vestigial structure / estructura vestigial: estructura, como el apéndice humano, que no parece cumplir función alguna y que tal vez pudo haber funcionado en el cuerpo de un antepasado. (Cap. 6, Sec. 2, pág. 170)

virus / virus: estructura que contiene material hereditario rodeado por un revestimiento proteico y que sólo se desarrolla en el interior de organismos vivos. (Cap. 2, Sec. 3, pág. 54)

zygote / cigoto: nueva célula diploide que se forma cuando un espermatozoide fecunda un óvulo; se divide mediante mitosis y se desarrolla en un nuevo organismo. (Cap. 4, Sec. 2, pág. 106)

Index

The index for *Life's Structure and Function* will help you locate major topics in the book quickly and easily. Each entry in the index is followed by the number of the pages on which the entry is discussed. A page number given in boldfaced type indicates the page on which that entry is defined. A page number given in italic type indicates a page on which the entry is used in an illustration or photograph. The abbreviation *act.* indicates a page on which the entry is used in an activity.

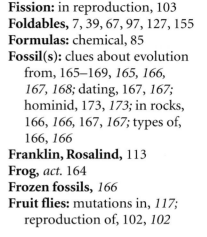
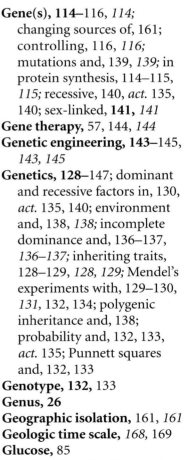

Index

Index

Arnold, Inc.; **88** (t)Runk/Schoenberger from GH, (b)AH; **89** MM; **90** Lappa/Marquart; **91** The Just/Garcia/Hill Science Web Site; **92** (tl)Michael Pogany/Columbus Zoo, (tr)Bachman/PR, (b)Jim Strawser from GH; **93** CNRI/ Science Photo Library/PR; **96** Biophoto Associates/PR; **96-97** Zig Leszcynski/AA; **97** MM; **98** (l)Dave B. Fleetham/ TSA, (r)Cabisco/VU; **100** Cabisco/VU; **101** (t)Michael Abbey/VU, (others)John D. Cunningham/VU; **102** (l)MM, (r)Nigel Cattlin/PR; **103** (l)Barry L. Runk from GH, (r)Runk/Schoenberger from GH; **104** (l)Walker England/ PR, (r)TSA; **105** Runk/Schoenberger from GH; **106** David M. Phillips/The Population Council/PR; **107** (t)Gerald & Buff Corsi/VU, (c)Fred Bruenner/Peter Arnold, Inc., (b)Susan McCartney/PR; **109** (l)John D. Cunningham/ VU, (c)Jen & Des Bartlett/BC, (r)Breck P. Kent; **110** (tl)Artville, (tr)Tim Fehr, (c)Bob Daemmrich/SB/PQ, (bl)Troy Mary Parlee/Index Stock/PQ, (br)Jeffery Myers/Southern Stock/PQ; **116** Stewart Cohen/Stone; **118** (t)Tom McHugh/PR, (b)file photo; **119** Monica Dalmasso/Stone; **120** Philip Lee Harvey/Stone; **121** Lester V. Bergman/CB; **122** (t)John Mitchell/PR, (c)Camille Tokerud/PR, (b)David Scharf/Peter Arnold, Inc.; **123** (l)D. Yeske/VU, (r)GH; **126** David Phillips/Science Source/PR; **126-127** MB; **127** Geoff Butler; **128** Stewart Cohen/Stone; **131** (bkgd)Jane Grushow from GH, (lr)Special Collections, National Agriculture Library; **132** Barry L. Runk From GH; **134** Richard Hutchings/PR; **136** (t)Robert Maier/AA, (b)Gemma Giannini from GH; **137** Gemma Giannini from GH; **138** Dan McCoy from Rainbow; **139** (l)Phil Roach/Ipol, (r)CNRI/Science Photo Library/PR; **140** Gopal Murti/PhotoTake NYC; **141** Tim Davis/PR; **142** (l)Alan & Sandy Carey/PR, (r)Renee Stockdale/AA; **145** Tom Meyers/PR; **146** (t)Runk/ Schoenberger from GH, (b)MB; **147** Laura Sefferlin; **149** KS; **150** David R. Frazier Photolibrary; **154** Bios (Klein & Hubert)/Peter Arnold, Inc.; **154-155** Nigel Cattlin/Holt Studio International/PR; **155** AH; **157** Barbara Cushman/DRK; **158** (l)Tim Davis/PR, (c r)Tui De Roy/Minden Pictures; **160** (l)Gregory G. Dimijian, M.D./PR, (r)Patti Murray/AA; **161** (t)Darek Karp/AA, (b)Vonorla Photography; **162** (l)Joe McDonald/AA, (c)Tom McHugh/PR, (r)Tim Davis/PR; **163** James Richardson/VU; **163** Frans Lanting/Minden Pictures; **165** (l)Dominique Braud/ES, (c)Carr Clifton/Minden Pictures, (r)John Cancalosi/DRK; **166** (bl)John Cancalosi/DRK, (t)Larry Ulrich/DRK, (cl)Ken Lucas/VU, (cr)John Cancalosi/Peter Arnold, Inc., (b)Sinclair Stammers/Science Photo Library/PR; **167** John Kieffer/Peter Arnold, Inc.; **170** (l)Kees Van Den Berg/PR, (r)DM; **171** Peter Veit/DRK; **172** (l)Mark E. Gibson, (r)Gerard Lacz/AA; **173** (tl)Michael Dick/AA, (tr)Carolyn A. McKeone, (b)John Reader/Science Photo Library/PR; **174** (l)John Reader/Science Photo Library/PR, (r)Archivo Iconografico, S.A./CB; **175** Francois Ducasse/Rapho/PR; **176** Kenneth W. Fink/PR; **176-177** AH; **178** (t)Lara Jo Regan/Saba Press Photos, (b)VCG/FPG; **180** (tl)Fritz Polking/VU, (tr)Dan Guravich/PR, (bl)Pascal Goetgheluck/Science Photo Library/PR, (br)Joe McDonald/VU; **181** (l)Koster-Survival/AA, (r)Stephen J. Krasemann/DRK; **182** Tom Tietz/Stone; **186-187** PD; **188** (t)Carolyn A. McKeone/PR, (b)J. & P. Wegner/AA; **189** (tl)Yann Arthus-Bertrand/CB, (tr)Barbara Reed/AA, (bl)Chanan Photography, (br)J-L Klein & M-L Hubert/ Okapia/Photo Resarchers; **190** (tl)Renee Stockdale/AA, (tr)Joan Baron/PR, (bl)Carolyn A. McKeone/PR, (br)Yann Arthus-Bertrand/CB; **191** (tl)Stephen Green/TSM, (tr)J & P Wagner/AA, (bl)Jane Howard/PR, (br)Ulrike Schanz/AA; **192** Timothy Fuller; **196** First Image; **199** Dominic Oldershaw; **200** StudiOhio; **201** First Image; **203** Richard Day/AA; **206** Paul Barton/TSM; **209** Charles Gupton/TSM; **218** MM; **219** (t)NIBSC/Science Photo Library/PR, (bl)Dr. Richard Kessel, (br)David John/VU; **220** (t)Runk/Schoenberger from GH, (bl)Andrew Syred/Science Photo Library/PR, (br)Rich Brommer; **221** (t)G.R. Roberts, (bl)Ralph Reinhold/ES, (br)Scott Johnson/AA; **222** Martin Harvey/DRK.

PERIODIC TABLE OF THE ELEMENTS

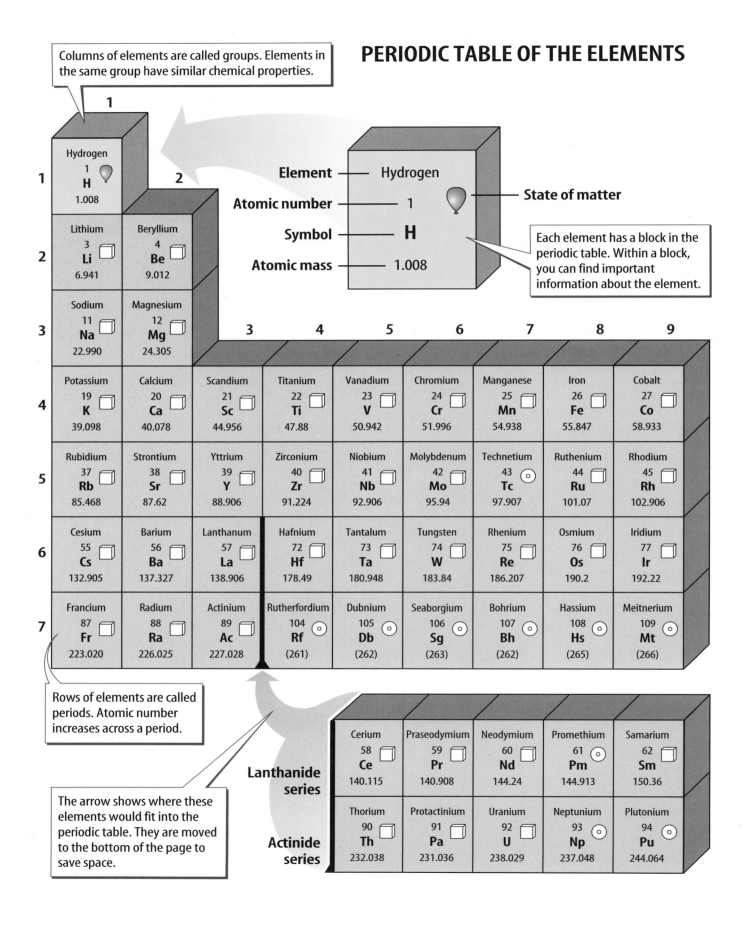

Columns of elements are called groups. Elements in the same group have similar chemical properties.

Element — Hydrogen
Atomic number — 1
Symbol — **H**
Atomic mass — 1.008
State of matter

Each element has a block in the periodic table. Within a block, you can find important information about the element.

1

1								
1 Hydrogen / 1 / **H** / 1.008								

2

1	2
2 Lithium / 3 / **Li** / 6.941	Beryllium / 4 / **Be** / 9.012
3 Sodium / 11 / **Na** / 22.990	Magnesium / 12 / **Mg** / 24.305

		3	4	5	6	7	8	9
4	Potassium / 19 / **K** / 39.098	Calcium / 20 / **Ca** / 40.078	Scandium / 21 / **Sc** / 44.956	Titanium / 22 / **Ti** / 47.88	Vanadium / 23 / **V** / 50.942	Chromium / 24 / **Cr** / 51.996	Manganese / 25 / **Mn** / 54.938	Iron / 26 / **Fe** / 55.847	Cobalt / 27 / **Co** / 58.933
5	Rubidium / 37 / **Rb** / 85.468	Strontium / 38 / **Sr** / 87.62	Yttrium / 39 / **Y** / 88.906	Zirconium / 40 / **Zr** / 91.224	Niobium / 41 / **Nb** / 92.906	Molybdenum / 42 / **Mo** / 95.94	Technetium / 43 / **Tc** / 97.907	Ruthenium / 44 / **Ru** / 101.07	Rhodium / 45 / **Rh** / 102.906
6	Cesium / 55 / **Cs** / 132.905	Barium / 56 / **Ba** / 137.327	Lanthanum / 57 / **La** / 138.906	Hafnium / 72 / **Hf** / 178.49	Tantalum / 73 / **Ta** / 180.948	Tungsten / 74 / **W** / 183.84	Rhenium / 75 / **Re** / 186.207	Osmium / 76 / **Os** / 190.2	Iridium / 77 / **Ir** / 192.22
7	Francium / 87 / **Fr** / 223.020	Radium / 88 / **Ra** / 226.025	Actinium / 89 / **Ac** / 227.028	Rutherfordium / 104 / **Rf** / (261)	Dubnium / 105 / **Db** / (262)	Seaborgium / 106 / **Sg** / (263)	Bohrium / 107 / **Bh** / (262)	Hassium / 108 / **Hs** / (265)	Meitnerium / 109 / **Mt** / (266)

Rows of elements are called periods. Atomic number increases across a period.

The arrow shows where these elements would fit into the periodic table. They are moved to the bottom of the page to save space.

Lanthanide series

Cerium / 58 / **Ce** / 140.115	Praseodymium / 59 / **Pr** / 140.908	Neodymium / 60 / **Nd** / 144.24	Promethium / 61 / **Pm** / 144.913	Samarium / 62 / **Sm** / 150.36

Actinide series

Thorium / 90 / **Th** / 232.038	Protactinium / 91 / **Pa** / 231.036	Uranium / 92 / **U** / 238.029	Neptunium / 93 / **Np** / 237.048	Plutonium / 94 / **Pu** / 244.064